From Shadows to Life

A Biography of the Cancer Survivorship Movement

Judith L. Pearson

From Shadows to Life: A Biography of the Cancer Survivorship Movement

A Lincoln Square Book
Published by Lincoln Square Books
www.lincolnsquarebooks.com
New York, New York
ISBN (paperback): 978-1-947187-12-2
Library of Congress Control Number: 2020949323

Cover Design: Neill Fox/Foxnoggin

What the critics are saying about
From Shadows to Life...

"When it comes to cancer, medical education and training focus almost exclusively on diagnosis and treatment. Life beyond this immediacy of cancer itself is too often neglected. *From Shadows to Life* tells the stories of the heroic individuals who founded the survivorship movement and continue its vital legacy into the present. Medicine has much to learn from their advocacy."

—Damon Tweedy, MD, author of the New York
Times bestseller *Black Man in a White Coat*

"Judith Pearson gives life and voice to what has been an astonishing revolution within the world of cancer. *From Shadows to Life* reminds us of the powerful impact of advocacy in any successful movement, whether for self or others. Imbued with hope, this previously untold history of the cancer survivorship movement should be recommended reading for all cancer survivors and those who care for and about them."

—Julia H Rowland, PhD, FAPOS, Senior Strategic
Advisor at Smith Center for Healing and the Arts and former Director, NCI Office of Cancer Survivorship

"We can't fully understand how to tackle the future of cancer advocacy, research and development and eradication without understanding the rich history of previous generations. Judith Pearson's *From Shadows to Life* has done that expertly, shaping the story of cancer pioneers into a narrative that makes it a compelling read regardless of your personal connection to cancer. Particularly stirring is the section devoted to breast cancer, which chronicles and honors the everyday patients and boldfaced names whose refusal to back down transformed the way doctors treated not only the cancer in a woman's body, but the woman herself."

—Ali Rogin, Foreign Affairs Producer, PBS NewsHour, author of *Beat Breast Cancer Like a Boss*

"I love it! It's history, biography, science, intrigue, drama, all wrapped into one. After reading *The Emperor of All Maladies* I was left thinking 'but what about PEOPLE who actually had cancer?' This is that book. While Siddhartha Mukherjee's book was about cancer and science, this book is about cancer and PEOPLE, and for me that is more interesting."

—Brad Zebrack, PhD, MSW, MPH, Professor, University of Michigan School of Social Work, cancer survivor

"As an oncology nurse since 1975, reading *From Shadows to Life* was like walking down memory lane. Judith Pearson's storytelling is so evocative of the times she was recounting. This book should be of interest to anyone who has an interest in cancer, cancer care and the history of cancer. Her highlighted key figures such as Fitzhugh Mullan, Susie Leigh, Ellen Stovall and so many others so clearly demonstrate what Margaret Mead said long ago. Pearson shows that on every page. It would be a nice companion book to *The Emperor of All Maladies.*"

—Deborah K. Mayer, PhD, RN, AOCN, FAAN, Director of Cancer Survivorship, Lineberger Comprehensive Cancer Center and University of North Carolina School of Nursing, cancer survivor

"Information is necessary if we want to make a difference in the cancer world and when it is combined with inspiration it changes our lives, the results of cancer treatment and its incidence. Pearson's book provides important information we need to know and understand if we are going to make a difference in the cancer world. We need to empower patients and inform medical providers so they can teach survivor behavior and not just treat a diagnosis. Reading

From Shadows to Life can help the transition to prevention and healing rather than our continuing to fight wars and battles against cancer."

—Bernie Siegel, MD, author of *Love, Medicine & Miracles* and *Faith, Hope & Healing*

"This is a well-written and fascinating history of cancer survivorship in America. Pearson takes the reader through each decade's political climate and social standing in the fight for recognition of survivorship as a part of the cancer continuum. Today, there are over 17 million cancer survivors and we are proud to be included in this group of cancer conquerors! We highly recommend this great read!"

—Tamara Green, LCSW, and David Dachinger, authors of *Live Calm with Cancer*

"Judy Pearson masterfully zooms in for the personal stories and zooms out for the milestones—scientific, political, social, and cultural—that drove the history of cancer survivorship. Riveting prose shows how we got to today and inspires hope for a better tomorrow."

—Wendy S. Harpham, MD, regular columnist, *Oncology Times*, and author of *Healing Hope: Through and Beyond Cancer*

For the cancer pioneers—doctors, nurses, social works, psychologists AND survivors—who have given quality of life to all who come after.

Never doubt that a small group of thoughtful, committed citizens can change the world; indeed, it's the only thing that ever has.
—Margaret Mead, cultural anthropologist,
author, and speaker

Table of Contents

Acronyms xiii

The Demons of Survivorship xv

Prologue xvii

Chapter 1: Owl's Eyes. 1

Chapter 2: Prisoners of War 14

Chapter 3: The Catalytic Agent 26

Chapter 4: What More Can We Do? 42

Chapter 5: The Empire 59

Chapter 6: "Someone Who Knew My Terror" 74

Chapter 7: "The Uncharted Land" 91

Chapter 8: Victims No More 108

Chapter 9: "A Streak of Stubbornness
and a Loud Voice" 125

Chapter 10: Like a Grapevine 142

Chapter 11: Tickling the Dragon's Tail 161

Chapter 12: Illumination. 179

Chapter 13: The Office 196

Chapter 14: The March 214

Chapter 15: Lost in Transition 233

Chapter 16: Helping Is Healing 252

Epilogue 273

Acknowledgments 277

Notes. 279

About the Author. 305

Acronyms

AACR	—	American Association for Cancer Research
ACS	—	American Cancer Society
ADA	—	Americans with Disabilities Act
AEC	—	Atomic Energy Commission
AIDS	—	Acquired Immunodeficiency Syndrome
AMA	—	American Medical Association
AOSW	—	Association of Oncology Social Work
ASCO	—	American Society of Clinical Oncology
CARRA	—	Consumer Advocates in Research and Related Activities
CoC	—	Commission on Cancer
DCLG	—	Director's Consumer Liaison Group
FCDA	—	Federal Civil Defense Administration
FDA	—	Food and Drug Administration
GWCCS	—	Greater Washington Coalition for Cancer Survivorship
HPV	—	Human Papillomavirus
ICC	—	Intercultural Cancer Council
IOM	—	Institute of Medicine
IVF	—	In Vitro Fertilization
LTC	—	Living Through Cancer
MSKCC	—	Memorial Sloan Kettering Cancer Center
NASA	—	National Aeronautics and Space Administration
NCCS	—	National Coalition for Cancer Survivorship
NCI	—	National Cancer Institute

NIH	—	National Institutes of Health
NOW	—	National Organization for Women
NTS	—	Nevada Test Site
OCS	—	Office of Cancer Survivorship
ONS	—	Oncology Nursing Society
PHS	—	Public Health Service
PLTC	—	People Living Through Cancer
PTSD	—	Post-Traumatic Stress Disorder
PWA	—	People with AIDS
RECA	—	Radiation Exposure Compensation Act
SCP	—	Survivorship Care Plan
SIG	—	Special Interest Group
TCGA	—	The Cancer Genome Atlas
U of A	—	University of Arizona
UCLA	—	University of California, Los Angeles

The Demons of Survivorship

*It is as if we have invented sophisticated techniques to save
people from drowning, but once they have been pulled from
the water, we leave them on the dock to cough and splutter on
their own in the belief that we have done all that we can.*

—Dr. Fitzhugh Mullan

Cancer doesn't end when treatment does, and Dr. Mullan's words
are as true now as they were in 1985 when he wrote them. While
each cancer survivor has his or her own list of demons, the following eight are the most prevalent, experienced to a greater or lesser
extent by each of us.

- Discrimination—including employment, insurance, and
  social
- Communication with the medical community—including
  disease disclosure and details of the disease and its treatment
- Self-image—including reconstruction and feelings of
  inadequacy
- Intimacy, relationships, fertility—including lack of resources
  and lack of information
- Government and corporate cover-up—putting public image
  and personal goals before public safety
- Psychological soup—including PTSD, fear of recurrence,
  and guilt
- Social apathy—including misunderstanding of survivorship

- Long-term challenges—including treatment-induced diseases, physical issues, and financial hardships

Since its founding, the National Coalition for Cancer Survivorship has striven to direct a spotlight on these demons in an effort to eradicate them. Confronting them is one of the driving forces behind this book.

Prologue

If you were saved it is because you have something else to do in this world.
—Artist Mary Cassatt to Theodate Pope Riddle,
survivor of the doomed ship *Lusitania*

New Mexico is known for expansive, high desert vistas, and rich Hispanic and Native American cultures. Its capital city, Santa Fe, is famous for upscale museums and galleries, not to mention frequent celebrity sightings. But its most populous city is Albuquerque. In October, 1986, however, despite being bigger than Santa Fe by a factor of ten, Albuquerque's greatest claim to fame was the Hot Air Balloon Fiesta; the 14th annual installment had just occurred a few weeks earlier.

Autumn in Albuquerque is a mélange of weather. Some years, snow not only makes an appearance on the tops of the surrounding pink granite peaks of the Sandia Mountains, but creeps down toward the city as well. Other years, glorious sun and mild temperatures endure long past Halloween. The landscape literally glows from the golden leaves of the city's ubiquitous aspen.

That late-October daytime temperatures hovered in the mid-60s, while the mild evenings encouraged gatherings around outdoor chiminea fireplaces. The distinctive odor of their burning piñon wood wafted through the air, announcing the change of seasons. Reminiscent of incense, the smell would certainly have been noticed by the group of visitors arriving at the Barcelona Court Hotel on Friday, October 24.

The group could not have been more diverse. It consisted of twenty-three individuals from eleven different states and was made up of doctors, nurses, lawyers, authors, and business people, ranging in age from 28 to 63. But they all had one thing in common—everyone had a connection to cancer.

While researchers of the day were arduously seeking a cure, they had scarcely moved the needle since President Nixon declared his "War on Cancer" fifteen years earlier. In fact, up until a few years ago, some physicians were continuing the practice of not even informing their patients of a cancer diagnosis. The terrifying scourge occupied the same space on the fear and loathing scale that venereal disease had during the first half of the twentieth century.

It was called the "Big C," and was spoken of in hushed tones. And it was almost never discussed in public. Cancer evoked specters of a slow and agonizing demise, spouseless mourners, and parentless children. Cancer "victims" existed in abject isolation and were a drain on society. The very word aroused terror and reeked of death. Worst of all, cancer was thought to be contagious. The notion of hairless, skeletal, surgery-maimed individuals was too much for people to think about. So, they didn't.

Most of the public was completely uneducated about cancer's causes, risk factors, or ancestry. The new arrivals in Albuquerque that fall evening knew all about the fear and phobias enshrouding cancer. More than half of them had met the disease head-on and the rest had either watched a loved one face it down, or had devoted their lives to cancer-related work. They had assembled not to cure the disease, but to begin curing the myths.

As if battling cancer wasn't bad enough, patients also battled unseen and unexpected demons. In 1986, nearly half of all cancer diagnoses were fatal. But the half who didn't die, including those assembling in Albuquerque, sought to live vibrant lives, to help others fight against those demons, and to feel free to discuss out loud their challenges *and* their triumphs.

They wanted to shake off the cloud of discrimination against them simply because they had fallen ill. They hoped to illuminate the need to heal psychologically from cancer, overcoming issues of poor self-image and post-traumatic stress disorder (PTSD). They aspired to encourage honest communication between themselves and their doctors, and to address their challenges in relationships, intimacy, and fertility. They were willing to call out corporations, industries, even the United States government—any entity knowingly poisoning the population and sowing cancer seeds. Most of all, they wanted to shed a light of hope for those who were newly diagnosed, to be true representations of the valuable life they could and *should* live after cancer.

The driving force behind the weekend-long assembly was a dynamo named Catherine Logan (later Catherine Logan-Carrillo) , a woman well acquainted with social change. She was in Mississippi in 1964 during the Civil Rights Movement, and was even tossed in jail for her beliefs in equality. She later graduated from the University of Illinois with degrees in sociology and psychology, and spent time in the Peace Corps before becoming a community organizer in Chicago. After seven years, she left the Windy City to pursue her true love: jewelry-making in the Native American arts mecca of Albuquerque.

And then the unthinkable happened. Catherine was one of the 16,000 American women diagnosed with invasive cervical cancer in 1979. The treatment was a complete hysterectomy, followed by radiation. For an unwed woman of 34, that not only shut the door on any hopes of childbearing, but enveloped her with a sense of being unworthy of marriage as well.

As she worked through the shock, disappointment, and anger of her diagnosis and treatment, Catherine developed friendships with several other women who had survived cancer. Together, in 1983, they founded Living Through Cancer. LTC, as it came to be called, had two main goals: to be a safe place for people with a cancer history to share fears and experiences, and to serve as a local clearinghouse for the latest information on cancer.

And this is how Catherine first heard of Dr. Fitzhugh Mullan. Fitz had trained as a pediatrician in the Bronx. Like Catherine, Fitz, too, had experience in social reform movements, his being in health care. In 1972, he had been commissioned in the US Public Health Service and practiced in New Mexico as one of the first physicians in the National Health Service Corps. Three years later, at the age of 32, he had taken a chest X-ray of himself at his Santa Fe hospital. The X-ray revealed a cauliflower-shaped tumor that proved to be a solid, cancerous seminoma.

What should have been a routine chest surgery devolved into a nightmare of complications from which Fitz nearly died. His recovery took a full two years. Having always been an eloquent writer, Fitz detailed his cancer journey in a 1983 book, *Vital Signs: A Young Doctor's Struggle with Cancer.* And since he had a healthy Rolodex of medical contacts from coast to coast, he embarked on a national speaking tour to promote his book.

After he moved to Washington, DC, Fitz authored a thought-provoking piece for the July 1985 *New England Journal of Medicine* titled "Seasons of Survival." In it, he likened life after cancer to the seasons of the year, progressing from the newness and uncertainty of spring to the seasoned acceptance of winter. For anyone remotely interested in life after cancer, it was eye-opening. For someone with a passion for the subject, like Catherine Logan, it was a battle cry.

In 1985, Catherine was waiting for Fitz in the vestibule outside one of his speaking engagements. Her appearance was a follow-up to a letter she had sent him previously. They were on the same wavelength about life after cancer, she told him. Because of the 1971 National Cancer Act, which was feeding unprecedented sums into research, cancer survivors were growing in number and desperately needed one another to forge through the stages of their new lives. She told him about LTC and the other grassroots cancer support groups across the country about which she was accumulating information. With passion and persuasion, she pronounced that they needed to get organized, to form a coalition. And to accomplish that, she needed him, and his considerable Rolodex of contacts.

Fitz agreed, partly because he believed she would continue to stalk him until he said yes, but more importantly, because he knew she was right. Cancer survivors were increasing in number, but their physical and emotional needs were completely closeted.

With Fitz's treasure trove of Who's Who in the cancer world, Catherine's mailing list grew. She sent a total of eighty-three letters to cancer organizations, researchers, and individuals—anyone who evidenced a remote interest in life post-cancer. She detailed their joint vision—having convinced Fitz that "joint" was the only way to word it—to create a network of like-minded people. In her letter, recipients were asked whether they would be interested in being a part of a national coalition, and what they'd like to see the coalition do.

Then—as now—survivorship organizations were protective of their turf, fearing the loss of stakeholders to newer, shinier programs. It was an absurd notion in an industry whose alleged mission was to support patients. Still, of the eighty-three letters she sent out, recipients of thirty-one responded affirmatively, and twenty-two of them agreed to gather that October to investigate this new vision for life beyond cancer.

Albuquerque was not known as a research or health care mecca. It had no prestigious medical school or acclaimed hospitals. The fact that this group, including accomplished and well-known individuals from around the country, was willing to make the trek to such an unlikely destination speaks volumes about both the subject matter and the respect held for both Fitz and Catherine.

A few weeks before the meeting, a Phoenix nurse who had been invited to attend learned she had a scheduling conflict. She contacted an acquaintance, another nurse who had worked with cancer patients and in cancer research at the University of Arizona Medical Center in Tucson, who agreed to go in her place.

So, on Friday morning, October 24, Susie Leigh headed for New Mexico in her white 1982 Toyota 4-wheel drive pickup truck. Her interest was piqued by what might be waiting at the end of her 450-mile trek. In addition to being an oncology nurse, she was also one of the nearly five million Americans in 1986 who had fought and survived cancer. It had been fourteen years since that diagnosis, and within the Albuquerque group that would give her the unique title of being the most senior in terms of life after cancer. But there was much more about Susie Leigh that made her unique.

In 1972, eight months after her return from a twelve-month tour of duty as an Army nurse in the Vietnam War, she had been diagnosed with the virulent, rare, and often fatal Hodgkin's disease (now known as Hodgkin's lymphoma). She had received a brand-new type of treatment that was showing impressive survival rates. Nevertheless, while the punishing treatment regimen made her a chemotherapy pioneer, its toxicity was debilitating.

Susie's body had soon begun to feel like a foreign thing. The treatment was an assault that made her feel unfeminine and damaged. She had fallen into a deep depression and, being introverted by nature, had isolated herself from other people. Her chemo caused long-term side effects, and the ensuing radiation would ultimately be responsible for as-yet undiagnosed cancers and cardiac issues. None of these reactions or conditions were unusual. All those treated for cancer knew that the disease hadn't really ended when their treatment had. But each thought their situation was the result of their own shortcomings, and not something to be shared with others.

At thirty-nine, Susie had fought in military and medical battles. She was a warrior and a survivor in every sense of the word. Her disease had motivated her to become one of the country's first oncology nurses, giving her the advantage of experiencing cancer from both sides of the hospital bed. But what lay ahead would not only change her life, it would change the lives of millions of people battling cancer far into the future.

Chapter 1: Owl's Eyes

In 1965, 285,362 Americans die of cancer, while there are 1,400,000 living survivors of the disease.

In 1830s London, Thomas Hodgkin's first medical appointment was one not often sought: he was the "Inspector of the Dead" and curator of the museum at Guy's Hospital. He performed autopsies and saved the good bits; when he encountered unusual or undocumented bodily conditions, he preserved pathological specimens for further study. In 1832, he wrote a paper about a collection of troubling specimens, the donors of which were mostly young men. In "On Some Morbid Appearances of the Absorbent Glands and Spleen," Hodgkin tried to make sense of what had taken the lives of these young people.

More than sixty years later, in 1898, Austrian pathologist Carl Sternberg was studying one of his own patient's glands, with a microscope more advanced than the one Hodgkin had, when he found a string of peculiar cells with dual nuclei. They looked, he said, like "owl eyes." Referring back to Hodgkin's 1832 paper, Sternberg realized that the "Inspector of the Dead" had identified a type of lymphoma. And the naming rights belonged to Thomas Hodgkin. Lymphomas attack the body's lymphatic system, a part of the circulatory system that serves as an accessory return route for blood, and as a defender of the immune system. Identifying Hodgkin's disease was one thing; surviving it, however, was something else. No one had ever been known to be completely cured of it, until an odd discovery from an unexpected source. (Note: As time passed, Hodgkin's disease became known as Hodgkin's lymphoma, and then Hodgkin lymphoma. The precise dates of these transitions are contradicted in research, therefore the timeframes for use of the names in this book are approximate.)

Chemical warfare was the bane of soldiers in the trenches during World War I, and the most often used chemical, mustard gas (nitrogen mustard), caused a lethal attack on the hematologic (blood) system.

By the start of World War II, fearing a repeat of those attacks, Allied Forces began experimenting with possible antidotes. In researching the medical records of men affected by the gas twenty-five years or so earlier, two doctors at Yale University, Louis Goodman and Alfred Gilman, noticed that many of the men they were studying had a surprisingly low number of immune cells in their blood—cells that, if mutated, could go on to develop into leukemia and lymphoma. If nitrogen mustard could destroy normal blood cells, Goodman and Gilman hypothesized, couldn't it also destroy cancerous ones?

They experimented successfully on animals, but it was a human subject, known today only as J.D., that tipped the scale. In 1942, J.D.'s lymphoma was so advanced that his jaw tumors prevented him from eating or sleeping, and he couldn't cross his arms because of the size of his chest tumors. After each treatment with "substance X"—Goodman and Gilman's code name for nitrogen mustard—J.D.'s lymphoma showed signs of slowing, and his tumors shrank. Although the lymphoma officially went into remission, it recurred, and J.D. died six months later. But the experimentation against lymphomas continued.

In early 1951, at a cocktail party on the opposite side of the country, Stanford University radiologist Dr. Henry Kaplan overheard news that a university physicist was experimenting with an "electron linear accelerator." The goal of its eventual six million electron volts was atom smashing. But Kaplan's mind went immediately to the treatment of his cancer patients. He was using X-rays to treat solid tumors in humans, after having experimented with the process on animals with leukemia. Perhaps the thing that had been designed to smash atoms could also be used to smash cancer?

Scoring a grant of $18,381 from the American Cancer Society in August of 1951 (the equivalent of $177,126 in 2021 dollars), Kaplan and Stanford engineer Edward Ginzton completed the redesign of the linear accelerator in one year. As described at the time, its knife-like precision beam "reportedly can penetrate healthy tissue without injuring it." This newly retooled, six-million-volt machine was first used in 1956 on a two-year-old boy for a tumor in his eye. The treatment not only saved the child's sight, it saved his life.

Kaplan next aimed his linear accelerator at Hodgkin's disease. Stage I patients' results were so successful it began to look like the incurable disease might suddenly have fallen into a new category. Eighty-five percent of the stage I patients who were treated with the linear accelerator would be alive and well five years down the road, the magic goal line to be considered a cancer survivor. But the later-stage patients were still not faring well.

A year later, in 1956, oncologists at the National Cancer Institute (NCI) injected a patient with methotrexate. The chemical actually cured her choriocarcinoma, an aggressive type of uterine cancer. And she remained cancer-free. Word spread: if one cancer could be cured by a chemical injection (known as chemotherapy), perhaps all cancers could be cured that way? Having had some success in animals with "combination" chemotherapy—using two drugs rather than one—NCI researchers took the brave step of bringing it to the fight against childhood leukemia. And they expanded the chemical regimen to four drugs.

VAMP (the acronym for the first letters of its chemicals, vincristine, amethopterin, mercaptopurine, and prednisone) trials began in 1961. The harrowing treatment eradicated nearly all the white blood cells in the medically fragile children, leaving them defenseless against infection. But with both the successes and the tragic deaths, more knowledge was added to the plus side of the ledger in the fight against cancer.

There were those at NCI who believed that by using combination chemotherapy they could make great strides against Hodgkin's. Dr. Vincent DeVita was one of those.

In 1966, Hudson Falls was the kind of place Norman Rockwell might have painted: a small town in upstate New York, perched at one of the bends of the Hudson River. Weekdays, the houses along the tree-lined streets spilled forth children riding bikes to or from school and men commuting to and from work. Their wives mainly stayed home to keep house, waving to neighbors as they shook rugs or hung laundry.

On Tuesday evening, September 12, the two-story house at 3 Colman Avenue in Hudson Falls was bustling with activity. Mary and Harrison Winne's eldest daughters, Christine and Debbie, were co-hostesses for a small party being given in their mother's honor.

The girls had planned it all on their own, and pooled their funds to pull it off. The money had been earned from a variety of household chores, and had been originally earmarked for a Schwinn Fair Lady bicycle, with coaster brakes, a flower-trimmed wicker basket, chrome-plated full-length fenders, and a Silver Glow saddle. Having a bike like that was important to a nine- and a seven-year-old. But this party was more important.

Two years earlier, at age twenty-six, Mary Winne had been diagnosed with Hodgkin's disease. It was dire news: the national five-year survival rate for all cancers combined at that time was 37 percent. Mary's illness, the local paper reported, caused her to find it "somewhat difficult to meet the normal requirements of housework and rais[e] children." It didn't mention that her treatments left her horribly debilitated. Cobalt radiation was being used in an optimistic effort to eradicate (or at least shrink) the tumors in her chest and around her neck. It left her skin burned and peeling, with chronic fatigue as a constant companion.

The side effects of the nitrogen mustard injected into her veins were far worse. Days of unrelenting nausea were followed by days of little to no appetite. And the itching! Her body felt as though thousands of ants crawled everywhere on her skin, persisting even in her sleep.

Nonetheless, with children's enthusiasm, Christine and Debbie figured nothing would cheer up their mother more than a surprise party. So that's what they threw. They invited sixteen local family friends and served refreshments, organized bingo and other games, and purchased a pair of earrings for their mom. They even arranged for babysitting for their three younger siblings: David, age four; Patrick, age three; and Lisa, age two. Mr. Winne made himself scarce, toiling at his second job doing home repair work on appliances. The additional income was crucial to meet his wife's mounting medical bills.

Two decades earlier, a 20¢ booklet had been published jointly by the American Cancer Society (ACS) and the NCI, featuring a disturbing graphic. It showed four hospital beds, topped by the heading "Of Every 4 Persons Who Have Cancer…." Below each bed was a prediction. The first: "One is saved by treatment…surgery, radium or X-ray." The second: "One dies because cancer was discovered too late." And below the two last beds: "Two die in the absence of new discoveries."

In other words, only 25 percent of those diagnosed in 1947 were expected to survive their disease. Given that nearly 200,000 would die that year, an ACS newspaper ad proclaimed that one American died of cancer every three minutes. Yet at the annual conference of the American College of Surgeons the following year, a symposium was optimistically titled, "Cancer Is Curable." If that was truly the case, why wasn't it happening?

On the medical side, manpower and money were lacking. As the 1947 ACS/NCI booklet pointed out, "Today pure science competes with industry for the best of the young researchers who come out of the universities—industry can pay more."

Then, as now, being short of money is the great deterrent to progress. Raising it was a major part of the ACS mission. Legions of volunteers rallied the public to give, particularly during their annual drive each April, known as the "Cancer Crusade." Full-page ads ran in newspapers across the country in 1948, with statistics meant to stir Americans, still fresh from World War II. "How Much for Your Life?" screamed a box in the center of the page. The ad went on:

> Two hundred eighty thousand lives—three hundred seventeen billion dollars—that's the price the nation paid for World War II. Every death cost us over a million dollars!
>
> During that same period, 607,000 Americans died of cancer, while only two million dollars were spent for cancer research. Those were "cheap" lives—not much more than $3.00 apiece!

The emotional appeal finished with:

> Immediately, when you give to conquer cancer, your money becomes a weapon to battle one of mankind's greatest scourges. The funds of the American Cancer Society are constantly at work—never idle—and the Society's only reserves are in the hearts of the American people.

"Mankind's greatest scourge" was also one of our greatest fears. Some took the route of ignoring any abnormality in their health, no matter how severe, because they simply did not want to be told they had cancer. It was as if by ignoring it, they could will the health issue away. And in an effort to assuage that fear, many in the medical field supported the notion of not publicizing cancer warnings.

Money played a part on the patient side, too. Research done in 1947 at New York's Memorial Hospital (now Memorial Sloan

Kettering Cancer Center) pointed out that "people with higher education showed a greater regard for their health than those with not more than grammar-school education." The need to earn a living took people out of school in the first half of the twentieth century. And even if they had stayed in school, lack of funds prevented many from earning a college diploma.

Since individuals who were more highly educated at that time were also more likely to be young, age was factored in as well. "Among patients over 60 years of age included in the study," the research report stated, "more than two-thirds had poor medical care habits."

Ignorance, too, had a role. A University of Michigan study showed that 49 percent of those diagnosed with cancer the previous year (1946) didn't recognize a single one of the highly publicized "seven danger signals": change in bowel or bladder habits; a sore that does not heal; unusual bleeding or discharge; thickening or lump in the breast or elsewhere; indigestion or difficulty in swallowing; obvious changes in a wart or mole; nagging cough or hoarseness.

By 1966, those same warnings were still being publicized. But now, the ACS also threw the word "cure" all over its full-page Cancer Crusade announcement. And there was cause for some celebration on three big fronts. First, one in three who had been diagnosed were now being "saved," meaning they were still alive five years after treatment. Second, there were 963 "cancer clinics," diagnostic and treatment centers approved by the American College of Surgeons, more than double the number there had been in 1947. The final triumph was that research had produced twenty-four drugs being used in cancer treatment, where there had been none just two decades earlier.

In 1964, the same year that Mary Winne was diagnosed, Dr. DeVita created another four-drug chemo cocktail. He called it MOMP, again using the first letters of its ingredients: methotrexate, Oncovin (he needed a vowel so used the brand name for vincristine), nitrogen mustard (using the *m* from mustard) and prednisone. Only fourteen patients were treated with it in the first clinical trial, and all suffered the same lack of immunity their VAMP brothers and sisters had experienced.

Dr. DeVita went back to the well, modifying the recipe once more. Methotrexate (the drug that had worked on the choriocarcinoma) was replaced with procarbazine, the letters were rearranged, and the chemo soup was now known as MOPP.

"The treatments were tough, the doubters many," DeVita said of the early clinical trials of MOPP. "It took plain old courage to be a chemotherapist in the 1960s and certainly the courage of the conviction that cancer would eventually succumb to drugs."

Preserving lives was one thing. Preserving the quality of those lives was quite another. Since there had never been long-term cancer survivors, all the brilliant minds that had gone into treatment discoveries had no reason to wonder what, if any, long-term effects their weaponry against the world's most feared disease might beget.

"Together let us explore the stars, conquer the deserts, eradicate disease, tap the ocean depths, and encourage the arts and commerce," John F. Kennedy declared in his inaugural address on January 20, 1961. His words were met with booming applause. But hidden within them was a question of priorities. Which comes first, the moon or the slums, the unexplored or the unemployed, supporting young artists or saving those with life-threatening diseases? The range of choices was endless.

As is typical in government, advisors were appointed and committee ideas hatched, including the President's Commission on Cancer, Heart Disease and Strokes. Research done over the previous ten years had produced advances in heart surgeries, revealed the health risks of high fat diets and smoking, and led to some strides in the fight against cancer. It wasn't enough.

Adding more committees would produce even greater problems. There was a looming conflict between the departments, and within departments, between the policymakers and the scientific experts. Each cautiously guarded their territory, convinced that letting the others in might render them unnecessary. The Heart Disease-Cancer-Stroke Commission (the arrangement of the words changed each time they were written) would cross into the domain of the National Institutes of Health, already heavy with bureaucracy.

A single bullet, fired on November 22, 1963, sidelined this commission, along with all other dreams the young president had for the nation. Seven weeks later, President Lyndon Johnson delivered his first State of the Union message on January 8, 1964. He declared an unconditional war on poverty, talked of budget cuts, called for an end to discrimination, and pledged a more peaceful world. By February, in a health message to Congress, he spoke of eliminating the "dark corridor of fear" that accompanied old age. This would be done by adding hospitalization benefits to the social security program for Americans over the age of sixty-five. Johnson, too, referred to the fact that the nation's medical research had developed techniques that were marvels to the scientific world. Unsaid was that many of those marvels were beyond the reach of millions.

On March 7, Johnson's newly created President's Commission on Heart Disease, Cancer, and Stroke took on America's "big three" killers. It included familiar names of the era: Doctors DeBakey, Mayo, and Farber; Emerson Foote, co-owner of the monster ad firm Foote, Cone & Belding; and former First Lady Bess Truman.

Like Kennedy, Johnson saw value in creating task forces to provide expert advice on policy. But unlike his predecessor, Johnson directed his task forces to work in secret. Highly sensitive to public opinion, Johnson hoped to prevent his programs from being derailed by criticism of proposals that had not yet been reviewed. The fourteen secret task forces studied nearly all major aspects of

United States society under the guidance of presidential advisors Richard Goodwin and Bill Moyers.

After the task force reports were submitted to the White House, Moyers began a second round of review. The recommendations were circulated among the agencies concerned, and strategies were developed for getting the proposed legislation through Congress. The twenty-eight esteemed members of the Commission on Heart Disease, Cancer, and Stroke would function no differently. Beginning with their organizational meeting, held in Washington, DC, on April 17, their work flew far below the public's radar.

Meanwhile, Johnson's larger plan for the country was dripped out slowly on May 7, 1964, when he told the student body at Ohio University in Athens, Ohio: "...I say merely as a statement of fact: America is yours—yours to make a better land—yours to build the great society."

That was the plan. Franklin Roosevelt—whom Johnson idolized—had his New Deal. Kennedy's New Frontier had been aborted by his assassination. The Great Society would be Johnson's goal.

The report compiled by the Commission on Heart Disease, Cancer, and Stroke was released in December 1964, and brought with it a stunning headline: "$3-billion War on Cancer, Heart Illness, Stroke Urged." As Chairman Michael DeBakey wrote: "Our stated goals...must be achieved if we are to check the heavy losses these three diseases inflict upon our economy—close to $30 billion each year in lost productivity and lost taxes due to premature disability and death."

To ensure that the latest methods of treatment would be more readily available to the "victims" of cancer, heart disease, and stroke, the commission proposed a system of sixty regional centers where Americans could get the best in diagnosis and care for the three diseases. Twenty-five centers would be for heart disease, twenty for cancer, and fifteen for strokes. They would accomplish three goals: clinical investigation, teaching, and patient care. In addition, a network of 450 stations across the nation would serve as initial stops, where the diagnoses of heart disease, strokes, and cancer could be provided, along with rehabilitation. Patients could then be referred on to the regional centers for further care if necessary. Two hundred of the stations would be for treating cancer, 150 for heart disease, and 100 for stroke.

In an earlier briefing, Dr. DeBakey had avoided press questions as to why Dr. Hugh H. Hussey, scientific director for the American Medical Association (AMA), had resigned from the commission in September (although he did stay on as a consultant). The fact was, the AMA had pledged opposition to all federal intervention in the field of medical practice. It demurred from a statement about the commission's report, saying it had not yet had time to study it. But behind closed doors, it was girding for battle. The AMA didn't want any part of the upcoming Medicare program, and it surely didn't want any part of this.

America's concern over socialism was never higher than in the 1950s and '60s. Doctors in the US watched with great concern the difficulties their British counterparts were encountering as the United Kingdom's vastly underfunded National Health Service struggled to find its way. Allowing even a government toe into medicine might spell the same challenges on this side of the Atlantic.

Nonetheless, when Johnson addressed the nation in his State of the Union on January 4, 1965, the road to the Great Society was ready to begin construction with some very well-laid plans. He pledged a concerted drive in Congress and the nation to buttress federal efforts against cancer, heart disease, and strokes. The aim, he said, is "to put more firmly in place the foundation for the healthiest, happiest and most hopeful society in the history of man...a health program to match the achievements of our medicine to the afflictions of our people."

To make that a reality, bill H.R. 3140/S. 596 went before the Eighty-Ninth Congress. The bill asked for $50 million for the current fiscal year, $90 million for fiscal 1967, and $200 million for fiscal 1968. And it should have been a shoo-in. The Democrats had won by a landslide in the 1964 elections. The House of Representatives was the most liberal House since 1938. The bill did indeed pass in

September. But the war on cancer President Johnson thought he would be declaring was nothing of the kind. Only a shadow of the original bill Johnson sent to Congress was passed; the budget was trimmed to $860,000—less than 30 percent of what was originally requested. Why the changes?

Making good on their promise to oppose federal interference in medicine, the AMA had launched a lobbying campaign. Their officials met with the President personally in the White House, sitting around the table in the Cabinet room. The next day they trotted over to the Department of Health, Education and Welfare, and twenty amendments were added to the original bill after the AMA all but threatened to sabotage the new bill, which had finally been achieved after twenty years of bitter battling. An AMA press release concluded: "The already existing misgivings among some members of the medical profession about the AMA's liaison relationships with the Department of Health, Education and Welfare would have been markedly aggravated by the enactment of another law so strongly opposed by physicians." Simply put, they didn't want government interference in medicine. It was their way or the highway.

Yet even before the wings of Johnson's war on cancer were clipped by the AMA's stand, the shadow of another war loomed. In August 1964, the handful of military "advisors" who had been sent to South Vietnam by Presidents Eisenhower and Kennedy were replaced by 3,500 United States Marines who came ashore at Da Nang, the first American combat troops to enter the country. This was only the beginning of the chain of events that would categorically and forever connect the two wars—Vietnam and Cancer.

———————

On a mild Saturday night in September 1967, Mary Winne died of her cancer at the Glens Falls Hospital. When she was buried the following Wednesday, she left behind a heartbroken group: her husband, her five children, her parents, and her ten siblings. Few people beyond her family and community ever knew Mary Winne. But her disease would become famous.

DeVita's MOPP chemo cocktail, when combined with Kaplan's linear accelerator, caused the survival rate for nearly all stages of Hodgkin's disease to skyrocket from zero to over 70 percent. Hodgkin's became the first adult cancer that could be conquered.

Sadly, the treatment's discovery was too late for Mary Winne.

Chapter 2: Prisoners of War

In 1970, 625,000 Americans are diagnosed with cancer.

By 1954, the French had tried to occupy, transform, and improve Vietnam for nearly a century. The Vietnamese had grown sick and tired of imperialistic and brutal tactics used against them by invading foreigners. When the French were driven out after the battle of Dien Bien Phu that spring, the country was divided into Communist North Vietnam and non-Communist South Vietnam.

Fearing a "falling domino" principle of Communist takeovers of other Southeast Asian countries, President Eisenhower said, "You have a row of dominoes set up ... and what will happen to the last one is a certainty that it will go over very quickly." Before you knew it, the theory went, the Communists would be knocking on America's front door. And so, America ignored the vital history lesson the French had just learned, and took France's place.

A year after the French left, and as the Cold War between the US and the Soviet Union grew chillier, President Eisenhower sent some seven hundred military personnel as well as military and economic aid to the government of South Vietnam. But by 1961, as John F. Kennedy became president, not only was this effort foundering, the new president was painfully aware that Fidel Castro's recent rise to power in Cuba meant a Communist state was now on America's doorstep. It seemed, to some, the domino theory was proving true.

President Kennedy quickly authorized sending "an additional five hundred Special Forces troops and military advisors to assist the pro-Western government of South Vietnam." By the end of 1962, there were approximately eleven thousand military advisors in South Vietnam … By the end of 1963, the numbers had risen to sixteen thousand.

After Kennedy's assassination, newly sworn-in President Lyndon Johnson unhappily inherited the problem of this far-off and little-understood country. As election day neared, Johnson told his Secretary of Defense, Robert McNamara, "I feel like a jackass in a Texas hailstorm. I can't run, I can't hide and I can't make it stop."

Fearing that Vietnam was political quicksand and that it would diminish support for his Great Society and all its programs—including his war on cancer—Johnson decided massive military force was not a viable option. But his advisors begged to differ with him.

Then, on August 2, 1964, came the infamous Gulf of Tonkin incident. The USS *Maddox* was attacked by North Vietnamese torpedo boats. Two days later, American radar technology appeared to detect another attack. Whether or not the second attack was widely exaggerated, if not fabricated (as retrospective analysis of the evidence suggests), Johnson ordered air strikes on North Vietnamese patrol boat bases. Gradually, the policy toward Vietnam changed, morphing from retaliatory warfare to a widened war with systematic bombing.

Johnson handily won the 1964 presidential election with a vote count so large, he was nicknamed "Landslide Lyndon." Two months after taking office in March 1965, coinciding with the Marines' landing in Da Nang, Johnson launched "Operation Rolling Thunder." The three-year campaign would consist of sustained bombing of targets in North Vietnam and along the Ho Chi Minh Trail, the elaborate system of mountain and jungle paths used by the North Vietnamese combatants to infiltrate troops and supplies into South Vietnam.

Anti-war Democrats complained that spending on the Vietnam War would choke off the Great Society. And they were right. When 1966 dawned, it did so with a new federal budget, one with many of the Great Society programs trimmed back to make more funds available for defense. Senator Robert Kennedy said the financial demands of the war in Vietnam should not be allowed to delay the other war that had been declared—on poverty. The 1966 budget also badly impacted government medical programs, including spending on cancer research.

He was the epitome of an American military hero: tall, blond, square-jawed. Sergeant First Class Phillip A. Hesse had joined up in 1955 at the age of eighteen, eventually flying lighter-than-air craft at Lakehurst Maxfield Field in New Jersey. (The joint military base had been the site of the horrific Hindenburg disaster in 1937.) In 1958, Hesse transferred to the 101st Airborne, and then joined the Special Forces in 1961. Three years later, while stationed in Germany, he was diagnosed with chondrosarcoma in his right leg—a cancer originating from the cells that produce cartilage. After three operations, including the removal of part of his hip, he was offered retirement from the Army with a 100 percent medical disability rating. Hesse declined.

The doctors persisted, telling him he had no more than five years to live, and probably only two. By this time Hesse was married with a two-year-old daughter. But he would not be deterred. He trained for months to strengthen his diseased leg, and then volunteered for duty in Vietnam. Arriving on February 25, 1966, he survived mortar attacks and jungle sorties unscathed, only to be medically evacuated on May 16 as the result of his cancer's spread.

Sergeant Hesse's story eventually made its way to the White House. It was exactly what the president needed. Johnson was still stinging from the watered-down version of his heart disease, cancer, and stroke bill the AMA had engineered. And he took personally the growing public concern about America's lack of success in Vietnam. Drawing attention to Hesse would garner much-needed positive publicity for both issues. Here was a guy who was so in favor of the war in Southeast Asia, he volunteered for duty there despite having cancer!

Johnson awarded Hesse the Bronze Star. Its accompanying citation read: "Sergeant Hesse's strong motivation, meritorious service and outstanding performance of duty under adverse circumstances reflect the utmost credit upon himself, the US Army and the armed forces of his country."

On June 13, 1966, the award was presented in a special hospital ceremony by Major General Philip W. Mallory, the commanding general at Walter Reed Army Medical Center in Maryland. A few days later, Hesse's right leg was amputated just below the hip. He had originally refused the surgery, figuring he'd rather live five years on two legs than ten years with one. But his pretty wife, Marion, pointed out that a father with one leg was better than no father at all. Their daughter was now six and she had a one-year-old little brother. Doctors were careful not to be overly optimistic about the soldier's future; the fact was, his odds for survival were questionable. But Hesse was determined. More than anything, he wanted to return to his other war, the one

---

For the first time in history, Americans were being given a ringside seat to war, as footage of the days' battles in Vietnam streamed into living rooms on the nightly TV news. There was mud and explosions and body bags and fear on every face caught on film. Five hundred soldiers were dying every month and Americans were getting angry about it. The World War II generation wanted the military to run the "conflict" like a war. Much of the younger generation, who had watched their buddies being sent in, wanted no part of it. By 1967, the summer solstice had officially become the Summer of Love.

This social phenomenon launched the hippie movement, powered by anti-establishment, anti-government, anti-war youth. They made San Francisco's Haight-Ashbury district their headquarters. And they became the topic of dinner table conversations across the country. They embraced flower power, and swapped a handshake for casual sex. They transformed clothing and public awareness. They created a line in the sand of time: the years *before* the Summer of Love and the years *after.*

But flowers and love weren't all that that summer produced. Race riots ripped cities apart from Boston to Memphis, and from Durham to Milwaukee. The worst occurred in Detroit, leaving the city a burning battlefield. President Johnson sent in the Army to restore order, and by the time it was over, forty people had died, two thousand more were injured, and five thousand were left homeless.

At 7:55 p.m., on June 23, 1967, President Johnson and his eldest daughter, Lynda Bird, arrived via helicopter at the Century Plaza Hotel in Los Angeles. The President was to deliver a speech at a $1,000-a-plate Democratic Party fundraiser. The L.A. Police Department knew that a coalition of eighty antiwar groups would be demonstrating outside the hotel. They expected between one and two thousand protesters. Instead, ten thousand showed up. The President began his speech at 10:30 p.m., and then listened to the Supremes sing, "Stop! In the Name of Love." He and Lynda Bird left at 11:35 p.m. via the helicopter on the rooftop.

Below, on the Avenue of the Stars, what seemed like a sea of demonstrators were resisting police demands to disperse. Violence erupted and when the protest ended, fifty-one people had been arrested and hundreds injured by the 1,300 nightstick-wielding police officers.

Two months later, President Johnson announced plans to send 45,000 more troops to Vietnam.

The dawn of 1968 brought was greeted with breathless anticipation by Ellen Lewis. The twenty-one-year-old was beginning the last semester of her junior year at Penn State University. But perhaps even more importantly, she had met a handsome architecture student in whom she was very interested. And John Stovall was just as interested in Ellen. He had grown up in metropolitan Washington, DC She grew up in small Honesdale, PA, thirty minutes northeast of Scranton. Despite the difference in their hometowns, there was no denying the sparks that flew between them.

Over two thousand miles away, in Tucson, Arizona, twenty-year-old Susie Leigh was also beginning the second semester of her junior year. Her drive to become a nurse had brought her to the University of Arizona. This shy girl from Prescott, a small town in the northern part of the state, had worked hard, despite an ongoing concern about earning enough money to get to the educational finish line. Susie's past couldn't have been more different from Ellen's. But the events that unfolded over the next eighteen months would have lifelong effects on both young women.

On January 30, 1968, the Viet Cong launched a stunning series of orchestrated attacks against key cities in South Vietnam that came to be known as the Tet Offensive. President Johnson had already lied repeatedly about America's military progress. He continued the practice in statements about the Tet Offensive, assuring the country that victory was just around the corner. In reality, 1968 would become the deadliest year of the war, with a total of 16,592 American deaths.

As fatalities mounted, Johnson's approval rating dropped until it hit 36 percent. Gripped with anxiety, insecurity, uncertainty over the Vietnam War, inner-city riots, the failure of his war on poverty, and his war against cancer and heart disease, the president addressed the nation on the evening of Sunday, March 31, 1968.

After thirty-nine minutes of discussing the Vietnam War, including that he was partially halting the US bombing, he dropped a bombshell of his own in the last minute of his speech. "Accordingly, I shall not seek, and I will not accept, the nomination of my party for another term as your president."

More shocks were in store for the country. Five days after the speech, Martin Luther King Jr. was shot and killed in Memphis, Tennessee. And two months after that, in June 1968, while on the campaign trail, Robert Kennedy was shot and killed shortly after his victory in the California primary.

When election day arrived on Tuesday, November 5, 1968, three names appeared on the ballot: the current Democratic Vice President, Hubert Humphrey; Republican (and former Vice President) Richard Nixon; and former Alabama Governor, George Wallace, running as an independent. The vote counting went on until the early hours of Wednesday morning, when, by the narrowest of margins, Richard Milhous Nixon became the thirty-sixth president. Like Kennedy and Johnson before him, Richard Nixon was about to wade into the same two wars: Vietnam and cancer.

On his last day as president, January 20, 1969, Lyndon Johnson awarded Mary Lasker the Medal of Freedom. It's the highest civilian honor the Chief Executive can bestow. Dubbed the "fairy godmother of medical research" by *Business Week* magazine, Mary was a force of nature. She declared that she was "opposed to cancer and heart attacks the way I am opposed to sin." Medals be damned; Mary was out for cures.

Cancer came to Mary's social awareness plate as the result of two events. The first was a dream. In it, Mary was a child, visiting her family's laundress, who was recovering from a radical mastectomy. Not long after the dream, Mary's housekeeper was diagnosed with uterine cancer, for which surgery was the only available treatment. Those events caused Mary to believe she was being led toward a mission.

In 1940, Mary had wed the millionaire ad man Albert Lasker. She was forty and he was sixty. Albert's ad agency, Lord & Thomas (which would become Foote, Cone & Belding) was legendary and included big-name clients like the Sunkist brand, Palmolive soap, and Pepsodent toothpaste, along with Lucky Strike cigarettes. It was Albert who had created the clever acronym "L.S./M.F.T." (Lucky Strike Means Fine Tobacco). The ad's target was women, whose smoking habits at the time lagged behind those of men. As early as 1912, it was suspected there was a link between tobacco and cancer. By 1954, rigorous studies had been published in the US and Europe that concluded smokers of thirty-five or more cigarettes a day increased their odds of dying from lung cancer by a factor of forty.

In 1942, Mary and Albert founded the Lasker Foundation, whose mission was to support medical research and health programs. One of Mary's first targets was the American Society for the Control of Cancer, which she initially visited in 1943. The stodgy organization was made up of doctors and scientists who focused solely on the treatment of the disease. They subsisted on a $50,000 annual budget (the equivalent of $696,000 in 2021 dollars), with none of that amount marked for research. Mary was appalled, made a $5,000 donation, and went home to plot out the future of cancer research.

Under Albert's tutelage, Mary learned the science of swaying public opinion. After all, Albert was an expert; he did it for a living. He taught her the delicate nuances of "fund raising" and "friend raising." Many of their well-heeled "friends" were tapped for their "funds." Then, in 1945, Mary and Albert staged a coup of the American Society for the Control of Cancer, rechristening it with a name that flowed far more easily off the tongue: the American Cancer Society (ACS).

As with other journalists, Pittsburgh columnist Elsa Maxwell assisted the Laskers during their very first ACS fund drive in April 1945. At that time, Elsa explained, only $5 was spent per cancer "victim." She illustrated the need for that year's $5 million dollar fundraising goal, explaining that "… over $50,000,000 was spent [last year] to advertise cigarettes, breakfast foods and dental creams. We might well have done without those things and been none the worse." Ironically, those were the very things that had made Albert a millionaire. Elsa continued, "But we can't do without control of cancer. It is an invisible enemy."

Elsa's words were just a few of the millions written that year about the people now dubbed "Laskerites." They were a veritable army of philanthropists, scientists, and politicians, rabidly working to raise money to conquer "the greatest enemy of mankind." In the first year of the Laskers' influence, ACS raised $4,292,000 and allocated $960,000 of it for research (the equivalent of $59,741,300 and $13,362,450 respectively in 2021 dollars). This was a far cry from the $50,000 budget Mary had originally encountered.

As an ACS lobbyist explained, Mary Lasker was convinced that the way to lick cancer "is to find something simple: a simple pill that a simple physician can give to a suffering patient..." And if the simple pill treatment sounded like an impossible dream to most cancer scientists, Mary felt they were simply too pessimistic.

Her efforts redoubled when her beloved Albert died of stomach cancer in 1952. Sixteen years later, when President Nixon trimmed the cancer research budget by 3 percent eight months after taking office in 1969, Mary was ready for war.

That same year, Ellen Lewis became Ellen Stovall. She left Penn State and moved to Silver Spring, Maryland. The newlyweds settled in nearby Gaithersburg, and John began his career in architecture. Since social welfare had always piqued Ellen's interest, her position as a project coordinator for a consulting firm, Social Educational Research and Development, was perfect. The firm handled projects involving schools and education within low socioeconomic areas. She ultimately rose to the position of vice president for administration and planning.

On the other side of the country, Susie Leigh's college financial woes had melted away, thanks to a military nursing program. It was a great package for women "who wish to spend at least a part of their career in the Army Nurse Corps." Via the brochure, the military—desperate for nurses—promised Susie enough money to cover university fees and books. They would cover the cost of housing and food, and give her the equivalent of enlisted pay that would take care of her $400 student loan. They would give her medical and dental care, a rare benefit in 1968. Plus, she would have the opportunity to take military hops to exotic places.

The program also afforded Susie the right to shop at Tucson's Davis-Monthan Air Force Base, where everything from food to housewares to gasoline could be had at a discount to members of the military. And to top it off, Susie would receive an officer's commission upon graduation. But more importantly, it was probably the only way Susie would be able to finish nursing school. She just couldn't earn enough money over the course of the summer to cover all her school bills. Of course, the Army Nurse Corps also required a two-year stint in the Army. Susie figured, with her limited experiences at that point in her life, wherever the Army sent her would be an adventure.

On Saturday, May 31, 1969, 4,200 students graduated from the University of Arizona. Army Second Lieutenant Susie Leigh was among them. After a visit with her parents in Prescott, her real Army life began with six weeks of basic training at the nearly one-hundred-year-old Fort Sam Houston in San Antonio, Texas. She graduated from basic at the end of September and received her first official assignment: Letterman Army Medical Center, on the grounds of the Presidio in San Francisco.

Wounded servicemen had been deposited at Letterman since the 1898 Spanish-American War. In 1969, most of the patients were from Vietnam, filling almost all the 929 hospital beds. Susie was a staff nurse in the neurosurgical ward, working with young men who had spinal cord injuries. They were para- and quadriplegics, a heartbreaking life sentence given that the average age of infantrymen in Vietnam was twenty-two.

The patients' monotonous days were spent in CircoLectric beds. An electric motor turned what resembled two small Ferris wheels, with a bed suspended between them. It allowed the paralyzed patients to change position, from vertical to horizontal and everything in between, movement prohibited by their injuries but vital for their circulatory systems. The Circo-Lectrics couldn't be operated by the patients, so that task was added to Susie's list. Her visits were the highlight of the patients' days: she joked with them, played cards with those who could, and looked the other way when their buddies snuck in pizza.

And then, as she presumed it would but kept pushing the thought from her mind, the day came when newly promoted First Lieutenant Susie Leigh was posted to the Republic of South Vietnam. It was July 27, 1970.

"I was so socially naive and inexperienced," she would later say, "that my initial fear was not necessarily of the war, but rather of surviving the incredibly unbalanced male-female ratio!...And with a name like Lieutenant Leigh (pronounced *lay*), what I really needed was a sense of humor."

In its original form, the purpose of Johnson's 1965 bill on Heart Disease, Cancer and Stroke was "to encourage and assist in the establishment of cooperative arrangements among regional medical schools, research institutions, and hospitals for research and training, including continuing education, and for related demonstration of patient care...." It certainly appeared like a logical way to approach these deadly diseases.

Despite the cutbacks as the result of the AMA's reticence at mixing government and medicine, fifty-six regions were established, covering the nation, including Puerto Rico. In December 1965, the National Advisory Council on Regional Medical Programs (RPM) met to initiate the program, and the first planning grants were awarded the following April. These were followed by the first operational grants ten months later, in February 1967. At the end of the year, sixty-one Regional Medical Centers had been designated and four of them were operational. Most of the programs were located at or near university medical schools.

In 1968, the RMP office was transferred to the newly created Health Services and Mental Health Administration. Later that year, the RMP was extended and the program expanded, resulting in a total of forty-four centers (of the original sixty proposed) becoming operational. As 1969 neared its close, and Richard Nixon won the presidency, the RMP was reauthorized for two more years.

And then it was all over. In late 1970, the program was phased out. Research for the original chronic diseases, including cancer, once again seemed to be put on the back burner. Tired of seeing tens of thousands of its young people sent to the war in Southeast Asia only to come home traumatized, physically injured, or dead, America became focused on ending it one way or another. Lyndon Johnson's war on cancer became a forgotten part of history, while a huge and unexpected population of returned service men and women, along with displaced people from Southeast Asia, settled down in America. Among them, however, was a sizable population who had been or were yet to be diagnosed with cancer.

Chapter 3: The Catalytic Agent

In 1971, there are 3 million cancer survivors in America.

Covering 15,600 square miles and sometimes called the "Nine Dragon river delta," the Mekong Delta is a vast maze of rivers, swamps, and islands, home to floating markets, pagodas, and villages. The fertile soil is ideal for agriculture, and rice paddies are everywhere. In fact, half of the country's supply of rice is grown in the delta.

This relatively flat part of South Vietnam has two weather seasons: dry and wet. Susie Leigh arrived at the 3rd Surgical Hospital just in time for the monsoons. Short but torrential rains fell every day, and rainfall averaged a whopping eleven inches a month. Once the ground became sodden—which it did almost immediately during the season—the rainfall had nowhere to go and flooded everything.

The hospital was part of a cluster of American entities that included an air base and a navy base. Lakes formed everywhere. And despite the hospital's name, Susie wasn't a surgical nurse. She worked in the wards taking care of medical patients whose maladies were as foreign as everything else. Scores of men arrived with FUOs (fevers of unknown origin), some of which eventually blossomed into deadly diseases. Because of the days the troops plowed through jungles and swamps, they presented with bacterial and fungal infections, intestinal worms, and liver flukes (the parasitic worms found in Vietnamese rivers). They suffered from cholera, malaria, and a litany of diarrheal diseases, including *E. coli* infection.

Most of the troops with whom Susie served were like her—so young they had limited life experiences to help them cope. They were separated from the safe and familiar. Consequently, Susie's patient ranks also swelled with those whose diseases came as part of the unsafe and unfamiliar. In an effort to numb their senses, the troops turned to excessive drinking and sex. Sex was available everywhere in Vietnam and venereal diseases were rampant.

And oh, the drugs. Mama-sans (Vietnamese women) tossed bags of heroin-laced marijuana over the base fences to get the GIs hooked. That led to injected heroin, and they'd soon become steady customers. When their addictions were discovered, they'd be hospitalized to get clean, and heavily guarded as they were considered criminals. To complete the upside-down, crazed scene, the guards themselves often sold the soldiers drugs right in the hospital wards. For Susie, it was gut-wrenching to watch young men with their entire lives ahead of them die from overdoses.

Susie had always been a fan of the underdog, and was more comfortable out of the limelight that those wounded in battle attracted. The men in her ward needed her skills, and caring for them gave her a sense of purpose. Nonetheless, the work was exhausting. The fear was exhausting. It was all exhausting. Yet, she slogged through, and on July 26, 1971, Susie stepped back onto American soil, her Vietnam experience over.

Mandatory chest X-rays, given to all men out-processing from the war, were usually staged in a massive airplane hangar using portable X-ray machines. Lines of shirtless men gathered at the machines to await their turn for their last military "photo." Because of her gender, Susie was sent to the base clinic, outfitted with a standard X-ray machine and techs to run it. Her X-ray was read, she was given a cursory medical exam, and, in no time at all, she was proclaimed in perfect health. Just like that, she was officially relieved from active duty.

Susie wanted to emotionally heal and do some serious decision-making about the rest of her life. She wasn't even certain she wanted to continue in nursing. She sold her 1965 red Mustang and bought a Volkswagen bus. It was perfect for her plan to stop and smell the roses; you couldn't get anywhere fast with a vehicle like that. She was still plagued by the fatigue she had experienced in Vietnam. Back at her parents' house, her mother became concerned by her shortness of breath and an irritating cough. To appease her mother, Susie made a trip to her hometown doctor. His opinion was that there was nothing wrong with her that rest couldn't cure. So, the Volkswagen rambling continued.

Back home a few months later, Susie received a letter from Steve, one of the corpsmen who had still been on duty at the 3rd Surgical Hospital when she left Vietnam. He told her that shortly after her departure, he had been air evaced to Saigon, where he was diagnosed with Hodgkin's disease. From there, he was sent to Japan to have his spleen removed, often a part of Hodgkin's treatment at the time. He almost died of a postsurgical infection before he could be sent stateside. Steve was now at Tripler Army Medical Center in Honolulu, midway through the gruesome MOPP combination chemotherapy treatment.

Susie rounded up another corpsman who had been in Vietnam with them and they flew to Honolulu for a pre-Christmas visit. They called Steve at the medical center as soon as they arrived, expecting to go straight to the hospital. But he waved them off. When they arrived the next day, Steve looked horrible: gray and haggard, and far older than his twenty-four years. He explained that nothing was available to stave off the horrific nausea that overwhelmed him after every infusion.

Susie's knowledge of Hodgkin's disease at the time was minimal, not surprising since it comprised less than 1 percent of all cancer diagnoses. What little she did know came from her nursing textbooks—which stated that Hodgkin's was always terminal—and her mother, whose father had had the disease at the age of thirty-six. It was, her mother had told her, a slow, painful, and certain death.

Meanwhile, Mary Lasker was charging toward her goal of a cure for cancer. Her approach was simple: if you threw enough money at a problem, it would resolve. That theory had worked time and again in her husband Albert's advertising business. Clients' problems were most often either image- or sales-related. With the right investment, which bought the right message in the right advertising mediums, the problems were solved.

In the biomedical field, polio had been defeated in exactly that way. Because President Franklin Roosevelt's paralysis was a result of the disease, he became the face of it, and of the massive fundraising effort to cure it. In 1938, he and colleagues formed the National Foundation for Infantile Paralysis, which ten years later recruited Dr. Jonas Salk to its ranks. It took Salk and his team just seven years to develop the vaccine that conquered the dreaded disease. And for his amazing discovery, Salk was awarded the 1956 Lasker Award, an annual recognition from the Mary and Albert Lasker Foundation which they had created fourteen years earlier. Mary then turned her attention to a new enemy—cancer.

Polio was caused by three different viruses, but its small family consisted of just a single disease. By the 1960s and early 1970s, cancer researchers were beginning to realize just how Hydra-like their nemesis was. One type of cancer behaved nothing like its cousins. Mary was unimpressed by that knowledge, and she wasn't interested in research into new treatment options. She wanted it gone. She wanted a cure. Returning to her theory of the power of money, she told broadcast journalist Edward R. Murrow that what was being spent on that goal was "... well, it's just piddling!"

Albert had taught Mary that an increase in funding would not happen by appealing to agency heads—those at the NCI, for example. A more powerful target, like Congress or the president, was the way to go. To that end, Mary, a staunch Democrat, placed herself among the top twenty individual contributors to congressional campaigns. She personally gave $69,400 (nearly half a million in 2021 dollars) to Hubert Humphrey's 1968 presidential campaign against Richard Nixon. And she got her wealthy and influential friends to follow suit.

And then there was the congressional lobbying. "Nobody lobbies as well, or has the access Mary Lasker does," an aide to the Senate subcommittee on Health and Scientific Research once told a Knight Ridder reporter.

It was that lobbying a decade earlier that had allowed Mary to press Congress to provide millions of dollars to the NCI for a cancer drug program. This, at a time when the notion of drugs curing cancer was thought to be ludicrous. Furthermore, Mary insisted that the money be allocated to research contracts, as opposed to the traditional grant-making process. Mary Lasker's message was clear: if you want the money, you play by her rules. Researchers had no choice but to comply. And the proof was in the pudding. Throughout the 1960s, those research contracts produced the drugs that cured a variety of childhood leukemias and eventually led to the MOPP chemo cocktail for Hodgkin's disease.

From her Manhattan penthouse, with its snow-white interior, Mary insisted, "I am just an agent, a catalyst. I have no power, but I have access to people who do."

———————————

At 9:32 a.m., on Wednesday, July 16, 1969, the National Aeronautics and Space Administration (NASA) launched the Saturn V space vehicle *Apollo 11*. On Sunday morning, July 20, Neil Armstrong and Buzz Aldrin entered the lunar module, *Eagle,* and set it down on the surface of the moon, at Tranquility Base, at 4:18 p.m. EST. Armstrong reported, "The *Eagle* has landed."

He descended *Eagle's* ladder at 10:56 p.m., and became the first human being to set foot on the moon's surface, proclaiming, "That's one small step for (a) man, one giant leap for mankind."

It was an event that breathlessly captivated the entire world. There were, however, those who saw the achievement as a distraction from more important issues. That position was made most clear in an editorial appearing in many newspapers that Sunday morning.

(Author's note: when the editorial was written, the writer had in mind NASA's original prediction that the inaugural moonwalk would take place on Monday, July 21. But the mission was actually five hours ahead of schedule. Thus, the reference to Monday, despite the fact that Armstrong had done it on Sunday.)

President Nixon asks America to spend Monday concentrating in a "national day of participation." I hope that America also spends Monday in a 'day of meditation' and thinks about the priorities of our country.

Is one of our national goals to pay farmers not to grow food and let children go to bed with an empty tummy?

Is our purpose to spend billions on chemical warfare yet deny drugs to the sick because they cost too much?

Is it necessary to fight a war to make an Asian country 'safe and secure' when we don't dare walk the streets at night in the big cities without getting robbed or raped?

Is it wise to spend billions and billions on sophisticated weapons like ABM and MIRV when we haven't even done our homework and solved cancer, heart disease and the aging process?

Mary Lasker was fully on board with the editorial writer. But she wasn't just going to meditate; she was going to use the historic moonwalk to light a fire under the NCI. In her view, they were still moving too slowly. A country that had put a man on the moon only eight years after President Kennedy had made the challenge, Mary said, was going to be the same country that cured humankind's most feared disease. Focusing on that image, a new 1969 thrust was given the moniker "the moonshot to cure cancer." And with rising numbers of diagnoses and deaths, there was no time like the present to launch.

This prompted Professor Sol Spiegelman, Director of the Institute of Cancer Research at Columbia University, to comment acidly, "...an all-out effort at this time [to find a cure for cancer] would be like trying to land a man on the moon without knowing Newton's laws of gravity."

Still, research *was* happening, including a search for cancer viruses. That same year, then-president of the ACS, Dr. Jonathan E. Rhoads, predicted: "The decade of the '70s will be as crucial in the war against cancer as were the 1880s and '90s with regard to infectious disease."

But Mary wanted more. So, she created the Citizens Committee for the Conquest of Cancer, which would speak through her personally sculpted American Cancer Society. To really drive their case home, the committee published a full-page ad on December 9, 1969, in the *New York Times,* with the heading, "Mr. Nixon: You can cure cancer." It went on:

> This year, Mr. President, you have it in your power to begin to end this curse...more than 318,000 Americans died of cancer last year.
>
> As you agonize over the Budget, we beg you to remember the agony of those 318,000 Americans and their families.
>
> We urge you to remember also that we spend more each day on military matters than each year on cancer research. And, last year, more than 21 times as much on space research as on cancer research...
>
> Why don't we try to conquer cancer by America's 200th birthday? What a holiday that would be! Cancer could be then where smallpox, diphtheria and polio are today—almost nonexistent...
>
> Surely, the war against cancer has the support of one hundred percent of the people. It is a war in which we lost twenty-one times more lives last year than we lost in Vietnam last year. A war we can win and put the entire human race in our debt.

The impassioned plea urged "the public, cancer patients, their friends and relatives" to write or wire the president.

Next, Mary headed to see a friend in the Senate, Texas Democrat Ralph Yarborough, chairman of the Committee on Labor and Public Welfare and its health subcommittee. She persuaded him to introduce a resolution to create the National Panel of Consultants on the Conquest of Cancer. The panel's purpose would be to recommend how the government might better fight the disease. The resolution sailed through the Senate and the panel was officially created in April 1970.

Although newspaper reports stated that it was Yarborough who created the panel, it had Mary's fingerprints all over it. Culling from her Christmas card list, it comprised thirteen cancer specialists and thirteen citizens. It included big names in medicine and research, and ACS officers and board members, along with titans of industry and five of her personal friends. Besides Senator Yarborough, the Who's Who panel listed among its members Dr. Sidney Farber (head of the Boston Children's Cancer Research Foundation and a former player in Johnson's war on cancer), pioneering oncologist Dr. James Holland, Dr. Henry Kaplan, author Solomon Garb, Emerson Foote (the fellow to whom Mary's husband had sold his ad agency, and another player in Johnson's war on cancer), and Benno Schmidt (partner in an investment firm and a major donor to what is now Memorial Sloan Kettering Cancer Center. He was also a pal and major donor to President Nixon. Mary wanted the panel to be a bipartisan effort to endear it to the president). Over the course of the next six months, the panel put together its recommendations in the "Yarborough Report."

Released in October 1970, the report contained three main prongs. First, a National Cancer Authority would be created, "whose mission is defined by statute to be the conquest of cancer." NCI would fall under this authority, and it would be led by a presidentially appointed administrator. Second, the report included never-before requested sums of money for research, $1 billion ($6.28 billion in 2021 dollars) by 1976. The tagline was that America would cure the world's most feared disease by our bicentennial celebration. In other words, cancer would be cured in just six years.

Last, approval for anti-cancer drugs would be moved from the Federal Drug Administration to this new cancer authority. These were astounding demands. But for Mary Lasker and the Laskerites (who were also less kindly known as "the benevolent plotters," "the health syndicate," "the Lasker Mafia," and "Mary's little lambs"), the National Institutes of Health (NIH) and NCI deserved a shakeup. The panel believed that removing bureaucratic obstacles would almost surely speed research toward improved treatment protocols and a cure. What they were really creating was more bureaucracy. The Senate had approved the Yarborough resolution to get the ball rolling, but passing an actual bill in both the Senate and the House would be a very uphill battle.

And then politics intervened. Yarborough was defeated in his November 1970 reelection bid. Before he left the Senate, he introduced his "Conquest of Cancer Act" in December. Once the Senate reconvened in early 1971, Senator Ted Kennedy took Yarborough's place as ranking chairman of the Committee on Labor and Public Welfare. Kennedy vowed to reintroduce the bill and would add Republican Senator Jacob Javits as co-sponsor. But Mary knew that wouldn't cut it. Nixon wouldn't consider anything that had the Kennedy name attached. Her political clout was so hefty that Senator Kennedy withdrew his sponsorship when Mary asked him to. He was replaced as the bill's sponsor by New Mexico Republican Pete Domenici.

————————————

Despite the fact that a human being had just walked on the surface of a heavenly body during his administration, President Nixon nevertheless had dozens of problems he could not easily resolve. In foreign affairs, there was an unwinnable war in Southeast Asia, and a Cold War with the Russians and to a growing extent the Chinese; while on a national front, racial tensions were still high in the aftermath of the 1968 assassination of Dr. Martin Luther King Jr. And on a personal level, Richard Nixon just wasn't very likable.

He had been elected by promising a "secret plan" to end the conflict in Vietnam, already America's longest war. Yet at the dawn of 1971, no plan had emerged and the war raged on. So, taking a page from Johnson's War on Poverty, Nixon began to ponder in earnest a real "War on Cancer." It was the perfect enemy, and it was surely a bipartisan crusade. After seeing the Yarborough report, he knew Democrats worried about cancer as much as Republicans did.

So, in his January 22, 1971, State of the Union speech, Nixon declared:

> I will also ask for an appropriation of an extra $100 million [over half a billion dollars in 2021 dollars] to launch an intensive campaign to find a cure for cancer, and I will ask later for whatever additional funds can effectively be used. The time has come in America when the same kind of concentrated effort that split the atom and took man to the moon should be turned toward conquering this dread disease. Let us make a total national commitment to achieve this goal.

As a part of the Senate hearings on the Conquest of Cancer Act, a chart was introduced into evidence to further explain the necessity of the act. The numbers continued to be mind-boggling. According to the national budget figures, the average cost per person on spending for cancer research in 1970 was 85 cents. This was a shocking number when compared to other per capita expenditures: $20.42 for space research, $45.67 for education, $390.58 for national defense, and an additional $138.52 for "Special Southeast Asia defense operations." Who wouldn't get behind a bill to reprioritize figures like that? Well, the National Cancer Institute, for one.

Every word printed and spoken about the Conquest of Cancer Act smacked of the suggestion—verbalized or implied—that the researchers at NCI just weren't working hard enough. Of course, nothing was further from the truth, particularly in light of the success Dr. DeVita had recently had in his breakthrough combination chemotherapy for the treatment of Hodgkin's disease.

NCI convened their own committee to address the bill's content: the NCI Assembly of Scientists. When they met on March 1, 1971, their purpose was an analysis of the Senate bill Yarborough had introduced. According to their official meeting wrap-up memo, "The bill was analyzed line by line. Preliminary to the evaluation of the bill there was *a brief and spirited discussion.*" (Emphasis added.)

The memo continued: "This philosophical discussion can be summarized somewhat as Joshua Lederberg [professor of genetics, Stanford University] recently did in the *Washington Post* [February 14, 1971]—the crusade for a 'cure for cancer' or 'conquest of cancer' like all crusades is a vast oversimplification and it has potential for backfiring if unachievable hopes are aroused.... In addition, it was felt that it would have been wise to have one or two members from NCI on the Committee of Consultants on Cancer."

Translation: what did an author, an ad man, and an investment firm partner know about cancer research? What qualifications did they have to tell NCI scientists how to spend their days?

Finally, the memo pointed out, "We are concerned that Congress and the public should not be misled to believe that the cancer field is at a stage where the major theoretical problems have been resolved and where a 'Manhattan Project' or 'NASA man on the moon' approach would guarantee success."

In other words, they wisely wanted no part of over-promising and under-delivering.

It was time for Mary Lasker to call in her old friend Ann Landers and ask her to take up the charge. Ann's column on April 20, 1971, began:

"Dear Readers: If you are looking for a laugh today, you'd better skip Ann Landers. If you want to be part of an effort that might save millions of lives—maybe your own—please stay with me."

Astutely pointing out that practically no one reading her column was so lucky to not have had their lives changed in some way by "this dread disease," Landers said that more people had died of cancer in 1969 alone than had died in all four years of World War II. Cancer was still killing at a rate of 50 percent, and it took more children's lives than any other illness.

She supported the creation of the National Cancer Authority (the Yarborough bill's recommendation), likening it—as others before her—to the way NASA functioned. She urged her readers to contact their senators and finished the column with a passionate plea:

> This Conquest of Cancer bill demands that the highest priority be given to devise better methods of prevention, diagnosis and cure of cancer at the earliest possible date. Today you have the opportunity to be a part of the mightiest offensive against a single disease in the history of our country. If enough citizens let their senators know they want Bill S-34 passed, it will pass. I urge each and every person who reads this column to write to his two senators at once—or better yet, send telegrams… No one can do everything, but each of us can do something.

Ann's words hit hearts, and a quarter of a million people did exactly what she asked. For his part, a few weeks later, President Nixon said in a statement that if his proposed $100 million wasn't enough to increase the research, he would provide more money.

Meanwhile, NCI also pushed back on the idea that cancer research should be moved to another entity entirely. On April 29, Dr. Carl Baker, then director of NCI, appeared on the *Today Show.*

"We feel the best place to put this activity is within the government research arm—NIH." Dr. Baker went on with the same wariness his colleagues on the Assembly of Scientists had voiced in their wrap-up memo: "We should caution about the statement of a quick cure within a year or two, comparable to the Manhattan Project. The situation in cancer is complex since it is a hundred different diseases."

Dr. Baker's concerns were echoed by many at NCI. A few days after his TV appearance, the NCI clipping service caught an article in an issue of *BioScience*, published by the American Institute of Biological Sciences. Underlined in red were the words all of them were most terrified of:

> The issue, posed by a bill in the current 92nd Congress, is whether cancer research in this country should be restructured into a new national agency, the National Cancer Authority, and the present National Cancer Institute of the NIH ... should be allowed to lapse.

Yarborough's bill S-34—written to "recommend to the Congress and to the American people what must be done to achieve cures for the major forms of cancer by 1976"—cleared the Senate with ease in a vote of 79 to 1 on July 7, 1971. Not so in the House, where the NIH was finally being heard.

As had been the case when their fellow medical professionals at the AMA pushed back against the Johnson war on cancer proposal, the NCI would not be bullied or told how to do their work by politicians and businessmen. And they would certainly *not* be controlled by an agency outside of NIH. They didn't yet know how cancer worked, they protested, including how cancer cells grow so uncontrollably. They further asserted that "cancer won't yield to a crash-cure program."

Won't yield? Clearly cancer didn't know Mary Lasker! Still, the hearings slogged on for five months. Once again, America's cancer survivors and those yet to be diagnosed became prisoners of war, this time of politics.

A letter arrived at the White House in mid-December 1971. Its author, Stanley Goldman of Wayne, New Jersey, was not aware of all the finite details standing in the way of committing more money to cancer research. He only knew that his daughter was dead.

"An open letter to the leaders of mankind," Mr. Goldman began his White House message,

> I write this letter in a rage of frustration. Our beautiful daughter, Laurie, died of Ewing Sarcoma, a form of bone cancer, at 3:35 a.m., December 3, 1971. She was eleven years and eleven months old.
>
> In four years, this dreadful disease crippled her, gave her pain and misery and finally killed her...The cure to this killing by cancer is simple. It is no more complicated than a polio vaccine, Penicillin, perhaps even a change in diet...We seek the solution piecemeal, an effort here, an effort there, uncoordinated, duplicated deadends [sic], short of intelligent, trained people, short of money.
>
> You who are our leaders must have the courage, the imagination, the intelligence to join together to eliminate this horror, cancer.
>
> As a father in anguish at the loss of his child, as a man in fear for your life, your loved ones as well as my own, I beg, I demand that we unite in one mighty effort to find the answer. We must cure cancer now!

Unbeknown to Mr. Goldman, President Nixon was already weighing the scope of his options. His scientific advisors were objecting to the risky war on cancer platform as it was being laid out. But Nixon's mind was made up. This war, *his* war, would ensure his 1972 reelection. And to ramp up the excitement, the White House P.R. department insisted on using the Lasker timeline. The war on cancer would be won in five years, coinciding with America's bicentennial. With enough money, anything was possible and this bill had been written to provide ample funding for Mary Lasker's long sought-after cure.

Under pressure from both sides of the aisle, concessions in the House were eventually struck. The NCI would remain under the auspices of the NIH and the funding was restructured a bit, although still at previously unseen levels. Most important of all, eradicating cancer was now in the forefront of everyone's mind.

On December 23, 1971, Richard Nixon signed the National Cancer Act in the state dining room of the White House, officially declaring a war on cancer. A jubilant Nixon proclaimed, "It is my hope that history would look back on this as being the most significant action taken during this administration."

America was thrilled. Because of the National Cancer Act, this horrific disease would soon be under human control. Those who were diagnosed would no longer face a 50-50 chance of survival. They would be cured, and would return to their previous lives as healthy, happy, and grateful individuals, living as if nothing had ever happened to them.

Two months earlier, on October 22, 1971, John and Ellen Stovall had welcomed a son, Jonathan, into the world. But the new parents' joy was short-lived. Ellen had been experiencing an odd list of symptoms for four years: itching mistaken for allergies, three miscarriages, and anemia. One doctor prescribed Valium and, by her account, "patted me on the head and said, 'Go home, little girl.'"

A throat irritation that just wouldn't go away finally drove Ellen to seek yet another opinion. Feeling that her family doctor in Honesdale would at least be more sympathetic, she, John and little Jonathan left Washington, DC, for Pennsylvania the week after Thanksgiving. Her appointment was scheduled for December 3, and since her twenty-fourth birthday was the day before, the family had left a day early to combine the appointment with a birthday celebration at her parents' home.

The day after her birthday, Ellen's Honesdale doctor delivered the horrible news: she had Hodgkin's disease. Her treatment began at Georgetown University Hospital the day Nixon signed the National Cancer Act. That night, Nathan Lewis called to check in on his daughter after her first treatment. In an effort to cheer her up, he told her, "Do you know what the President has done for you? He's launched a war on cancer!"

Chapter 4: What More Can We Do?

In 1972, 650,000 Americans are diagnosed with cancer, 4,900 of them with Hodgkin's disease.

Three miles from the White House, on December 23, 1971, while President Nixon was signing his National Cancer Act, Ellen Stovall was lying still and flat on her back under the cobalt therapy unit in Georgetown University Hospital. Although Dr. Kaplan's linear accelerator was rapidly becoming the radiation machine of choice for Hodgkin's disease, Georgetown didn't have one yet. Ellen had felt some relief in her diagnosis, an answer at least to all the odd little things that had been bothering her for some time. But there was no comfort in her prognosis. She had seen a small army of doctors after returning to Washington from Honesdale. One gave her a less than 20 percent chance of survival. Another dismissively said, "Why do you want statistics? It's either 100 percent or nothing for you." A third was more hopeful. If she made it two years without the cancer coming back, her chances of living five years past diagnosis would increase to 50 percent.

So, there she was, staring at a ceiling of asbestos tiles. The doctors had told her to use imagery while undergoing the treatments. But all she could see was peeling paint, smoke alarms, air-conditioning ducts, and sprinkler heads. And the cobalt machine. She later said it was the loneliest time of her life.

Further concerning her was that the radiation was going to be the only treatment she would receive. She had heard about

Dr. DeVita's new combination chemotherapy, and had asked to be part of his clinical trial. But she wasn't eligible, since she was eight weeks postpartum. Her pesky, still fluctuating hormones would have interfered with the purity of the trial, skewing the results. The researchers had figured only people who weren't new mothers would be using the drugs.

Ellen's sixty total nodal radiation treatments were not, at the time, considered curative for her stage and type of disease. That belief wasn't discussed with her prior to her treatment out of fear that she might defer or refuse it altogether. Another fact not mentioned was that for nearly all who received it, Ellen's radiation protocol rendered nearly everyone infertile. She described it all later in the forward of the 2010 book *Cancer Symptom Science*:

> The 1970s were an era where a diagnosis of some common cancers in children was no longer an immediate death sentence, yet where pain and suffering for adults diagnosed with cancer was not uncommon, where outcomes for many adult cancers were virtually uncertain, and where most of the research on the psychosocial and behavioral aspects of cancer was concerned with whether or not to tell the diagnosis, how to prepare for death, how to manage bereavement, and generally, how to reduce suffering.

It was February and Susie Leigh was at a house party in Georgia, where she was visiting friends. Swaying to Don McLean's newly-released ballad, "American Pie," she felt short of breath. And this wasn't the first time. When she coughed up a small amount of blood-tinged mucus, a doctor friend who worked at the nearby army base hospital took her in for an X-ray. The film showed a large mass in her chest between her lungs, and swelling of the lymph nodes in the area. Shocked, she headed home.

Back in Prescott, the local radiologist retook her chest X-ray and told her she needed specialists in a larger city. Since she wasn't working yet and had no insurance, but was a veteran, she elected to go to Tucson to be admitted to the Southern Arizona VA hospital. They began running tests and requested her discharge film that had been taken seven months earlier at the Oakland Army Base. Although it had been proclaimed negative, that X-ray, too, showed the same mass, albeit somewhat smaller. Now the mass had not only grown in size, but also had escaped the lymphatic system into the lining (parenchyma) of the left lung.

It was Hodgkin's disease.

In 1972, oncology was a neophyte specialty. There were only a handful of places that offered treatment, and Tucson, Arizona, was not one of them. The medical team there, however, knew about the research and successful treatment of Hodgkin's disease being done at Stanford University. The Palo Alto VA hospital had a growing relationship with nearby Stanford, and the military patients were the recipients of the cutting-edge oncology treatments Stanford had to offer. The prudent thing to do was to send Susie to Palo Alto. It meant she'd be seen by the very people who were doing the era's most important Hodgkin's research and treatment, so off she went. Susie did not realize it at the time, but the Tucson VA doctors had just saved her life.

The pattern of the pulmonary masses was atypical for Hodgkin's, as they were outside the lymphatic system. The Palo Alto doctors wanted to make certain that there wasn't another disease involved. Perhaps some bizarre fungal infection, possibly picked up in Vietnam, had invaded her chest cavity. A surgical biopsy of the nodes in her lung revealed that her highly irregular masses were, indeed, Hodgkin's.

As Susie explained years later, her discharge X-ray "clearly showed a large mediastinal [the part of the chest that lies between the sternum and the spinal column, and between the lungs] mass, and extralymphatic [outside of the typical lymphatic system] nodes in the left lung parenchyma [the substance of the lung outside of the circulation system that is involved with gas exchange]." The Army radiologist had completely missed all of this, reading the X-ray as negative. And that mistake delayed her diagnosis by seven months, allowing the disease to advance.

Despite the disappointment of the diagnosis—although, like Ellen, Susie was somewhat relieved to at least know what was wrong with her—with the newly concocted combined chemotherapy, better-targeted radiation equipment, and the brilliant men leading her treatment charge, Susie's outcome was likely to be life. This was in stark contrast to the Hodgkin's patients in her grandfather's era. Yet her treatment was still somewhat rudimentary. The port-a-cath (or port), for example, an implanted receptor for chemotherapy, wouldn't be invented until 1981. So, a prominent arm vein was the target of Susie's chemotherapist for her IV, with the specific vein changing with each infusion. (Oncology nursing had yet to become a specialty, so only doctors, often referred to as chemotherapists, were allowed to administer the intravenous drugs.)

Susie had two rounds of chemotherapy at the Palo Alto VA as an inpatient. Having been hospitalized for over two months, she asked if she could go back to the Tucson VA, where she could stay with her brother and receive treatment as an outpatient, for her next rounds. Her request was granted, but the transition wasn't smooth. Her treatment would be delivered by an older physician who had never before given chemotherapy. He automatically went to her large antecubital vein for the injection, not knowing that any leakage of drugs could cause a severe burn in the surrounding tissue and render the vein unusable for future use.

From its beginning, chemotherapy has had a bad reputation because of its serious side effects. The drugs' targets were the rapidly growing cancer cells in Susie's body. But other cells also fell into the rapidly growing category, starting with hair follicles. Her oncologist at Stanford suggested that placing a tourniquet around her hairline during the chemotherapy infusion just might prevent hair loss. This was simply an unproven hunch, but worth trying at that time. Yet, when Susie tried explaining this scalp application to the

Tucson VA doctor, he chided her for her vanity. Cells in her stomach lining would also be affected, and were responsible for severe nausea and vomiting. From the very first injection, the moment the nitrogen mustard hit Susie's vein, she tasted what seemed like the household cleaning product 409. Gagging commenced instantly. Anti-nausea drugs hadn't been developed for this type of chemotherapy, and the Palo Alto doctors suggested she bring peppermint candies to her treatments to mask the taste. A nice thought, but they really didn't help.

Susie returned to Palo Alto for her final course of chemo. By that time, the white blood cells in her bone marrow had been diminished by the drugs, too. They are the body's major infection defenders, without which her body was unprotected against any opportunistic germs. Consequently her doctors sent her home to Prescott to recuperate before beginning radiation.

As noted by the American Cancer Society, the earliest description of cancer (although the word "cancer" was not used) dates back to Ancient Egypt around 3,000 BC. It is part of an ancient Egyptian papyrus on trauma surgery. The author says about the disease, "There is no treatment."

ACS continues its history lesson. In the fifteenth century, "scientists like Galileo and Newton began to develop the scientific method, which was adapted to the study illness. Autopsies done by William Harvey led to his publication of a book about the circulation of blood through the heart and body in 1628 that had previously been a mystery…." A hundred years or so later, "the famous Scottish surgeon John Hunter suggested that some cancers might be cured by surgery and described how the surgeon might do it. If the tumor had not invaded nearby tissue and was 'moveable,' he said, 'There is no impropriety in removing it.'"

By the nineteenth century the development of anesthesia radicalized surgery through the increased treatment of women's ailments from poor birth experiences, and battlefield trauma and classic cancer operations such as the radical mastectomy were developed. Furthermore, up to the twentieth century, nearly all the world's most terrifying illnesses were contagious. Tuberculosis, bubonic plague, smallpox, cholera, dysentery, polio, and many others took children and adults with abandon. Whether spread by air, water, contaminants or bodily fluid, plagues and epidemics taught humans a valuable lesson: stay away from someone who's sick.

It's no surprise, then, that cancer would fall into a similar category. The disease was misunderstood and difficult to study. Doctors believed it was just one disease that struck randomly, since it attacked all organs and bodily systems, and displayed a variety of symptoms. Try as they might, the medical community was often at a loss when it came to treating cancer. For both doctors and lay people, the easiest explanation of its increase in incidence in the nineteenth century, when scientific oncology was born, was contagion. Cancer, many doctors thought, could be "caught," just like any other killer disease.

The newspapers of the day innocently perpetuated that theory. For example, on November 14, 1901, a report was released by the German Cancer Investigation Committee, led by Dr. Ernst van Leyden. It stated that "…cancer is rarely, if ever, hereditary, but he [Dr. van Leyden] does think that it can be communicated from person to person."

Nineteen years later, a personal health newspaper column included a question from a reader: "Would it be safe to give to the poor several articles of men's wearing apparel which were lately worn by a man who died of cancer of the stomach?" The responding doctor said he didn't imagine cancer was contagious. But neither did he resolutely claim that it wasn't.

In 1940, Dr. George Gallup, director of the American Institute of Public Opinion (which later became known simply as Gallup), surveyed Americans coast to coast, asking: "Do you think cancer is contagious?" Fifty-seven percent said no, leaving the other 43 percent somewhere between a definite yes and a solid maybe.

When a 1960 United Press International (UPI) headline shouted "Virus Type of Cancer Contagious?" the public assumed the contagion theory was back on the table. In that article, the Agriculture Department reported studies of poultry cancer which "...established a more firm belief that viruses cause forms of animal and human cancer." The story continued, "The report said this raised the possibility that some virus-produced cancers may be contagious."

Five years after that, in a "How to Keep Well" column, Dr. Theodore R. Van Dellen was asked if lung cancer was contagious. His reply fed fuel to the public's fear of a cancer epidemic, not unlike the polio epidemic that had just been tamed in 1958. "There is a remote possibility," he said. "The cause of lung cancer is not known, except that it is associated with inhalation of irritating smoke and polluted air."

When an American Cancer Society unit convened for a dessert smorgasbord in 1970, a board of doctors (including a surgeon, a radiologist, and a chemotherapist) fielded questions. The most often repeated was: "Is cancer contagious?" Their response still hovered in the vague range. "It is not contagious in the same sense as whooping cough, measles, diphtheria, etc. [And]...particularly not contagious while nursing a cancer patient in the home." But a definitive no was never uttered.

In 1972, around the time Susie Leigh received confirmation of Hodgkin's in Palo Alto, an Associated Press article boasted a bold headline: "Evidence that Some Cancers Contagious." At a Hodgkin's disease symposium taking place just a few miles away, on Stanford's campus, a Sloan Kettering Institute for Cancer Research doctor said, "The telltale biochemical fingerprint of a suspected human cancer virus has been found in the healthy relatives and friends of cancer victims."

Although the doctor stressed that his studies were preliminary and incomplete, every time the words "cancer" and "virus" and "contagious" appeared together, new waves of terror flooded the hearts and minds of anyone who heard or read about it. The cancer researchers weren't doing it deliberately, of course. But many hardships have been launched by such innocent ignorance. What's worse, the doctors at the Stanford symposium were the very ones whose research would be funded by Nixon's war on cancer. They were frantically looking for a cure to meet the 1976 deadline boasted by both the administration and the Laskerites. Finding conclusively that the disease was contagious would be a giant step toward that reality.

The dark side of the contagion controversy was that fear of the disease often drove those living with a history of it into isolation. Whether in treatment or among the now-growing 50 percent who survived, that population lived in the same kind of fear their secret would get out as early sufferers of AIDS would experience decades later. They could lose their jobs and their friends. They, and their families, would be pariahs and shunned.

The fact that heart disease, then as now, killed more people every year than cancer didn't matter. The vision of wasting away from the "Big C" was unbearable. The fear of catching it was unsurmountable. It would be another fourteen years before society would be forced to understand the damage those fears unleashed.

Once physicians completed their residencies, they often went on and became known as "fellows." Training for the fellows who went into oncology in those early days was pretty much trial and error. As chemotherapy was still in its infancy at the time of Susie's cancer, patients were often hospitalized while receiving their treatment. And because she did not live in the area, the VA hospital became her home for the duration.

It was a lonely existence. "I was a young female in a hospital system primarily housing older males, and on top of that, someone who had a disease that was historically terminal," Susie remembered. "There were no specially trained social workers either, so support was hit or miss... I remember feeling tremendously isolated."

Once a treatment plan was finalized, the oncology fellow came in to tell her she was to begin chemotherapy that day. On his way out, he told her matter-of-factly, "And by the way, you will be sterile." He then left before she could say anything.

It was a horrific gut punch! No one had ever discussed long-term side effects with her, especially not something as monumental as infertility. Susie cried for three days. "Nurses cared for me," she said, "but they generally did not have a clue as to how to support me, medically or emotionally."

The next time the fellow was on the ward making rounds, the nurses told him how distressed Susie was. He went to see her, and that's when he made his second huge blunder.

"We are going to cure you," he told her. "What more do you want?"

―――――――――――――――

Even as recently as 2009, the *New York Times* reported on a new study published in the journal *Academic Medicine* that suggested "even established clinicians could be better role models of compassion and care." Bedside manner, until recently, has not been offered as a medical school course. (Surgeons are considered some of the worst offenders, because their patients are mostly unconscious and they don't spend much time with them awake, followed by medical researchers, who rarely meet the people they help.) Consequently, the doctor-patient relationship has been a long and winding mountain trail, fraught with the falling rocks and landslides of miscommunications, mistrust, and devastation. In some cases—perhaps out of proportion with the number of occurrences, since bad stories are generally the ones most repeated in any arena—doctors have presented an air of paternal superiority to patients and their family members. Being smart doesn't automatically make you empathetic.

But in the cancer world, communication, or the lack thereof, was deliberate to the point that physicians would purposefully not tell their patients they had cancer. In the fifth century BC, Hippocrates wrote that "doctors should be economical with the truth ... Honest revelations have caused patients to take a turn for the worse." In the eighteenth century, doctors were told to tell "benevolent lies" and avoid making "gloomy prognostications." The position was that the emotional state of the patient directly affected their ability to fight off disease. True enough. At that time there was virtually no curative treatment for cancer. A diagnosis equaled a death sentence.

One of the 1915 ten commandments of cancer was that physicians, "Use good judgment in telling patients they have cancer. But tell relatives." Again, the theory was repeated: why depress patients and hasten their demise?

It wasn't until 1953, when Dr. Jacob Finesinger, a Harvard psychiatrist and researcher, conducted a survey with cancer patients at Massachusetts General Hospital that this prevailing theory was challenged. The survey participants expressed strong negative emotions about their disease: "... fear in almost every case ... guilt, 'It is my fault I have a cancer; I must have done something wrong,' in about two-thirds of the patients ... and feelings of inferiority."

Part of the problem, Dr. Finesinger felt, was that "... the doctor has difficulty in dealing with the patients because he knows the patient has cancer, yet does not know what to do or say." And then he said something totally out of character for his era: "Adequate treatment in cancer must involve treatment of the patient as well as of the lesion ...."

In other words, at a time when very little could be done to rid a patient of cancer, the doctors were also under psychological stress, as it fell on them to deliver bad news with no good news to follow. All their medical training was useless, and despite their *Father Knows Best* approach to treating their patients, they felt powerless.

Part of the noncommunication was also cultural, with family groups choosing not to tell their loved ones about the disease because that custom had been passed down through generations. Many patients knew anyway, of course, and a comical charade would be played out between doctor, patient, and family. For most, regardless of gender or culture, cancer was a word that just wasn't spoken. Ever.

In a sad side note, for all the progress Dr. Finesinger made in patient communication before his death on June 22, 1959, his obituary still followed the day's custom. It read that he had died at the age of fifty-six, "after an illness of more than a year." That was journalistic code for "death by cancer."

The nondisclosure drum was still banging in 1971 (just before Nixon signed the National Cancer Act), when Dr. J. L. Mathis, chair of the Psychiatry Department at the Medical College of Virginia, suggested:

> If, as evidence indicates, a certain constellation of personality characteristics predisposes an individual to the development of cancer, then it must be hypothesized that the rate of growth and progression of a known malignancy may in some way be connected with the same emotional factors.

Translation: not telling the patients of their disease might keep emotional factors, and by extension the disease, in check.

The air of cancer secrecy produced a crazy existence for everyone. Doctors didn't want to discuss the disease with patients. Families didn't want to discuss the disease with patients. And patients didn't want to discuss their disease, either because they didn't want to worry their families, or because they were afraid of the social stigma cancer conjured. The result of it all was a tsunami of stress.

The communication gap was never more tragic than in the case of a young woman in 1972, who, like Susie, had also been told that her chemotherapy had rendered her infertile. She had a break between treatments, and she and her husband went on what was to be a healing getaway. She returned, finished chemo, and had gone through several radiation treatments when a peculiar lump in her belly sent her back for tests. Had the cancer metastasized to her abdomen?

As a matter of protocol, a pregnancy test was given, although everyone expected it to be negative. Everyone was wrong. The couple hadn't used contraception, believing it wasn't necessary. Now, two people who had been told they'd never have children had to abort a fetus. After existing in a bath of toxic chemicals followed by deadly assaults of radiation, the baby would have either died in utero or been born with severe, and probably fatal, birth defects.

Even as this book is being written (2021), only one in two women are told their fertility might be at risk due to their treatments. Science has made advances in cryopreservation (allowing women to freeze eggs or fertilized embryos, and men to freeze sperm), but monthly storage fees are often too great a burden. Greater still are the costs of fertilization and implantation, not covered by many insurance plans.

A final tale of a lack of communication drives home the point. Lurleen Wallace was thirty-five in April 1961 when she gave birth to her fourth and final child via cesarean section. More than a beautiful daughter came into the light that day. The surgeon noticed suspicious tissue during the procedure and biopsied it. The tissue proved to be cancerous. Following the era's common practice, Lurleen's physician told her husband, George, the news, but not her. The man who a year later would become Alabama's governor and begin several attempts to become president soon after that, then insisted that his wife not be informed.

As a result, Lurleen didn't receive appropriate follow-up care, and when, in 1965, she saw a gynecologist for abnormal bleeding, his diagnosis came as a complete shock. She had uterine cancer. To make matters worse, one of her husband's staffers revealed to her that Wallace had discussed her cancer with them during his gubernatorial campaign. She was outraged. Nonetheless, she followed through on a plan George had to keep the governorship in the family. Despite his popularity in the state, Alabama term limits prevented him from seeking a second term. George figured Lurleen could win the spot in 1966, and then he'd take it back after her term was up.

Now it was Lurleen's turn to keep her cancer a secret. She began radiation in December 1965, had a hysterectomy in January 1966, maintained a brutal campaign schedule, and was inaugurated as governor a year later. By June 1967, another tumor was found on her colon and more radiation ensued. Six months later, she informed her staff (but not the public) that she had a cancerous pelvic tumor. Despite the prior surgeries on her uterus and colon, and the radiation treatment, Lurleen's cancer had spread. Her last public appearance as governor was at the 1967 Blue–Gray Football Classic, followed by a campaign appearance for her husband's presidential bid on the American Party ticket on January 11, 1968.

Yet, despite the fact that the cancer was in her liver and lungs, she weighed less than eighty pounds, and her illness had, by this time, been announced publicly, George still lied to the press about her condition, going so far as to claim in April 1968, "she has won the fight." A month later, Alabama's first woman governor died.

Dr. Arthur I. Holleb joined the American Cancer Society in 1948 as assistant director of the Service Division. One of Dr. Holleb's early assignments was to convince gynecologists and obstetricians of the value of a new cancer screening called a Pap smear, named for its developer, Dr. George Papanicolaou. Dr. Holleb initially encountered a great deal of skepticism. But by the end of 1949, the Pap smear had become the centerpiece of cancer awareness.

By early 1972, Dr. Holleb wrote a stirring perspective in the ACS magazine, *CA: A Cancer Journal for Clinicians*. Titled "The Cancer Patient—Too Often Alone," it read in part:

> …We are haunted by our failure to cure the patient, the family by their guilt and the patient by grief he cannot share. Even when the disease is controlled, the difficulties of rehabilitation, the chances of recurrence and the enormous cost

of treatment must be faced. Too often, solutions to these problems are sought in isolation—without help and without real understanding.

Following up on this sentiment, the American Cancer Society decided to hold a National Conference on Human Values and Cancer the following June in Atlanta, Georgia, focused on the belief that the "team approach" to treatment was as valuable in treating people as it was in science and medicine.

It was an extraordinary idea. The meeting was held June 22–24, 1972, at the still relatively new Regency Hyatt House on Peachtree Street in downtown Atlanta. Julie Nixon Eisenhower, the president's younger daughter, was the opening keynote speaker.

Dr. William Markel, the ACS vice president for Service and Rehabilitation, and the conference coordinator, was quoted in the press as saying, "the meeting will emphasize the humanistic problems of the cancer patient, including interpersonal relationships, rehabilitation, employability, insurability and hopes for miracles."

In the end, several hundred attendees, including surgeons, psychiatrists, nurses, psychologists, and social workers, spent three days talking about such human values through the lens of cancer. It was revolutionary. Many of those issues, if not all, had been for generations a large part of the list of previously unspoken "demons" of survivorship.

―――――――――――――――

You can write the most well-reasoned, well-documented third-person story in the world, and people may or may not notice it. But write personally, about yourself, and the phone will ring off the hook for days, sometimes for months. It seems that though people hunger for health information, they respond most strongly to stories about individuals.

By the time these words appeared in the forward of Natalie Davis Spingarn's 1982 book, *Hanging In There: Living Well on Borrowed Time*, she had become quite a cancer expert. The native New Yorker had used her 1943 Bachelor of Arts degree from Vassar College to become a journalist, writing on health and social policy for the federal government.

Natalie was a prolific writer. Among the topics she covered as a freelance journalist in books as well as magazine and newspaper articles were mental health, primary care nursing, and the politics of health research. She produced an anthology of true stories of the men and women of the US Public Health Service. She was hard-driving, often not even stopping for lunch on a work day. She certainly would not have had time to deal with a potentially life-ending illness, nor was it remotely on her radar.

Natalie had seen a doctor in the summer of 1974 for a routine exam. With a clean bill of health in hand, she prepared for a much-anticipated trip to Israel with her husband, Jerry. A few weeks later, in Jerusalem, she felt a lump in the upper part of her right breast. It felt big and hard, but Jerry was reassuring. She had had lumps before and they had proven benign, he told her. They continued their trip, stopping in Spain before heading home.

Once she was back in the States, the fifty-two-year-old called her doctor immediately, and was in his office that same week in September. Reminding her that she had what was known as "lumpy breasts"—breasts with fibrocystic disease—her doctor suggested a surgical biopsy (in those days it was done under general anesthesia). If the biopsy results were benign, he'd sew her back up and she'd be back on the journalistic trail in a few days. If he found cancer, he would do whatever kind of mastectomy he felt best. That protocol was called the "one-step mastectomy."

Trusting the man, Natalie agreed. But when she awoke from surgery, she discovered she had just one breast. In a calm, matter-of-fact voice, the doctor told her he had removed the breast because the growth was malignant, "garden variety," but *there*, nonetheless. As Natalie later wrote, "He thought my chances were good because he had 'gotten it all.'" In that era, that common phrase meant "as much as possible," and suited American zest for all or nothing.

Natalie continued the description of her mastectomy saga:

[I was] sitting on a bench near a hospital nursing station, waiting to be dismissed, when he [a resident] approached. "How are you?"

"Okay." And then, because that didn't seem enough, "I get a little blue once in a while, but that's all. The doctors tell me a little postoperative weeping is par for the course."

"Ah," he answered. "You like to read, don't you?" He had observed the books and magazines on her bed.

"Yes."

"Well, you should read *On Death and Dying.*"

Natalie was astounded.

Having consigned me to the grave, he allowed that the operation I had was often successful. Then he disallowed such optimism by going through Elisabeth Kübler-Ross's *On Death and Dying* thesis: At first, the dying person denies his situation, then feels angry, asking "Why me?"

After her second recurrence in 1979 (the first recurrence was in 1977), she shared another story of regrettable discourse with a health care worker. This *Washington Post* article ran in early 1980.

I am living still in my Washington hospital bed…A nurse comes in to check on me. 'What's the matter with you?' she wants to know…my disease seems to her my fault. She makes no move toward me, even to inquire if I need anything, and observes that I should have talked to the doctor about avoiding its spread.

As shocking as these experiences must have been, there can be little doubt that what began as very dark times in Natalie's life, as well as the lives of her family, would eventually became pivotal in her career. Coupled with her journalistic inquisitiveness and a powerful command of language, those experiences would soon compel Natalie to use her voice in support of her fellow cancer survivors.

Chapter 5: The Empire

In 1974, 655,000 Americans are diagnosed with cancer.

On the last page of the March 1973 American Public Health Association newsletter, below the personal and death announcements, another notice was posted:

American Cancer Society Announces Cancer Nursing Conference
September 10 &11, 1973
Palmer House, Chicago, Illinois

A description followed:
Cancer Nursing: Precepts, Principles and Practice. This conference, the first of its kind on a national scale, will emphasize current trends in nursing practice related to the prevention, treatment and rehabilitation of patients with cancer. Speakers will be leaders in their fields, and there will be an opportunity for audience participation. Sessions are open to professional nurses and professional nursing students only. Preregistration is requested. There is no registration fee.

The announcement suggested that, for more information, interested nurses could contact Virginia Barckley, the "National Nursing Consultant," at the American Cancer Society (ACS) in New York City. Such a simple announcement. But it would change the face of cancer care for millions. Virginia and the event's other organizer, Renilda Hilkemeyer of Houston's M.D. Anderson (now

MD Anderson) Cancer Center, expected a hundred attendees. More than twenty-five hundred registered.

Both organizers made a lasting impression on every attendee. It was particularly true of Virginia. She had completed her nurse's training, and gone on to earn a Bachelor's of Science in Public Health Nursing from the University of Pennsylvania. While completing it (which she did in 1943), Virginia worked for the Philadelphia Visiting Nurses Association. As a visiting nurse, she attended an ACS meeting whose program was the discussion of "terminal cancer"— in the common verbiage of the time—of which she would later say: "You couldn't be a visiting nurse without seeing a great deal of cancer, and you couldn't see a great deal of cancer, especially in the 1940s, without being deeply touched and deeply impressed." Her passion for cancer nursing evolved until she arrived at the point where "somewhere inside, you decide something's got to be done, and I want to be one of the people who do it." After volunteering for ACS, she joined the staff in 1962.

Even decades later, Susan B. Baird, one of the young nurses who attended the Palmer House meeting, remembered Virginia clearly. "This tiny woman, with both hands grasping the podium as if to help her see over its top, delivered a powerful message about the opportunity for nurses to make a strong contribution to cancer care. Her distinctive voice and wonderful storytelling ability are still with me and I know how privileged I was to have come into cancer nursing during her era and to have benefited from her experience and commitment."

After the conference ended, twenty of the attendees, all of whom were passionate about their work with cancer patients, crammed into a Palmer House hotel room to discuss the future. Depending on where they were located, the nurses were randomly called "cancer nurse," "oncology nurse," or "chemotherapy nurse." They conceived an idea of an organization specifically for cancer care nurses, a national network that would enable them to communicate and share information with one another.

The existence of nurses whose specialty was cancer had much earlier roots. In the 1915 meeting of the nurses' association for the state of Michigan (its eleventh annual), Dr. Reuben Peterson, medical director of the Ann Arbor university hospital, inspired his nurse attendees with: "Let your motto for cancer be what the students of this University of Michigan use when the football team is getting a little the worst of it, 'fight, fight, fight.'"

Earlier in his address, Dr. Peterson had asked for the support of the nurses' association in the fight against cancer. It was the trained nurse, he proclaimed, who carried out the anti-tuberculosis campaign that had occurred several years earlier. "I am free to confess that organized effort against the great white plague would have proved a dismal failure but for her [the nurses'] efforts." Sadly, Dr. Peterson's position was not one widely held.

As infectious diseases became more controlled in the early twentieth century, people began living longer. The nation's population was aging and more were entering the "cancer-prone" years. Thus, there were more diagnoses. At the same time, nurses, whose jobs had been to make dying cancer patients comfortable, found their work had expanded into unexpected, unfamiliar, sometimes even unrealistic, territory.

During the "conspiracy of silence," when the physician-run medical community considered concealing a diagnosis of cancer from a patient to be the humane thing to do, cancer care nurses were expected to use the same euphemisms as the doctors. It wasn't cancer being treated. It was a "growth," a "cyst," a "lingering illness," a "serious infection," or slightly more truthful, "metastatic disease." But those mild explanations gave root to extraordinarily difficult challenges for nurses.

Patients went into the operating room to have a "cyst" removed from their colon and came out to discover they were now forever attached to a colostomy bag. Nurses found themselves in an untenable position: either lie to the patients or ignore their requests for information. An immensely delicate dance ensued, as it was the nurses who were constantly with the patients, while the doctors were able to keep their patient face time relatively short.

Also a challenge, particularly in the first half of the twentieth century, was the radiation exposure experienced by cancer care nurses. It was a serious threat. They were advised to spend as short a time as possible with patients who were undergoing this little-understood treatment, a suggestion at direct odds with the kinds of care the patients needed. Radiation pellets, either implanted into an orifice, or taped onto the body, were expensive and had to be kept track of. Since surgical dressing changes were needed, it was the *nurses* who had to handle and count the pellets, taking care that the little things didn't get lost in the gauze or sheets.

Patients with skin cancer were treated with radium masks affixed over the cancerous area. Every hour during the eight to ten hours of daily treatment, it was the nurses who checked to make certain that the masks were in place. And nearly every radiation treatment resulted in patient tissue death. It was the nurses who removed the necrotic and radioactive skin that sloughed off.

By the time those twenty nurses came together in Chicago in 1973, the War on Cancer's money was flowing into research. As the numbers of cancer patients responding to their treatments rose, so too the need for cancer care nurses began to swell. The Chicago group clearly recognized that need. Most had wanted to be nurses since they were girls. Cancer was making more frequent headlines, and therefore becoming a more intriguing area of medicine to young nurses. Some had even had the disease themselves. But whatever brought them into the cancer world, none were prepared for what came next.

Early on, experience wasn't required for most cancer care nurses. The fact was, no one had experience since, in most cases, they were pioneers. What their jobs entailed had rarely been covered in nursing school. Years later, referring to experience, one nurse remembered, "We got it all and much more in the first year. We were long on shortages of all kinds—including more nurses—and short on long talks and reflections about our practice."

The lack of "talks" and "reflections" left great, dark holes in their professional lives. They identified with their patients, felt guilt at their deaths, and recognized their own mortality. Their emotional roller-coasters were magnified many times over, as compared to those of doctors, because they were the people who spent so many hours with patients.

While the newly developed treatments continued to show promise, nurses also saw the cost. Once the doctors left the patients' rooms, it was again the nurses who dried women's tears over their amputated breasts. They cleaned up after patients feeble from violent vomiting and diarrhea. And it was those same nurses who held patients' hands as they took their last breath when family members didn't arrive in time.

These nurses simply weren't prepared for the psychological needs of their patients and their families. They had had no training in this area and no one had warned them that this, too, would fall on their shoulders.

Medications to manage treatments were evolving, but nowhere near the pace of their needs. Those who needed pain management the most were still dreadfully under-medicated. Furthermore, both the medical community and patients had an overwhelming fear of drug addiction. It was a ridiculous scenario. If drugs, even dangerous ones, for dying patients couldn't be controlled in hospitals, what was the point of having them available? So, despite working in a country that was churning out significant cancer research, these young nurses were charged with caring for people with one hand sometimes tied behind their backs, and forced to watch the resultant pain-racked death.

The physical danger the cancer care nurses faced expanded as the use of chemotherapy increased. While they weren't allowed to administer the therapy until later, they were charged with mixing the new, highly toxic chemicals along with being exposed to the improved—and far more powerful—radiation treatments while relatively unprotected. The scenario caused a spectrum of physical reactions, from rashes to coughs to their own cancer diagnoses down the road. Since they weren't yet an organized group, there was no way to share information among themselves, and as a result no way to share warnings.

The nurses' extended time with patients also caused them to notice things that doctors didn't. They observed the difficult and traumatic effects extended treatments caused. For example, in an effort to ensure that breast cancer was completely eradicated from a woman's body (before metastasis was clearly understood), one nurse explained that early chemotherapy treatment went on in excess of a year. Women who quit early were labeled by their doctors as "noncompliant."

"We had no idea what would happen to them long-term," she said. "Yet those who stopped, survived best. It was us—the nurses— who understood. We knew our patients. And we supported their decisions."

And the reward for all their trial-and-error learning, mostly in complete social isolation? Their profession, until now, has been little more than a footnote in medical history. For some, the best way to recover from the death, depression, and fear of the cancer floor was to seek another specialty. After all, time in the obstetrics ward, where life began, was nearly always a far happier place.

In 1975, Dr. Fitzhugh Mullan, known to his friends as Fitz, had worked at *La Clínica de la Gente* (Clinic of the People) in Santa Fe, New Mexico, for the past three years. It was a community-governed medical practice to which he was assigned by his employer, the US Public Health Service. One March morning, the thirty-two-year-old doctor was standing in front of an X-ray developing machine. A young mother had come in earlier with her one-year-old child who was suffering from a cough and lack of appetite.

Fitz was now waiting for two films. One was the child's chest X-ray—Fitz assumed the little guy had pneumonia. The other was an impromptu chest X-ray he had done of himself. For over three months now, Fitz had suffered an occasional and strange pain in his chest. He had now developed a persistent cough. Fitz's diagnosis of the baby's condition was correct. But when he looked at his own film, he became alarmed. There, just to the right of his heart, sat a white density looking like a hazy cauliflower and about the size of a grapefruit. Fitz knew he needed a biopsy.

As a member of the Public Health Service, Fitz could seek medical treatment anywhere in the country. He chose the National Naval Medical Center in Bethesda, Maryland, since his parents lived in nearby Washington, DC. After his initial examination in Bethesda, it was agreed he would undergo a mediastinoscopy, done via an incision in his lower neck under general anesthesia. It would allow the surgeon to send a scope into the area between Fitz's lungs and around his heart, where the tumor was growing. The procedure finally took place on March 28. It was Good Friday.

Fitz suddenly went from seeing things from the physician's side to being a patient. In his 1982 book, *Vital Signs*, he describes this unfamiliar persona.

> When we arrived in the surgical area, I was parked in what proved to be the recovery room alongside a number of other supine, sheet-clad figures. Though I did no checking, I presumed that they also had left their pajamas in their rooms.... we were men and women, large and small, and our ranks continued to swell until the recovery room was fairly packed. We were surely an unusual congregation, nude, pensive and silent.

Fitz was finally wheeled into the operating room. And it wasn't long before everything went terribly wrong. His body had to be torn open, and he nearly died twice. As he slowly regained postoperative consciousness, Fitz realized he was on a respirator in intensive care, with large amounts of tape on his chest. His own description is terrifying.

...the tumor was massive and had grown around and through a number of vital structures in the mediastinum [his chest cavity], including the superior vena cava—the indomitable vein—a number of key nerves, the pericardium, and the right lung. Through the mediastinoscope it had been difficult to tell what was tumor and what was not.

The vena cava carries massive amounts of blood back to the heart. And it ran just beneath the piece of tissue chosen for the biopsy. Erroneously cut, that vein's blood poured out. The surgeons performed an emergency thoracotomy, splitting Fitz's chest down the front and under his breast to the back. With the chest already open, surgeons decided to remove as much of the tumor as possible. It was identified as a seminoma, "an unusual [cancerous] tumor occasionally found in the chest, but one that was amenable to treatment and potential cure."

It was the perfect storm of medical horror. Cancer *and* a surgery so aggressive, Fitz was potentially open to pneumonia, congestive heart failure, internal bleeding, and infection. His breastbone had been split, with several ribs cracked. His heart had been manipulated and his lungs manhandled. Everything hurt: breathing, moving, and above all, coughing.

The medical team determined that Fitz's cancer should be addressed immediately. Beginning in mid-April, two weeks after his surgery, he would receive cobalt radiation every morning, five days a week for six weeks. Chemotherapy would begin three weeks postsurgery, delivered intravenously on a weekly basis. Half an hour after his first noxious dose, Fitz became fatigued and his temperature shot up. This was followed by extreme shivering as his temperature returned to normal. Twenty-four hours later, the nausea began, lasting two days or so. After a short respite of a few days, the whole wretched process began again.

As patients before him had, Fitz too asked himself why cancer had entered his life. Where had it come from? Was it his parents' fault, or from something he had done in his youth? Maybe it was the stress of being a physician? He even, as he explained, "entertained some fairly outlandish thoughts. Just two weeks before my tumor was discovered, a friend had sent me a chain letter with a complicated set of instructions that included a brazen threat to the health of anyone who failed to send the letter on." Upon remembering this grim message, Fitz also remembered the fact that he had not sent the letter.

At the end of his treatment and surgical recovery, Fitz surveyed the collateral damage. Radiation had destroyed a certain amount of the lung tissue in his chest and burned his esophagus, temporarily making eating painful. He had internal scarring and a partially paralyzed diaphragm from the emergency surgery. The nausea (and the burned esophagus) had caused considerable weight loss, although he had gained most of it back by the one-year anniversary of his diagnosis. The greater problem was how to assimilate the cancer experience into his everyday life. For example, when acquaintances asked, "How have you been?" the correct answer eluded him. "Fine" didn't work, nor did "pretty good, other than a touch of cancer." He didn't have the energy to spell out the entire saga, and there were those who still wondered if the disease was contagious.

Fitz had long been an eloquent writer. While recovering from his treatments, he finished a book he had begun before his diagnosis. *White Coat, Clenched Fist* (1976) was an autobiographical account of his political activities during medical school, internship, and residency. He now began to write *Vital Signs,* and would spend the next ten years sorting out his feelings about the disease that nearly ended his life.

The effort to create a nationwide specialized nursing organization turned out to be a much larger undertaking than the nurses in Chicago had imagined. But they would not be deterred.

They had two goals: identify other cancer care nurses across the country; and encourage the development of educational programs for medical staff and then create meetings at which those programs could be shared.

Virginia Barckley and Renilda Hilkemeyer, the organizers of the first meeting, were joined by Connie Henke, Shirlee Koons, Lisa Marino, and others, each of whom divided up the tasks required to accomplish their goals. This was, of course, in addition to their day jobs as nurses. During a November 1974 meeting jointly held in Chicago by NCI and ACS, a true organizational meeting for cancer care nurses was also scheduled. By this time, the original twenty had become seventy-one. They discussed whether to affiliate with a more established organization like the American Nurses Association. Cindi Mantz (now Cantril), a nurse attendee who had consulted with an attorney on the group's behalf before the meeting, shared the lawyer's somewhat negative musings. While writing their own ticket as a stand-alone organization would be easy, they "would have little clout, since communications with other groups would be difficult." Still, the nurses were not deterred. By January 1975, their goal of identifying cancer care nurses in the country had produced a list of more than four hundred names.

Mother's Day weekend arrived amid an unusual national weather pattern. No matter where you were—New York City, Washington, DC, Chicago, or San Diego—coast to coast, the forecast for Friday, May 9, was warm spring sunshine, interspersed with gentle showers, and temperatures in the mid-60s and 70s .

Nine days earlier, Saigon had fallen to the Viet Cong, officially closing the book on the Vietnam War. Newspapers across the country were still discussing the war's impact and what a unified Communist Vietnam would look like.

That weekend, two events of note took place. First, Sony's Betamax home videotaping system went on sale in Japan. The unit contained a color TV, the recorder, and tapes, and retailed for $2,488 ($11,653 in 2021 dollars). The device would have an impact for generations to come.

The same was even more true for the second event: the joint meeting of two cancer research behemoths. Representatives of the American Association for Cancer Research (AACR) and the American Society of Clinical Oncology (ASCO) met at the Town and Country Convention Center in San Diego. The cancer care nurses had scheduled a meeting to occur at the same time. However, the space allotted them at the conference center wasn't large enough to accommodate all those who wanted to attend. Local nurse Florence Downs arranged for space at the nearby San Diego Community College, necessitating a commute in a very cramped bus. Upon arrival, the fifty or so nurses in attendance filed into a hot, poorly ventilated lecture room, and sat at school desks ready to make nursing history.

They voted to create a formal and independent organization for their specialty, which they agreed would officially be called Oncology Nursing. It followed, then, that their organization would be the Oncology Nursing Society (ONS). The next step was to put out a call for members and send out applications.

The young organization's applications had to be accompanied by a letter of reference, and in this pre-fax and pre-internet era, everything was handled via the US Postal Service. Between Mother's Day and August, eighty-five nurses sent in their membership applications. By the beginning of October, the number had grown to 238. When charter membership officially closed in January 1976, the official charter membership listed 488 names. And they were well on their way to planning their first annual meeting, which they called a congress, to be held in Toronto that May. Their first order of business would be to create standards of care for cancer patients across the country and around the world.

―――――――――

In between her radiation treatments at Georgetown University Hospital, twenty-four-year-old Ellen Stovall focused on being a wife and mother. She couldn't imagine not being alive to raise her son, couldn't imagine not growing old with her husband. But she was pondering what one of the first doctors she saw had told her—if she made it two years post-treatment, she'd have a 50 percent chance of making it to five years. As many had done before and have since, Ellen struck a bargain with the universe. She vowed that if she did indeed survive to the two-year mark, she would devote the rest of her life to doing something about cancer. And Ellen Stovall was as good as her word.

Shortly after her treatment ended, Ellen asked a hospital social worker where she might find other young adults with whom to discuss the challenges of life post-cancer. Hers was a strange, dark world where she had both a baby *and* hot flashes. She was depressed and frightened. The future loomed with ominous uncertainty. She was sure others must have similar post-cancer trauma symptoms. The hard fact was, she learned, the support she was seeking wasn't available in Georgetown. So together with the social worker, Ellen started the first peer support group for young adult cancer survivors at Georgetown University Hospital.

Volunteering ran in Ellen's blood. Her tightly knit family had always been engaged in the community. As a child, she had tagged along with her mother to roll bandages for the American Cancer Society (ACS). She had been a Girl Scout and at twelve had completed a Red Cross water safety course at a camp. The DC-area young adult support group was just the first step in Ellen's payback.

The Leukemia Society (the organization's name would be changed to the Leukemia and Lymphoma Society in 2000) next benefited from Ellen's energy and talents. Following that, she returned to ACS, where she became a full-time volunteer fundraiser and then the coordinator of their DC CanSurmount support program. All this cause-related work opened Ellen's eyes to an important but nonexistent element of cancer care: patient advocacy.

Advocacy is generally thought of as public support for a particular cause or policy. In the cancer community, advocacy took on both a broader and a more intimate definition. An advocate could be either a single person, monitoring an individual cancer patient's treatment, care, and survivorship; or an organization doing the same kind of thing for an entire community of cancer patients—or any variation in between.

Ellen realized she had had cancer under the best of circumstances. She had access to a comprehensive cancer center; she had a husband and family who supported her; they had great insurance coverage and the financial means to cover the expenses the insurance did not. It wasn't long before Ellen came to realize how vastly different the cancer experience is from person to person.

Cancer is indeed the "emperor of all maladies," as Dr. Siddhartha Mukherjee christened it in his 2010 Pulitzer Prize-winning book of the same name. This "emperor" rules four realms. The first two have received attention for decades—the realm where there is a search for a cancer cure, which Mary Lasker and her Laskerites were certain was just around the corner; and the realm that encompasses advances in cancer treatment, which scientists had been working steadily to improve.

Now a third, new realm was gaining attention: cancer prevention. Five years earlier, even before the cancer war had been declared, a July 1971 headline had proclaimed "Cancer: Prevention Is the New Watchword." At the same time, the World Health Organization estimated that 85 percent of all cancer was caused by environmental factors. And public enemy number one was tobacco.

Throughout the 1960s, the "war on smoking" had held the public's attention. In 1961, the ACS, the American Heart Association, and the National Tuberculosis Association asked President Kennedy to appoint a commission to investigate the link between smoking and health. Tales of the battles waged against big tobacco have filled volumes. The condensed version of the result is that in 1966, a warning appeared on all cigarette packs: "Caution: Cigarette smoking may be hazardous to your health." This took on more punch in 1970, when it was changed to: "Warning: The Surgeon General has determined that cigarette smoking is dangerous to your health."

Broadcast cigarette advertising—always focused on the theme that classy, beautiful women and rugged, handsome men were cool because they smoked—was targeted too. The last television cigarette ad aired at midnight, January 2, 1971. That timing had given the "Marlboro Man" one final shot at viewers during the New Year's Day college football bowl games before he rode off the screen forever.

The campaign against smoking fed into the ultimately larger campaign for cancer prevention. As a steady stream of smokers quit, a wave of consciousness was aroused in Americans about their consumption, their environment, and their activities. Later, in an article appearing on April 20, 1978, national correspondent Frank Greve was concise when he wrote: "If the cancer crusade loses its status as a holy war, it will happen on the prevention battlefield. Cure and treatment have no enemies; prevention has plenty of them."

A growing number of scientists and congressmen were adamant about a major new emphasis on prevention. They proposed placing tighter controls on environmental and workplace pollutants; they pushed to eliminate carcinogenic products like pesticides, food additives and dyes, the artificial sweetener saccharin, and more. The parent corporations fought to the death—in some cases— not to be labeled as cancer-causers. *Big* money was at stake, entire industries in danger of annihilation.

Doctors boldly talked to patients about lifestyle changes, an area in which few had previously ventured. The ACS taught nurses, who in turn taught their female patients, how to do breast self-exams. The Division of Cancer Prevention was created by the National Cancer Institute, and in turn, it gave birth to cancer prevention and control programs in cities from coast to coast. Cancer prevention became America's grand new love affair, spreading its influence worldwide.

But there was also an almost invisible fourth realm of cancer, except for those who inhabited it. By 1975, there was a growing population of Americans experiencing a painful discrimination.

In a country that prided itself on equality and compassion for those less fortunate, these Americans were losing their jobs, their insurance coverage, and their friends at an alarming rate.

The "normal" population avoided this group at all costs, ostracizing them because of who and what they were. They were served food on disposable plates with disposable eating utensils at dinner parties, their children were kept at a distance from the children of "normal" people, all for fear that their disease—cancer—was somehow contagious, even in remission. In 1975, there were more than three million cancer survivors in America, the equivalent of that year's combined populations of Detroit, Houston, and Washington, DC. Dismissed, shunned, and mostly ignored, these cancer survivors were shadow people. But they were about to emerge into the light.

Chapter 6: "Someone Who Knew My Terror"

In 1979, 765,000 Americans are diagnosed with cancer.

July 4, 1976: America's Bicentennial had arrived. It was a nationwide celebration the likes of which no one had seen, nor likely would again. The *Tucson Daily Citizen* made that quite clear, publishing:

> ...that distinctive American way of expressing pride and the human condition through skyrockets, stomach-stuffing, baseball, beauty queens and drum-and-bugle cadence...No matter that 200 years ago this stretch of desert was an isolated argument between a few Spanish soldiers and the Apaches...Tucsonians will be doing their part for the nation this weekend.

Coast to coast, newspapers excitedly covered fireworks, parades, and festivals. An astounding 11,738 communities across the country were given special recognition for their Bicentennial commissions supporting local projects. Businesses jumped on board with clever, and obvious, sales ploys. A New Jersey salon, Joseph's Haircutting Room, advertised, "Celebrate the Bicentennial with a shampoo, cut, style and blow-dry for only $7." A Mississippi western store proclaimed, "A glorious time for America. Men's short sleeve western shirts, $7.99 and up." And in California, Dave's Fine Furniture announced a "Revolutionary Sell-a-bration," offering an additional 20 percent off their regular low prices.

But not a single American newspaper mentioned that July 4, 1976, was the deadline President Nixon, his bevy of advisors, and Congress had set for curing cancer. When the war on cancer countdown arrived at zero, the one thing most remembered about Richard Nixon was his disgraceful departure from the White House, the fallout from the Watergate scandal. In the two years since he had left on August 9, 1974, 1.5 million Americans had been diagnosed with the disease. And nearly half of them would die.

But make no mistake, cancer *was* making news in 1976. In April of that year, Pennsylvania nurses competed for the title of Miss Hope. The purpose was to spotlight the hopeful aspects of the war on cancer. The winner would be selected for her poise, intelligence, and credentials.

A more serious announcement noted that, despite the NCI's yearly research budget of $700 million (the equivalent of more than $3 billion in 2021 dollars), doctors were winning few battles. The staggering truth was that cancer was killing an American every 90 seconds. Why weren't people being cured?

It depended on what was meant by "cured." In 1976, the medical community and the ACS defined a "cured" cancer patient as someone who was still living five years after their original diagnosis. This caused science reporter Joseph Hixon to ask, if someone experienced a recurrence from the same primary cancer at year six, would they still be considered "cured"?

And then as incivility grew worse—part of the societal aftershock of growing distrust in institutions that followed the earthquake of Watergate—accusations were aimed at Congress over misappropriation of research funds, while members of Congress blamed one another for the same thing. Cries of fraudulent research circulated within the scientific community. Hoax cures peddled by modern-day flimflam artists were purchased by desperate, dying patients. The heavy atmosphere caused Dr. Donald Kennedy, head of the Food and Drug Administration, to tell the still war-weary populace that the war on cancer had become "a medical Vietnam." Actually, it was much worse.

Over a fourteen-year period, the United States had spent $118 billion (nearly half a trillion in 2021 dollars) throughout Indochina before and during the Vietnam War. Simultaneously, and infinitely more costly, America had watched 46,370 of their best and bravest lose their lives. (Note: these figures fluctuate depending on their origins and what exactly they include. The author used this particular data, produced in the era being described, to best make the comparison with the statistics to follow.)

Meanwhile, over a forty-year period (beginning in 1937), the country had spent only $7 billion fighting cancer, with 382,000 Americans dying in 1977 alone. In other words, science was fighting a losing war with fewer resources and far more casualties.

Cell research scientist James Watson had warned at the dawn of the war on cancer that too little was known about how *normal* cells work, much less trying to understand and kill *abnormal* cancer cells. Recalling the space metaphor used to discuss the likelihood of success—"we landed a man on the moon, we can do this"— Watson likened the fight against cancer to "trying to put a man on the moon in 1920 before missiles were invented…[by giving] contracts to cannon manufacturers, ladder builders, and many, many administrators but no support for missile research."

It was the very definition of putting the cart before the horse.

In the 1970s, there was virtually no understanding of the complicated and often disturbing post-cancer life in which Susie Leigh now existed. Unlike her pre-Vietnam combat training, Susie remembered, "There was no basic training for this type of conflict. Survival was trial and error. My care focused strictly on physical survival. The rest of me seemed superfluous to most of those caring for me."

No one ever addressed the need to grieve; to deal with physical and emotional changes; to live with anxiety, fear, and uncertainty. Susie's priorities had drastically changed. Getting married, having children, the things that were *supposed* to happen to a woman her age, weren't in her future. It was difficult to relate to old friends, and equally difficult to feel socially comfortable with new ones.

What the cancer world needed at that moment was nurses who were willing to listen to their patients and who were trying to understand. What Susie needed was to do *something* in oncology. No nursing specialty program existed yet at the University of Arizona (U of A). But a new hematology/oncology program did, and fortuitously, Susie's oncologist, Dr. Steven Jones, was its assistant director.

"We're expanding so fast" he told her. "Would you like to work with us part-time as an oncology research nurse?"

It was perfect. It was nursing, in a specialty that intrigued Susie personally and professionally. It was part-time, so she could take off and roam the world when she wanted to. It would allow her the ultimate proximity to her own oncologist at the university, should her health take an unexpected sudden turn south. Susie took the job without blinking.

Dr. Jones already had two full-time nurses working in the program when Susie arrived in April 1976. She fit right in as the part-timer, eagerly helping with research protocols and administering chemotherapy. The latter was a new task for nurses, as doctors had begun to relinquish their hold on drug administration. She felt her personal experience with cancer would enhance her on-the-job training. And as Dr. Jones had said, "You can swap war stories with the patients."

Suddenly, Susie's life had meaning. Her cancer had meaning! And there was more excitement on the horizon: both full-time nurses had just joined the Oncology Nursing Society (ONS). They had missed the annual congress, held that year in Toronto, but another meeting was being held in Boston in a month. They invited Susie to join them on the trip and she was thrilled. Susie recognized the need to gain expertise in cancer treatment from the nurse's side of the bed. Why wouldn't she join a national organization that was created to share ideas and knowledge about how to care for this special population?

She knew there was a lack of specifics in oncology for nurses. She hoped that ONS would change all of that. Susie had experienced firsthand doctors' laser focus on *quantity* of life. Medical and radiation oncologists, including hers, seemed driven by the same questions. How aggressive can our treatments be? How much can patients take? How can we extend their lives for even a few more days?

Doctors were much less aware of the *quality*-of-life issues that were arising from patient treatment. Since the nurses held far lengthier conversations, they saw that for patients, quality nearly always far outweighed quantity in importance. Sharing patient quality-of-life lessons was one of the most crucial tenets of the newly birthed ONS.

Susie felt that, between her personal experiences and her love of nursing, she might have something unique to offer. She jumped in with both feet, with an ulterior motive. After all the drugs and radiation she had received, she remained very concerned about what might happen to her physically in the future. Not a single doctor she had encountered could tell her what awaited her five or ten years down the road. However, if she remained immersed in oncology nursing, she would have access to news and advancements well before they were released to the public. She would also have access to the plethora of experiences that her sister oncology nurses had gleaned in their careers.

The fee for the ONS fall conference was $50 for nonmembers, but a mere $20 for members. It was a no-brainer, and off Susie and her two nurse colleagues went to Boston. The conference was hosted by the Sidney Farber Cancer Center, newly named for the man who was considered the "father of modern chemotherapy." His early work had paved the way for Dr. DeVita to create his successful MOPP protocol. While the meeting did not warrant even a mention in the *Boston Globe,* it didn't matter to the assembled nurses. The program's objectives were bold and exciting. Listed on page one of the brochure, they included increasing "the nurse's awareness of the perspective of the patient/family" and "the nurse's awareness of the current roles of nursing in this area." The sessions were even more provocative, with titles like "Controlled Clinical Trials: Where's the Nurse?" "Economics of Long-Term Survival," (which Susie, at four years, could already speak to), and "Sharing Information with Your Patients."

The two-day meeting was an eye-opener. Susie returned to Tucson with new purpose. She made herself available to any patient who needed to talk, and could tell them "I understand" and mean it. There were still no support groups available in Tucson, but she could share her personal concerns with her patients while she listened to theirs. Bonds grew. And contrary to everything she had been taught in nursing school, she became close to some of those under her care. Further complicating issues with regard to cancer patients was an odd and growing dichotomy. Society was beginning to speak more openly about death and dying as a part of the human life cycle. But when it came to cancer patients, death was seen as a failure.

Susie dove into her work. She would say later that her patients became her first peer support group. Working with them had made her realize how she hadn't really worked through her emotions about her own cancer. A lot of energy was going out, with little coming back. Susie felt somewhat isolated in a world where she was both cancer patient and cancer caregiver. Then came the straw that broke the proverbial camel's back.

Leticia was a lovely, young, single mother of a five-year-old daughter. She was being treated for recurrent Hodgkin's disease. Susie, who delivered her chemotherapy, had helped her overcome her terror of the needles by teaching her relaxation techniques. When Leticia's cancer recurred for a third time, it was left to a resident to tell her. Susie felt that a stranger who had never seen Leticia before should not be the one to deliver this terrible news, and she told the resident that she would go with him to offer support. It was an extremely difficult conversation, and she cried after she left the room.

No one knew what to say to her. Many of the doctors Susie worked with felt she was hypochondriacal when it came to her own health, and over-emotional when it came to her patients. One of them proclaimed that since she couldn't control her emotions, she should be kept away from patients.

What they didn't know was that it wasn't only sadness Susie felt. She felt real fear seeing someone so young dying of the same disease she had had. In 1978, two and a half years into her oncology nursing career, Susie knew it was time to leave.

In 1919, less than sixty days after the end of World War I, President Woodrow Wilson proclaimed, "This nation has no more solemn obligation than healing the hurts of our wounded and restoring our disabled men to civil life and opportunity." To that end, he created the Federal Board for Vocational Education, offering aid to every one of the 200,000 soldiers then in hospitals, including those suffering from "shell shock," what we now call PTSD. The war's continued effect on the psyche of those who were shell-shocked often prevented them from holding a steady job, and in the saddest of cases, caused them to take their own lives.

Two and a half decades later, in the throes of World War II, "shell shock" became known as "battle fatigue." It was a different name for the same condition, but with no better outcome. Some thought those experiencing it were simply cowardly and looking for a quick and easy way out of combat duties. General George Patton famously slapped a young man in a field hospital, called his condition "hooey," and threatened to shoot him on the spot.

The dismal story was repeated again in the '60s and '70s, when men who had served in Southeast Asia exhibited symptoms of the same condition, then known by yet another name, "Vietnam syndrome." As with previous wars, many of those men couldn't reenter their lives. They lost jobs and families, replacing them with drugs, crime, and suicide. It took until 1980, five years after Saigon fell, before the condition became a psychiatric diagnosis with an accurate name: post-traumatic stress disorder.

Officially, according to the NIH, PTSD "develops in some people after a shocking, scary, or dangerous event." Flashbacks occur, as the sufferer relives the trauma over and over again. Sometimes the flashbacks seem so real that physical symptoms, like a racing heart and profuse sweating, occur just as if the event were actually happening.

The NIH definition included not just war veterans, but children and people who have been through physical or sexual assault, abuse, accident, or disaster. Noticeably absent from the definition was the cancer experience, despite the fact that more Americans living at the time had been diagnosed with the disease than had collectively served in a theater of war. Since so few patients survived their disease prior to the 1970s, there was little "post trauma" to deal with. That might have made the NIH definition excusable then. But it stands unchanged still (2021), with survivorship numbers approaching 17 million.

And PTSD might have been what Susie experienced when Leticia died.

Catherine Logan was born in 1945, the same year that her parents' former neighbor, Harry Truman, became president of the United States. Truman may have made Independence, Missouri, famous, but Catherine Logan would go on to change more lives in her lifetime. Her father—a Presbyterian minister—taught Catherine two important lessons. The first was compassion, as the family often took in refugees from around the world. The second was flexibility. Assigned to a variety of churches around the Midwest, Reverend Logan moved his family numerous times.

That compassion and flexibility led Catherine to her studies in social work and psychology, a stint in Puerto Rico with the Peace Corps, and back to Chicago (her degree came from the University of Illinois) for social work and community organizing. Her love of horses and jewelry-making finally brought her to the place she would call her forever home: Albuquerque, New Mexico. Her half-acre homesite had a house with adobe walls, a corral for her horses, and a Native American sweat lodge. Her jewelry business was a dream come true, and her reputation grew among Albuquerque residents as well as those living in the nearby pueblos. Then, in 1979, at the age of thirty-four, Catherine was diagnosed with invasive cervical cancer. She closed her shop for six weeks to undergo surgery and radiation. Once treatment was over, rebuilding her business became her focus.

It was then that she realized her notion of getting back to normal as soon as treatment ended was a pipe dream. Her family and friends had been supportive, but none had actually been cancer patients. The aftershocks—isolation, anger, and treatment side effects—weighed her down for a full year. She finally saw a therapist, and realized it was the first time she'd really talked about all of this. She also realized that her health was not totally out of her control, and she was not a helpless victim. Those realizations brought substantial relief, along with an idea. Each time she had the opportunity to speak with other cancer patients, another brick in her wall of isolation fell. She learned how to navigate the medical establishment and how to make use of the resources that were available at the time.

> "There are people who've been dealing with cancer for years," Catherine said in a 1988 newspaper article. "It seemed a huge waste if they were not passing on what they'd learned. We needed a place to share the combined wisdom, to learn about what to eat, how to relax, all sorts of techniques for living better with the disease—and to talk openly about the fear of death."

Some years earlier, Catherine's oncologist mentioned his neighbor, Audrey Wilson, who had recovered from breast cancer. Audrey later described the moment of her diagnosis. "I went numb. With my own parents and my husband's family, there was a great deal of denial ... At the first public gathering I went to after diagnosis, I was asked to use disposable table and silverware and asked not to use the restroom."

A coworker told Audrey not to tell anyone about her cancer; she would surely lose her job as a cognitive language development specialist. Another highly educated acquaintance told her, "Cancer's a psychological disease, you know."

These experiences created the same concerns in Audrey as they had in Catherine. The oncologist suggested they meet, and it took the two women no time to bond. Then, they took action. They organized a day-long conference in Albuquerque called Living Through Cancer, to be held August 6, 1983. For six dollars, participants would hear from local cancer experts speaking on topics ranging from Western medicine to traditional healing to nutrition. As advertised, the featured workshops would also include "self-help and healing techniques that can supplement essential medical care."

By November, Catherine and Audrey, along with sister cancer patients Jeanne Stover, Helene Abrams. And Grace Muir, were ready to launch an organization with the same name: Living Through Cancer (LTC). It was created to be a support system for survivors and their families. They held the first meeting at Audrey's house. Those who attended, and all the others that came after, did exactly what the founders hoped. They forged strong bonds, exchanged knowledge, voiced fears of cancer recurrence, and shared their newfound appreciation for life.

Word spread about LTC via the newspaper and word of mouth. Some people even moved to Albuquerque from smaller towns around New Mexico just to be part of the experience. Catherine's renown spread. She had seen too many fellow cancer patients discriminated against and living unfulfilled lives. The compassion she had learned at an early age kicked in. It was time, she said, to stir the pot.

"There's a misconception that mutual aid groups [the early name for support groups] sit around feeling sorry for themselves," Catherine told a reporter. "What happens is you gather a sense of yourself as a survivor, you talk about goals healthwise in your lives, address potential as well as current problems. You don't complain, but talk about how to do your best in the situation; it's sort of an orientation for life."

Ellen Stovall, meanwhile, was volunteering for the Leukemia Society in 1980. She met a young man—we'll call him Adam—whose story further fueled her advocacy fire. After graduating from college in the late '70s, Adam was unable to find work because of his leukemia diagnosis. In that era, it was perfectly permissible to ask potential employees about their health history, and disclosing a cancer diagnosis was like disclosing a prison term served for murder. Based on misconceptions about the disease, employers assumed those who had had it would be plagued by physical limitations and missed workdays due to further illness. Not to mention the biggest misconception of all, contagion.

Adam couldn't afford to live on his own, so he had returned home. His mother feared he carried "cancer germs." She purchased an autoclave to sterilize his dishes, and washed his clothing separately to keep any "cancer residue" from the rest of the family's clothing. Adam shared all of this at a small gathering of other former leukemia patients that Ellen was facilitating.

Ellen was a mother herself, and the story tore open her heart. The very person who should have been most protective of this kid and advocating for him—his mother—was as unknowledgeable and unprepared to support him as a complete stranger. Ellen decided to double down on the vow she had made.

On April 19, 1981, she appeared as a guest on a brand-new television program called *Nice People*. The growth of cable—and the advent of cable networks—had created an enormous appetite for programming. Shows like *Nice People*, billed as offering profiles of people who make a difference, were the result. The host of the half-hour TV magazine, Bob Neal, interviewed Ellen about her work with cancer patients. Ellen's mind immediately went to Janet Morrison.

Like Ellen, Janet had spent over eighteen months being examined by various specialists, only to have them tell her they could find nothing wrong except "neurodermatitis" (nerves) as a result of "suburban anxiety." She had been prescribed tranquilizers, body creams, and aspirin, all to no avail. Both of her parents had died of cancer. And then, in 1981, at age 33, she was told—over the telephone—that she, too, had the disease. She described the experience in a March 9, 1983, *Washington Post* article.

> I kicked and screamed, I cursed and hollered, I banged my fists until my knuckles were bruised... and then I cried. Could my doctor, who had chosen to phone me that afternoon to announce that I had a malignant tumor in my chest, most likely lymphoma, possibly Hodgkin's disease, be wrong?
>
> I needed to find someone immediately who knew my terror; someone I could talk with on a personal—rather than clinical—level; someone who had "been there." I needed to find a survivor.

That "someone" was Ellen. They had been connected through mutual friends. Ellen explained to Janet how she had wanted to take the most negative experience of her life and somehow pull something positive out of it. So, she had become a patient advocate, not totally for selfless reasons, but because she needed fellow cancer patients as friends. Like Susie had done with her patients, Ellen needed to learn from her cancer friends as much as they needed to learn from her. Ellen walked Janet through all the steps of her Hodgkin's experience. They spent hours on the phone together, not meeting face-to-face for two months.

On March 8, 1983, the day before Janet's article appeared, Ellen got the opportunity to bring her advocacy message to a larger audience. She was asked to be a guest on a three-part *Today Show* series called "Learning to Live with Cancer." Ellen was listed in the program's *TV Guide* description as a Hodgkin's "victim." To those who knew her, like Janet, calling the petite blonde dynamo a "victim" was laughable.

Two days later, the two women appeared together on the show's third segment. Janet was in awe of Ellen's willingness to wear the "patient advocate" label. In 1983, it was, after all, a fairly unknown word combination. If a patient is an advocate, many asked, who is their adversary? It is cancer, Janet explained. And the advocate is not the physician or the medical team. He or she is an extra and knowing hand, reaching out and reminding us daily of the Sanskrit proverb:

Look to this day! For it is life...
For yesterday is but a dream, and tomorrow only a vision;
But today, well lived, makes every yesterday a dream of happiness,
And every tomorrow a vision of hope.

Not long after the *Today Show* appearances, Ellen was diagnosed with Hodgkin's disease for a second time. In the nearly twelve years since her first diagnosis, treatment had improved (she was treated with the very same MOPP chemotherapy regimen in whose trial she had been denied participation in 1972) and her son was much more self-sufficient than he had been as the infant. But a feeling of vulnerability gnawed at her, along with the recognition that cancer would always be lurking among the weeds in her life.

The concept of survivorship had first come to Fitz Mullan just after the publication of his book *Vital Signs*. It occurred to him that there must be others like him. "People got this godawful diagnosis," he said later. They had gone through the crucible of cancer treatment and come out the other side. But they had to live a set period of time before they could be called a "survivor," before they could graduate from the uncured to cured category on some nebulous balance sheet.

"Why was the idea of survivorship so constricted? It was an uncharted land. All survivors' lives changed, from minor to catastrophic."

Fitz was invited to speak at an April 16, 1983, event being hosted by the Baltimore chapter of the American Cancer Society. He would be a panelist at the "Cured Cancer Congress," speaking about his personal experience with the disease. The congress was the first of its kind in Baltimore, and was expected to draw three hundred people, "some of whom have been cured of cancer, and others who have not yet reached their five-year mark," according to a Baltimore *Evening Sun* story the day before the opening. It would be held at the Hyatt Regency.

On the day of the congress, after his participation, Fitz was in the vestibule outside of the conference room. A woman approached him, looking around furtively. She wore a scarf over what was most probably a bald head and said to him, "I'm not supposed to be here. I'm not really cured, I'm just two months out of diagnosis. But I'm really glad to be here. I hope to get where you are—six years out. I took the liberty of sneaking in so I could hear everyone speak about life after cancer."

In that moment, Fitz realized that what had happened to them—their cancer diagnoses—had created a real connection between them. The idea that they had to live a set period of time to be called a "survivor" was absurd. Fitz stewed on this and ultimately wrote a truly monumental article for the July 1985 issue of the *New England Journal of Medicine*. Titled "Seasons of Survival: Reflections of a Physician with Cancer," he eloquently likened the changing periods of the cancer experience to the changing seasons of the year.

It started with Acute Survival. "The first season begins with the diagnosis of the illness," Fitz wrote. "It is really the medical stage, dominated by the diagnostic and therapeutic efforts to stem the tide of illness." Next came Extended Survival, "when the patient goes into remission or has terminated the basic, rigorous course of treatment and enters a phase of watchful waiting, with periodic examinations and 'consolidation' or intermittent therapy." Finally, patients move to Permanent Survival. "The term permanent survival will not be found in the literature. It can be roughly equated with the phenomenon we usually call 'cure.'"

But this survivorship metaphor is, without a doubt, the most poignant: "It is as if we have invented sophisticated techniques to save people from drowning, but once they have been pulled from the water, we leave them on the dock to cough and splutter on their own in the belief that we have done all that we can."

Fitz continued by saying that thoughtful, coordinated national research should be undertaken to study survivorship as a phenomenon in itself, rather than a by-product or afterthought in cancer research. These cogent words, coming from a cancer survivor, added to the rumblings about bringing the shadow realm of cancer's empire into the light.

The article was wildly popular, reaching far beyond just those who subscribed to the *New England Journal of Medicine*. And the mail began pouring in. Fitz received correspondence from around the country, including a letter from Catherine Logan in Albuquerque. She, too, had read "Seasons of Survival." She told him it resonated loudly with her and the rest of her LTC members and volunteers. And then she added a throwaway phrase that intrigued Fitz: "We really should have a(n) [cancer] alumni association."

In early 1986, Catherine met Fitz face-to-face at one of his speaking engagements. She had already begun compiling a list of cancer organizations for which survivorship was either a full or partial focus. They ranged in size from the American Cancer Society to smaller grassroots organizations like her own LTC. In addition, she had identified individuals who researched or wrote about survivorship. Hoping he would buy into her plan, Catherine also hoped to rely on his contacts, assuming they would be vast, considering his medical, speaking, and publishing work. Fitz fondly remembered Catherine as "... diligent to the point of almost being militant. She was like a dog with a bone and not about to give up." Seeing no other recourse, Fitz agreed to climb on board with her plan.

Catherine created a mailing list of eighty-three organizations and individuals from their joint contacts. In a letter, she explained the need for a network of like-minded people in the field of cancer survivorship. She then asked each of them whether they would be interested in being a part of a national coalition and what they'd like to see the coalition do. Thirty-one responded to her questions with interest, so another letter went out on August 15, 1986, inviting them to a national planning meeting. It included specific details of the gathering and requested $144.70, which would cover meeting fees and two nights at the Barcelona Court Hotel. RSVPs and checks began arriving at the LTC office in Albuquerque, including one that came from an Arizona oncology nurse.

Debi McCaffrey (now Boyle) was a Seattle oncology nurse and a melanoma survivor, whose treatment involved a large excision on her arm. Even before her 1980 diagnosis, she had known people who had died of melanoma, despite having intensive treatment. Not having traveled the chemotherapy/radiation path herself, Debi struggled with the "survivor" title. Would surgery alone keep her cancer-free? As was the case with others, she found very little information about survivorship in any form. The idea of a survey hatched in Debi's mind. How were other oncology nurses, who were also survivors, faring? She put out a call via the ONS circuit.

Susie Leigh was one of the people who responded to the call for survey participants. Debi was astounded at how effusive Susie was in her responses. Apparently, Susie was as well, finishing the survey by saying, "I didn't realize all of this was inside of me." When Debi was invited to speak at the university hospital, she contacted Susie, and the two became fast friends.

Debi was on Catherine's mailing list. By the time the initial letter arrived from Albuquerque, Debi had moved to Phoenix and was working at Good Samaritan Hospital as an oncology nurse clinical specialist. She answered Catherine's question about having interest in a national cancer network with a resounding yes. Regarding what she'd like to see the network do, she responded that she hoped such an organization would "negate the stereotype that all people with cancer die," that she would "encourage research on this topic," and further hoped to see the organization "survey the needs of survivors." Debi was eager to attend the meeting, and would do so representing the Oncology Nursing Society.

Given her profession, her cancer history, and her interest in survivorship, Debi had become a renowned speaker on the subjects, and was in great demand. Unfortunately, the inaugural meeting date that Catherine and Fitz ultimately selected was the same as that of a speaking engagement she had already accepted. She immediately thought of Susie and the passion for survivorship she had seen on Susie's face when they had met at U of A. "There's this group meeting in Albuquerque," Debi explained in a phone call. Was Susie available to go?

By this time, Susie was working with her friend and colleague Lois Loescher at the University of Arizona's Division of Cancer Prevention and Control. Susie laughs when she describes the phone call. "I remember wanting to scream, 'Cancer survivors! Someone is seriously interested in cancer survivors?' I could hardly contain myself. You bet I wanted to go!"

Whether you believe in fate, the alignment of the universe, or something more spiritual, this was a pivotal moment for Susie, and for the cancer survivorship movement.

Chapter 7: "The Uncharted Land"

In 1987, there are 5 million survivors in the US, making up 2 percent of the population.

Because of the newer and better-targeted treatments, as had happened with oncology nursing, other medical specialties were born as more patients survived their cancer diagnoses. For example, scattered across the country, prescient work in survivor quality of life was being talked and written about—and put into action—by individuals in the social and mental health sciences. Their passion and dedication would change everything for cancer patients in the coming decades.

The first research papers on patients' psychological reactions to cancer were published by clinicians at New York's Memorial Hospital (later, Memorial Sloan Kettering Cancer Center) in the early 1950s. One such paper was co-authored in 1952 by Jacob Finesinger, the same doctor who was so very outspoken about doctor-patient communication. Titled "Guilt Reactions in Patients with Cancer," it is a heartbreaking treatise. Fifty-six of the sixty patients interviewed "made statements indicating that they considered their illness to be their fault or the fault of others." They laid personal blame on a previous diagnosis of venereal disease, a sin or misdeed, a blow to the now-cancerous body part, or their own personal negligence.

The interviewees who blamed others for their cancer did so feeling they had caught the disease or inherited it. It might have occurred because they had worked too hard in caring for a sick loved one, or they'd been struck by a relative, again at the same site of their cancer. "Unlike tuberculosis, heart disease, and other chronic illnesses," Finesinger and his co-author, social worker Ruth Abrams, wrote, "there is relatively little in the literature about the attitudes of patients... toward their diagnosis of cancer. Meager also are the writings of psychiatrists and social workers regarding the manner in which their particular skills might best be utilized." Abrams would become a giant in the field of oncology social work and would go on to write the groundbreaking book *Not Alone with Cancer* in 1974.

Two years after Finesinger and Abrams's publication, another paper—authored by Dr. Morton Bard and Dr. Arthur Sutherland—dealt with the psychological impact of a radical mastectomy. Along with outlining the complicated relationship young women have with their developing breasts, the doctors also explained that mastectomy patients were routinely referred to their hospital's psychiatric service. Thus, not only did the women carry the guilt and stigma of having gotten what was considered a "dirty" disease, but they also faced the stigma of possible instability in their mental health.

Just as cancer's psychosocial component was beginning to be recognized, Jimmie Coker entered Baylor Medical School. Petite and bespectacled, with a kind face, she was one of only three women in her class, and intended to practice family medicine. But Jimmie's internship rotation in psychiatry changed the course of her medical career. Once she completed her residency, she took a position at Roswell Park Memorial Institute in Buffalo, New York—the nation's first cancer center, founded in 1898.

In the 1970s, the broadly held philosophy was that if a patient survived cancer, they should be happy to be alive, and simply not worry about post-treatment challenges. That didn't suit Jimmie at all. As a psychiatrist, she was interested in how people with otherwise good mental health responded emotionally and psychologically to life-threatening illnesses. She called this focus "psychological care of the medically ill." At Roswell, she encouraged oncologists who were conducting clinical trials to also include in their data collection questions about patients' quality of life. This led her to oncologist James Holland, Roswell's Chair of Medicine. The two ultimately fell in love and married, becoming Drs. James and Jimmie Holland. This created more than a little confusion during their esteemed careers.

After the Hollands relocated to New York City, Jimmie began research into stress among breast cancer patients at Montefiore Hospital in the Bronx. In 1976, it was news of that work that reached Columbia University graduate school student Julia Rowland. When one of Julia's instructors read her paper on cancer and the stress connection, she recommended that Julia might be interested in Jimmie's research. Julia was more than interested. She wanted to be a part of it, and, after meeting Jimmie and hearing more about her work, Julia wrote a letter to her offering to volunteer. Jimmie took her on.

In 1977, Jimmie moved to Memorial Sloan Kettering Cancer Center (MSKCC) to establish the country's first psychiatric service in a cancer hospital. Julia went with her, now in a paid position, while simultaneously completing her PhD. By the time she finished, the NIH-funded post-doctorate fellowship program in psychosocial oncology (led by Jimmie) had just opened to non-MDs. Julia became one of the first two PhD fellows to be trained. Upon completion of the fellowship, she held joint appointments in both pediatrics and neurology. She also helped to develop and was the first director of MSKCC's Post-Treatment Resource Program. The innovative program provided a full range of nonmedical services to patients and their families after the end of treatment. It was revolutionary.

The culmination of Jimmie and Julia's work together was the 1989 *Handbook of Psychooncology: Psychological Care of the Patient with Cancer*, which they proudly co-edited. It was the first time the word "psychooncology" had ever been used, and the book's editors didn't realize until after the printing that the word had a bizarre appearance without a hyphen. But the accolades far overshadowed the missing punctuation. (The hyphen is now part of the spelling.) Described as "remarkable" and "superb," the comprehensive volume was the first to cover the full range of psychological, social, and psychiatric problems facing cancer patients, their families, and health care staffs written specifically for oncologists, nurses, and mental health professionals.

Nearly 3,000 miles away, two California residents would also step into the exciting, and much-needed field of psychosocial oncology. As a first-year resident at the UCLA School of Medicine in 1973, Patti Ganz was considering a career in cardiology. But the dynamic new chief of hematology and oncology, who served as Patti's attending physician, sparked a different interest in her. When she received her first faculty appointment at UCLA, Patti was also given the opportunity to start a hospice at a UCLA-affiliated Veterans Affairs (VA) hospital. All her patients had had a cancer diagnosis, and some were still receiving treatment with an intent to eradicate their disease. It was, she said, "a [hospital] ward that wasn't just for people in the last few months of life. We were taking care of a spectrum of patients."

Her work profoundly altered her thinking. "I realized that all the things that hospice was proposing in terms of psychosocial support, symptom management, and so forth, we should be doing for everyone from the time of diagnosis." The concept of holistic—whole-patient—care became her battle cry.

Two of Patti's colleagues at the hospital were involved in a clinical trial, investigating the value of support groups for veterans and their families. To better understand what patients were coping with, the researchers visited Patti's clinic. Thanks to them, she was introduced to the tools of psychological science. It became clear the era's improvements in treatments were churning out more patients with a prospect of living longer. And when she attended a conference on cancer rehabilitation in 1982, Patti began to really hone in on what would ultimately become the focus of the rest of her career: the very broad topic of managing the aftereffects of cancer. Her passion for survivorship has benefited millions.

Further north, in San Francisco, Pat Fobair had also broadened her career. Having earned her master's degree in social work from the University of Kansas in 1963, Pat went to work in San Francisco's Mount Zion Hospital, providing clinical services for patients and their families. In 1967, she began a two-year research project for the local division of the American Cancer Society (ACS) that entailed a cancer patient survey of their needs for social services. As in the case of the others, that connection to cancer redirected Pat's career.

In her 2009 article for the *Journal of Psychosocial Oncology*, "Historical Threads in the Development of Oncology Social Work," Pat wrote, "The American Cancer Society was responsible for offering oncology social work a spotlight on the national stage with their invitations to participate in the multidisciplinary talks given at their Human Values Conferences, held throughout the country from 1972 to 1987." Julie Nixon Eisenhower spoke at the first of those, in Atlanta. Pat Fobair would go on to speak at two of them.

Those conferences sparked more interest in psychosocial oncology, and just like oncology nurses had done, social workers began meeting to support and educate themselves and others. In 1979, the national ACS office hired their first social worker, and a year later, the term Oncology Social Work became a part of the vernacular. With encouragement from the ACS, plans for a new professional organization were soon underway.

By this time, Pat had begun working at Stanford University as the coordinator of the Hodgkin's Patients' Rehabilitation Program. She supervised data collection and social work services to patients in the radiation oncology department at the medical center. Inspired by Fitz Mullan's *Vital Signs*, Pat created the survivor magazine *Surviving* in 1983. It was the first of its kind and produced on a mimeograph machine, an old-school, low-cost duplicating contraption that worked by forcing ink through a stencil onto paper, before being stapled in the corner. Survivors— Susie Leigh among them—grasped the newsletters as if they were life preservers tossed to drowning people. And the 100 percent patient-written magazines were exactly that! As Pat described them, "we lightly edited … [the articles] and threw them in. It was good for patients currently under treatment to read about patients on the other side."

After she graduated with a master's degree in social work from the University of Pittsburgh in the 1970s, and inspired by Eleanor Cockerill, a pioneer in oncology social work, Elizabeth Clark (Betsy to her friends) asked for a field placement in the hematology/ oncology unit of the medical center. A few years later, she and her husband relocated to Bethlehem, PA, where a community hospital had a grant from the ACS for a cancer support program. They had a steering committee of doctors, but no idea how to develop the program. It was Betsy's dream job, and allowed her to collect data for her 1981 doctoral dissertation, "The Role of Social Support in Adaptation to Cancer."

Betsy joined the others as a pioneer in the field of oncology social work. She was a charter member of the National Association of Oncology Social Workers when the organization was founded in 1984. (It would change its name to the Association of Oncology Social Work a decade later.) Betsy's peers recognized her for her work with awards many times over. Then, in 1985, cancer became personal for Betsy. Her sister, Eleanor, was diagnosed with multiple myeloma. The blood cancer requires lifelong treatment to keep it at bay, but is not without side effects. Eleanor died in 1998 after she developed leukemia. Living at a time when the disease was not nearly as manageable as it is now, Eleanor remained an inspiration for Betsy in her work as a hope advocate.

Many other bright and dedicated individuals contributed to psycho-oncology and oncology social work when those fields were still in their infancy. Their work is reflected in today's (2021) supportive services programs, which have become an ever more important part of cancer survivorship. But the work of these five pioneers—Jimmie Holland, Julia Rowland, Patti Ganz, Pat Fobair, and Betsy Clark—would take another national stage when survivorship became a movement.

By 1986, Catherine Logan's vision was that the National Cancer Survivors' Network would be a network that would "empower the survivorship movement in general." Trouble was, even though cancer survivor groups were springing up around the country, most of them weren't aware there even was a growing survivorship movement, nor indeed exactly what that meant. The weekend in Albuquerque would change all that.

The meeting had originally been planned for the first weekend in October to coincide with Albuquerque's famous Hot Air Balloon Fiesta. But Jewish invitee Estelle Weissburg, who would be attending on behalf of Pittsburgh's Cancer Guidance Institute, sent regrets that she wouldn't be able to make it as the weekend was also Rosh Hashanah, one of the holiest holidays in the Jewish calendar. Anxious to make the meeting as convenient as possible for everyone, Catherine moved the date to the last weekend in October.

They came from Arizona, California, Florida, Maryland, New Mexico, North Carolina, Ohio, Pennsylvania, Texas, Washington state and Washington, DC. The eldest in attendance was Harold Benjamin, the sixty-two-year-old founder of the California-based Wellness Community (now known as Cancer Support Community). The youngest attendee was twenty-eight-year-old attorney Barbara Hoffman from Philadelphia. In 1974, at the age of fifteen, she had been diagnosed with Hodgkin's disease but had the good fortune to be treated—as Susie was—by Stanford's Henry Kaplan with his groundbreaking radiation protocol. As a practicing civil rights attorney, specializing in the rights of individuals with disabilities, she was also the director of the Cancer Patients Employment Rights Project of the Foundation for Dignity in Philadelphia. Fitz was on the foundation's advisory board, and Barbara's impressive experience was the reason he had suggested she be invited to their founding meeting.

The weekend's home base was the two-year-old Barcelona Court Hotel. Previously an apartment complex, it was now a southwestern vision to behold. After a $12 million renovation, it had opened as Albuquerque's only all-suite hotel, complete with an 18,000-square-foot climate-controlled atrium at its heart. The corridors of each floor were open to the atrium, featuring handcrafted wrought iron railings. The hotel's crowning glory—with a $25,000 price tag—was a stained-glass skylight, towering thirty-eight feet above the lobby's stone floor, which had been quarried from Guadalajara, Mexico.

Catherine explained in her welcome letter to participants that the plan was for the weekend to be "open-ended, with agenda items defined by the participants themselves. Friday evening [October 24] will be set aside to meet and acquaint ourselves with one another's philosophy and work, and to set the agenda for the remainder of the weekend."

When Susie Leigh arrived at the hotel, Catherine greeted her in the same way she would all the participants: with a welcome packet and a request to be back in the atrium at 6:00 p.m. Then, much like a mother hen, Catherine herded the group of twenty-two along the four-minute walk to the Cooperage Restaurant for cocktails and dinner.

With its round structure, accented but generally dimmed lighting, dark wood paneling, and varnished floors giving the feeling of dining inside an elegant barrel, the aptly named Cooperage marketed itself for banquets and business meetings. Slabs of meat were the order of the day, and the ten-year-old restaurant prided itself on being "a great place for prime rib." A lobster tail and a visit to the forty-item salad bar could be had for just $10.95. The Cooperage was the perfect site for the welcome dinner of the organization.

The restaurant's owner, Jim Schumacher, also happened to be the president of the Bernalillo unit of the ACS. Catherine scarcely needed any of her persuasive skills to secure their dinner space. Jim readily agreed to host the meeting, welcoming them as if they were guests in his home. He had chosen the "R Room" for their gathering. There was an arch of rocks at the entrance, with a wrought iron gate reminiscent of an entry into a wine cellar. With a big rock

fireplace as the room's most imposing feature, it wasn't hard to figure out that the "R" of the room's name stood for rock.

Once everyone was settled in, the wait staff took drink orders.
Dinner had been pre-arranged, offering a New York strip or a
less celebrated chicken breast. Seed money for the organization,
and the dinner, had been donated by St. Joseph Cancer Center in
Albuquerque and St. Vincent's Hospital in Santa Fe.

The group was an eclectic mix. Fitz was convinced that if their
movement was to succeed, it would need medical professionals.
So, in addition to Fitz, who Catherine hoped would cofacilitate
the weekend, the roster included survivor psychosocial pioneer
Dr. Patti Ganz. Her involvement in the group proved to be a
stroke of genius. Michael Lerner was in attendance, representing
Commonweal, the California-based organization he had founded
a decade earlier, which offered programs for both cancer survivors
and health care professionals. There were three volunteers from
Catherine's organization, LTC. They included Alice Hiat, a psychotherapist and breast cancer survivor who led an LTC support group;
her husband, Al, who was also a psychotherapist and led the LTC
husband's group; and Gena Love, who Catherine had in mind to
act as scribe at their meeting. Diagnosed with Hodgkin's disease
four times, Gena, too, led an LTC support group. The impressive
list went on, later described as individuals with "leadership roles in
the emerging cancer survivorship movement."

Susie spent the majority of that first evening in her familiar persona of being the quietest in the room. It wasn't the surroundings.
The hotel was lovely and the food was great. But what made her
more observer than speaker was the company she was keeping. She
was in awe. The collective power of the attendees had been electri-
fying from the moment they assembled. But while the "who" of the
meeting might have been intimidating to Susie, the "what" was a
different story. For fourteen years, Susie had been beaten down at
every turn since her diagnosis and treatment. No one understood
her challenges as a survivor; most who'd never been diagnosed
didn't even realize challenges existed. No one really knew what

a "survivor" was, and there were no guidelines on how to survive *survivorship.*

Each time Susie had tried to express her feelings, the responses from friends, family members, work colleagues, and the medical community alike was, "Well, at least you're cured." She felt there should have been some kind of official survivor graduation, and often asked, "But how do I know I'm a survivor?" No matter to whom she posed this question, the response was always the same: "Well, you don't have cancer today, so you're cured."

This group, however, was clearly different, and Susie almost tingled with excitement. *This group* appeared to actually believe that survivorship—particularly survivorship beyond three or five years—was possible, although fraught with the same challenges Susie continued to face. As cocktails were served, they began talking about the importance of addressing survivor psychosocial and quality-of-life issues, and never slowed down throughout the entire meal.

Saturday morning, October 25, in Albuquerque, the "land of enchantment," dawned clear and crisp, with an expected high of 64 degrees. It was the last day of Daylight Saving Time and New Mexicans were thrilled at the prospect of gaining an hour of sleep that night. For the attendees of the fledgling National Cancer Survivors' Network, it meant an extra hour to talk about changing survivors' lives.

They convened at 7:30 a.m. in the LaPaz conference room on the hotel's main floor. The tables were arranged in a large rectangle so that everyone could clearly see one another. The walls were papered with giant blank pages, affixed with masking tape. At the back of the room was a commercial coffee maker, which worked nearly as hard as the attendees throughout the weekend.

It took America's Founding Fathers four months to complete their work at the Philadelphia Constitutional Convention. Their vision for a new country was born out of a melding together of their individual experiences and passions. That was exactly what was about to happen in Albuquerque. In fact, it was so successful, this moment has come to be known as the "Constitutional Convention" of the cancer survivorship movement. And it only took this group of twenty-three founding mothers and fathers three days.

In addition to those she had met at the Cooperage dinner the night before, Susie quickly became better acquainted with others. Wendy Traber was attending the meeting to represent *Surviving*, Pat Fobair's newsletter. Jan Kinzler attended on behalf of the Oncology Nursing Society. It was her first week on the job as membership director. Peggie Carey had come from Asheville, North Carolina, representing the support group Life After Cancer Pathways. Shannon McGowan was a Santa Monica psychotherapist and, along with Harold Benjamin, a cofounder of the Wellness Community.

Helen Crothers represented the American Cancer Society. Shirley Miller had been included on behalf of Florida's Cancer Hotline. Julie Becker had come from Cincinnati, the home of support organization Cancer Share. Amarillo, Texas-based Harrington Cancer Center had sent Barbara Waligora-Serafin. Her expertise was in patients' physical fitness and exercise. A founding member of Seattle's Cancer Lifeline, Pamela La Fayette, also had a seat at the table.

There were two others whose particular skills rounded out the group. Yvonne Soghomonian, was a cofounder of Candlelighters Childhood Cancer Foundation (now called American Childhood Cancer Organization). Her experience in support organization start-up predated that of all the others in attendance, and it was invaluable. Equally vital to the meeting was Neil Fiore, a California-based survivor, psychologist, and author of *The Road Back to Health*. Over the course of the weekend, he pulled together the group's agreed-upon ideas into a formal format.

The night before, they had discussed quality-of-life issues and long-term health, neither of which was currently being discussed by the medical community at large with regard to cancer survivors. The intensity in the conference room was palpable. Each attendee may have been laboring under different labels, but they were all working in the same universe, and, as Fitz would say decades later,

"We practically fell into one another's arms." For the first time, each of them could say to another, "I know you because you're working on the same thing I am." And Catherine was right; with his booming voice, Fitz was the perfect moderator.

Like all of them, Susie had been part of meetings and committees with clear hierarchies. This group, however, put aside egos and titles in favor of one focused agenda. She described her amazement of the weekend: "I concentrated on every discussion, and was overwhelmed with the energy, enthusiasm, and expertise in the room. These people were talking a language that I thought only went on in my head."

The blank pages taped to the wall started to fill up with headings like "Lobbying" (which was then crossed out and replaced with "Advocacy"), "Clearinghouse," "Voice," and "The Organization." Next, they began formulating a statement of goals and objectives, agreeing that they needed to change the semantics of cancer. The word was often used to portray something negative. A bad politician or policy, for example, might be known as a "cancer on the government." Odious individuals were a "cancer on humanity." The authors of those phrases never considered how their words might impact people living with an actual cancer history.

Equally repugnant to the group was the term "cancer victim," and being referred to as someone who had "suffered" from cancer. Those terms conjured up hopelessness, and were never applied to other first-world maladies like heart disease or diabetes. Thanks to advances in treatments, life after cancer was becoming something one could hope for, just like life after a heart attack. It was time, they all agreed, to let the world know these things loudly and clearly. But if they weren't "victims" or "sufferers" of cancer, what were they?

Up until this moment, a "survivor" of cancer was someone who had lived at least five years past the completion of their treatment. They were "cured." At this point, Fitz shared with the group the story of the woman who had approached him at the Cured Cancer

Congress. Even more absurd, he declared, was that in 1986 the word "survivorship" was nowhere to be found in medical literature.

If their group was sailing into what Fitz had called "the uncharted land of survivorship" and removing language about cancer they didn't like, they would also be focused on creating new language that would work for them. They would build an entirely new lexicon that would deal with a range of issues, separate from the biology of a cancer diagnosis. As a result of this expansive thinking, the paper on the walls quickly filled up, and together they crafted what would become the preamble to their charter:

> Cancer is an unwelcome intruder in life. Yet cancer is also an inescapable part of many lives. From the time of its discovery and for the balance of life, an individual diagnosed with cancer is a survivor. Surviving is an enormously important, often difficult, always challenging human enterprise that involves the individual, the family and the givers of care.

It was masterful. It was radical.

Lunch was delivered, and they ate while they worked, their marathon of enlightenment continuing. Next on the to-do list was developing a communications network and a comprehensive clearinghouse for survivorship materials, advocates for survivors' rights, and the study of survivorship. They assessed what services currently existed for those who were living beyond a cancer diagnosis and treatment, and considered what a "survivorship movement" might look like. They worked until it was time to go to dinner, a potluck at an LTC board member's home.

By Sunday evening, the group had carefully written the charter that followed their preamble. Thus, the structure of the infant organization, newly christened the National Coalition for Cancer Survivorship (NCCS), was born. For the first time, a network of survivorship organizations and individuals existed.

The group selected five founding members to serve on the board of directors, including Fitz as president and Barbara Hoffman as secretary. Rounding out the board were Pamela La Fayette, Barbara Walingora-Serafin, and Estelle Weissburg.

Two more survivors joined the board after the founding group parted that weekend. Edith Lenneberg had taken an active role in the development of the enterostomal therapy profession (a specialized field of nursing involving the care of patients with stomas, openings in the abdomen connected to either the digestive or urinary system to allow waste to pass out of the body). An acquaintance of Catherine's who had fought ovarian cancer twice, Edith had pointed out to her earlier that mutual aid would be at the very foundation of the survivorship movement. It was something she had been involved with since it first became part of health care and she had worked alongside Catherine in planning the organizational meeting.

Albuquerque attorney Grace Olivarez also joined the board, volunteering for the treasurer's position. In addition to a 1970 Notre Dame law degree—Grace was the first Hispanic woman to ever receive one—she had been a prominent New Mexican social research leader, the highest-ranking Hispanic woman in the Carter administration, and the owner of an Albuquerque Spanish language television station. Grace was also a cancer survivor, midway through a two-year battle with the disease that would eventually take her life in September 1987.

Catherine was never one to dole out heavy lifting without being willing to take on just as much herself. She agreed to serve as the NCCS executive director. She held that role at LTC, and it was in their office—a house at 323 Eighth Street, in a quiet Albuquerque neighborhood—that the official NCCS headquarters would co-exist, using space in the house's kitchen.

As it had been with ONS a decade earlier, without internet or email, all correspondence would be by US mail or the increasingly popular fax machine. Additionally, there would be fees associated with becoming a bona fide nonprofit, and the founders literally passed the hat for operational funds. They collected $921.85 ($2,000 in 2021 dollars) on the spot with another $3,450 ($7,600 in 2021 dollars) in pledges. But the money would mean nothing without the group pulling survivorship out of the shadows and into the light.

Every founder of the newly born NCCS had been emotionally affected by their weekend together. Hotlines and newsletters were discussed. And they told one another as they departed, "This isn't over."

In Susie's mind, the most poignant aspect of the weekend in Albuquerque was that the concepts they discussed—"a movement" and "support groups"—could actually be possible. In the 1980s, cancer support groups, as mentioned before, were thought of as mutual help groups, self-help groups, or peer-to-peer groups, and were disparate and localized. And a movement for cancer survivorship? That would mean dragging their unspeakable disease, and their collective experiences with it, from the dark recesses of their pasts and thrusting it onto a national, even an international, stage. But the newly formed NCCS would not be the first organization to unite people with a shared and terrifying disease. Nor would it be the first to help the public better understand a disease of which it was afraid.

For example, while mental illness is still somewhat misunderstood, it was more so in eras past. Mentally ill patients were also kept in the shadows, often shackled, ignored, and abused. But in the late eighteenth century, at a psychiatric facility outside of Paris, France, superintendent Jean-Baptiste Pussin first changed those practices. With his wife, Marguerite, and physician Philippe Pinel, Pussin advocated for humane treatment for the mentally ill. He also recognized the value of employing recovered patients as hospital staff. Thus, the first benefits of peer-to-peer support were recorded.

In 1983, six gay New York men officially established the Gay Men's Health Crisis in response to the alarming growth of AIDS (acquired immunodeficiency syndrome). They produced and distributed fifty thousand free copies of their first educational news-letter to doctors, hospitals, clinics, and the Library of Congress. And they created the landmark "buddy" program to assist PWAs (People with AIDS) with their day-to-day needs. These pioneering movements and others offered NCCS solid shoulders on which to stand.

An example already existed in the cancer empire. The waiting room of a hospital pediatric floor is a lonely and terrifying place for parents. Their perceived job is to protect their children at all costs. Yet illness and injury often render parents impotent. In 1968, Washington, DC, attorney Grace Ann Monaco found herself in that very space. Her eighteen-month-old daughter, Kathleen Rea, was diagnosed with acute lymphoblastic leukemia.

The good news for parents and children facing leukemias in that era was that medicine was finding more successful ways to treat them. But as the children survived the disease longer, a new set of problems emerged around their long-term care. They were often unable or unwilling to eat, or conversely were ravenous, causing them to fluctuate from skeletal to obese over the course of treat-ment. They fell behind at school as a result of long hospital stays, radiation to the head, and the brain fog that accompanies chemo-therapy. They were made fun of by other children, and shunned by those children's parents. They were not yet even aware of the fallout awaiting them when they became adults—infertility, fear of recur-rence, and emotional scars.

As the weeks of Kathleen Rea's treatment became months, Grace and the other parents she routinely encountered on the pediatric oncology floor began discussing their common needs and fears. They were a powerful and eclectic group of scientists, journalists, government workers, and lawyers. They met wherever they could find space in the hospital—including boiler rooms and the corri-dors outside the emergency room. One parent in the group was a congressional staffer and eventually snagged a conference room for them at the Rayburn Building, where members of Congress had offices. Bonds formed. Miracles sometimes happened. And sometimes they didn't.

Kathleen Rea died of her leukemia in 1970. But her mother turned grief into action. Together with the group of twenty-five parents she had met at the hospital, Grace helped found the first pediatric cancer support group: Candlelighters Childhood Cancer Foundation (the group Yvonne Soghomonian represented at the NCCS founding meeting). They lobbied, testified, and wrote, all the while meeting regularly to support one another as parents of children enduring the ravages of the disease and the grief it often left in its wake. The Candlelighters blazed a trail in cancer support and parent-peer support, and they, along with the AIDS movement and others like it, such as AA, gave the NCCS founders much encouragement.

The spark growing in Susie over that October 1986 weekend in Albuquerque had become a full-fledged fire by the time she arrived back at work in Tucson on Monday morning. She was so enthusiastic that Lois set up a meeting with the Cancer Prevention and Control director, and their boss, Dr. Frank Meyskens. Recurrence and secondary cancers, along with studying long-term disease and treatment effects, certainly seemed to fall under the "prevention and control" umbrella.

Susie was ready to hear what had become a typical response to survivorship: what do we need that for? But to her surprise, Dr. Meyskens gave them free rein. It was different from other programs. It was out-of-the-box thinking he loved, and he enthusiastically endorsed pursuing the survivorship trail to see where it might take them.

Chapter 8: Victims No More

In 1989, there are 3 million Americans who have lived five years or longer after their diagnosis and treatment.

Volume 1, Number 1 of the NCCS newsletter arrived in mailboxes in March 1987. The eight-page newsletter served as an introduction to NCCS and was sent to Catherine's ever-growing mailing list.

The "National Networking Publication" (as the newsletter was subtitled) described how the founding members had come together in Albuquerque, and was filled with tidbits about other organizations and individuals who were doing great work in survivorship around the country.

On the back page was a piece written by Barbara Hoffman titled "Employment Discrimination Against Cancer Survivors: The Current State of the Law." Barbara's article pointed out that in 1987, more than one million of the country's five million survivors would experience some form of employment discrimination solely because of their cancer history. Denial of new jobs, demotions, undesirable transfers, loss of benefits, and outright dismissal—not to mention coworkers' fears of contagion—were happening at that very moment across the country.

The Rehabilitation Act of 1973 prohibited discrimination based on handicaps in federally funded programs. Some survivors did have actual physical handicaps, while others' handicaps were perceived by employers. The act forbade both. At the state level, forty-five states had their own laws prohibiting handicap discrimination.

Only Arizona, Delaware, North and South Dakota, and Wyoming did not. But for survivors, the word "handicap" was a slippery slope. On the one hand, in order to be protected under that act, they needed to admit to a handicap. On the other hand, doing so might not only jeopardize their jobs, but also force them to admit at some level that they weren't "cured," which was the benchmark upon which so many things depended.

After President Reagan's July 1985 surgery for colon cancer, he never had to worry about his job security. In contrast, in that same year, 84 percent of blue-collar workers with a history of cancer, and half of their white-collar counterparts, experienced discrimination. They shared their work-related problems in an American Cancer Society study. Cancer specialist Dr. Stanley Marks told the *Pittsburgh Post-Gazette* that he knew of no suits or complaints that had been filed charging discrimination. However, he said, "I think most patients are frightened or certainly don't want the publicity. They may be too mentally and physically exhausted to mount a legal challenge."

Those comments mirror Jeffrey Ibbotson's story. He had been first in his college undergraduate class, and went on to earn a master's and then a doctorate degree in chemical engineering. He was recruited by the Gulf Corporation to leave his native England and move to the United States, where he topped off his education with an MBA. Although well-respected within the corporation, Ibbotson was laid off with ninety-five other employees in 1983. He was the most senior in the group, and the only one with a "handicap." In 1976, he had undergone a laryngectomy due to cancer of the vocal cords. He learned to speak again using his esophagus, making him sound as though he had laryngitis.

Over the next two years after being furloughed, Ibbotson sent out 130 resumes. He had interviews, but because he was nearly always asked about his voice, no job offers came. Although friends advised him to consider suing Gulf, he was reluctant because he didn't want to be labeled a troublemaker, which would further hamper his job-hunting efforts.

A forty-two-year-old bookkeeper named Jon underwent a colostomy for his colon cancer. "I received a death sentence twice," he said in the ACS study. "Once when the doctor told me I had cancer, then when my boss of ten years asked me to quit because my cancer would upset my fellow workers."

Frances Wright was also diagnosed with colon cancer and went to great lengths to preserve her job as a clothing store employee. She took all her chemotherapy on weekends to avoid absenteeism, but was still told to quit or be fired. She was ineligible for Social Security disability because her doctor didn't consider her disabled, and she wouldn't be eligible for Social Security benefits until she was sixty-two. She was fifty-four at the time.

Not only did this happen in the latter half of the twentieth century, it happened routinely. Barbara's newsletter article confirmed that the greatest impediment to ending discrimination was that very few survivors brought suits to enforce their rights to equal job opportunities. Consequently, the laws were unclear and untested. She stated that the NCCS was "working with federal and state legislators to introduce new laws designed to address the specific needs of cancer survivors." And in fact, fighting these injustices was the third objective in the NCCS charter: "To advocate the interests of cancer survivors to secure their rights and combat prejudice."

Barbara had learned firsthand about the discrimination faced by cancer survivors. In 1975, one year after her cancer treatment, she was on her way to a class as an undergraduate at Princeton University. She passed by two young men and overheard one of them talking about having spent his freshman year at Stanford while undergoing treatment for Hodgkin's disease. He was now angry about a roommate situation, not an uncommon occurrence in college. But this situation caught Barbara's attention. She recognized the speaker as Peter Bastone; they had a class together. She tracked him down to talk to him privately.

Peter's recent history had been tragic. He grew up on Chicago's West Side, where his father was a homicide detective. During the last part of Peter's senior year of high school, his father died of a heart attack on duty, while chasing a perpetrator through City Hall. A few months later, Peter found a lump in his neck. A biopsy revealed that he had Stage III Hodgkin's disease and he began treatment at the University of Chicago. But then his mother saw a newspaper article about Dr. Henry Kaplan's work with Hodgkin's. The article's headline proclaimed, "Device Can Blast Cancer," and described Kaplan as an expert on Hodgkin's disease. Before long, Peter, too, became an alumnus of the linear accelerator radiation club. His treatments were sandwiched in between freshman college classes at Stanford.

Having been an athlete all his life, when his treatment ended, Peter transferred to Princeton, where he joined the football team as a walk-on. (Designated a starter, Peter would go on to become captain of the freshman and JV teams, be selected Academic All-Ivy, and win two collegiate football awards from Princeton and the Caldwell Fellowship for Grad School. His next step was the Baltimore Colts football camp, but he suffered an injury and didn't make the cut.)

Peter refused to be characterized as weak or sick, instead forcing himself to bounce back from treatment quickly. But he knew his mother was worried about him, and he was equally worried about her now that she was alone. Not knowing what the future might hold, Peter gave his Princeton roommate his mother's phone number, just as a precaution, explaining his father's death and his cancer diagnosis.

The roommate's father was a doctor, who had recently read—and misconstrued—an epidemiological study. The study showed a cluster of Hodgkin's that was found to be genetic. But when the study was initially reported on, it suggested that Hodgkin's was virulent and contagious. The roommate's doctor father focused *only* on the first report. There was no way he would allow his healthy son to be exposed to the deadly disease Peter might still have. So, he telephoned Princeton's Health Services to complain vigorously. In response, they released Peter's medical records for the doctor to peruse without Peter's knowledge. This violation of privacy was only the first insult.

Shortly thereafter, a Health Services team escorted Peter to a single room at the McCosh Infirmary, where he was ordered to live. Peter was devastated. His mother was furious. And an impressive challenge was mounted. Both his original oncologist in Chicago, and Henry Kaplan himself, flew to Princeton on Peter's behalf. The phalanx of defenders also included his head football coach, Bob Casciola, and most of the team. Eventually, Peter was returned to the dorm to room with a teammate who wasn't the least concerned about "catching" the disease. In fact, the football team relished the idea that they had a guy in their midst tough enough to beat cancer.

Susie's chance attendance at the NCCS founding meeting was about to affect her life more profoundly than she could have imagined. She said a decade later, referring to her experiences as an oncology nurse, "It continually amazes me how disappointments can lead to challenges and opportunities." After hearing her enthusiasm about the survivorship discussions in Albuquerque, and the organization's founding, Debi McCaffrey realized that 1987 was the year to bring that part of the cancer experience to the Oncology Nursing Society (ONS) Congress. The annual event would be held that year in Denver on May 10–12.

Debi created an educational panel that included Susie, Fitz, and LaMarr Bomareto, a Denver survivor of three different cancers. Debi opened the panel with an emotional and tearful introduction about her personal cancer experience. And then it was Susie's turn. As she looked out over the crowd of two thousand nurses who had come to their session (nearly half of the entire congress attendance), Susie became so nervous she honestly thought she would lose all bowel and bladder control. Her knees knocked. Her mouth felt dry as an Arizona desert. But she kept telling herself, "You can't be wrong, you can't be wrong. You lived what you're speaking about. It's your own personal experience!" With a quivering voice, she began her twenty-minute presentation, and when the applause subsided, she realized she had actually enjoyed it. The shrinking violet had just blossomed on that stage.

Meanwhile, Lois, Debi, Barbara, and Susie co-authored a two-part review article in the *Annals of Internal Medicine.* Dr. Meyskens was also listed as a co-author. But a bona fide research project on the subject could really launch survivorship into the medical stratosphere. The first step before beginning any formal research project—and one that is often more time-consuming than the project itself—is to find funding to cover the costs of running that research. Susie and Lois received a one-year grant from the National Institutes of Health (NIH). They added three more women to their team, Lauren Clark and Jan Atwood from the U of A College of Nursing, and Gerri Lamb, director of nursing research at Tucson's St. Mary's Hospital. Debi and others added their skills as the study progressed.

For nearly twelve months, the team collected two phases of data from a group of adults who were at least two years out from the end of their treatments. They created a "Cancer Survivor Questionnaire" which consisted of twenty-two short, simply worded, open-ended questions focusing on the survivors' life changes, problems, concerns, and needs. The questions hit all the big challenges, most of which still ring true for survivors thirty years later: physiological issues, including development of second or third cancers and cardiomyopathy (chronic heart disease); emotional issues, including depression, and fear and anxiety about recurrence and death; and the socioeconomic effects of cancer, including insurance and employment issues.

Because Susie was both an oncology nurse and a survivor herself (for a remarkable fifteen years at that point), participants felt truly comfortable in speaking with a member of the "club." They were very candid in their responses, which made up the pernicious soup of survivorship spume that Susie knew all too well.

"Long-term cancer survivorship is a contradiction of terms in a society that has long equated a cancer diagnosis with inescapable death," began the study abstract, an overview for the rest of the paper. Published in the *Oncology Nursing Forum,* it continued: "Findings indicate that the cancer experience permanently changes life patterns."

Insomuch as U of A had been on the cutting edge of many other cancer-related programs, Susie and Lois saw no barrier to creating an innovative support program at the university's cancer center. They proposed an adult, long-term follow-up clinic, with physiological and psychosocial components, much like the existing pediatric survivor clinics. The two women had ticked all the boxes. They had been funded by the prestigious NIH and conducted appropriate research. And the need for survivorship support had been clearly demonstrated to the satisfaction of ONS, since its journal published their findings.

But despite their enthusiasm at the prospect that this was something whose time had come, their proposal was not accepted by the physicians in the oncology department. With grant money spent and no survivorship program to develop, Susie was once again without a job. However, she had learned she was not without a voice.

By the summer of 1987, over seventy independent and local organizations had joined the NCCS, along with hundreds of individuals. The advisory board had grown to thirteen, and the new additions included cancer survivor and founder of H&R Block tax preparation company Richard Bloch, psycho-oncology pioneer Jimmie Holland, and president of NBC Entertainment Brandon Tartikoff. Catherine was now working full-time for NCCS, as well as maintaining her executive director duties with LTC.

The next obstacle to overcome was finding a stable source of income. While companies and hospitals made contributions, and memberships flowed in, fundraisers filled the coffers as well. That's where the newly founded Bike America came into the picture.

Bike America's purpose was to raise public awareness and funds for a specific charity each year, and NCCS was to be their first beneficiary. Three cyclists left Portland, Oregon, on June 10, 1987, and biked 4,500 miles in ninety days, arriving at Philadelphia's Fox Chase Cancer Center on September 2. Along the way they solicited direct donations, netted one-day and per-mile sponsorships, and garnered a lot of media attention. That attention benefited not only Bike America for future rides, but NCCS as well.

During the ride, newspaper articles included quotes from Fitz and other board members, and since Philadelphia was Barbara Hoffman's home turf, she was there to welcome the team. Best of all, they raised $10,880. That figure (the equivalent of $24,220 in 2021 dollars) made up more than one-fourth of the first fiscal year's income for NCCS.

Their early growth was truly remarkable, given the state of communication technology in the 1980s. Other than the telephone, instant communication was *not* the norm. Computers existed, but they were either the size of a modern-day powder room, rarely existing outside of the workplace, or clunky "portables" like the Osborne and the Kaypro that were far from portable in real life. "Surfing the web" was limited to visiting various bulletin boards, while email was in its infancy.

Similarly, "mobile" phones weighed in at nearly two pounds, with a $4,000 price tag. The first commercial version—appropriately nicknamed "The Brick"—weighed two and a half pounds and had a battery life of less than thirty minutes. Traditional nonmobile phone usage required taking into consideration long distance fees, which weren't cheap. Fax machines, too, were subject to long distance rates, and Federal Express, though growing, had limited delivery. For a young organization like NCCS, minding every penny was essential.

When announcements, newsletters, and meeting agendas needed to be sent to members and organizations within their network, the NCCS staff used the era's most common and least expensive forms of communication—typewritten letters, duplicated by making a second (and sometimes third) copy using carbon paper or by mimeograph machines, which meant a lot of sore arms from hand-cranking the printing drum. It was all sent via the US Postal Service. Yet, word about the organization spread.

By the summer of 1987, a nonprofit company called Date*Able* (with the emphasis on "able") was looking for a volunteer match-maker. The company focused on helping people with the stigma of physical limitations meet others. Ellen Stovall was looking for a new challenge. The DateAble job was to personally interview each applicant after they had filled out a basic questionnaire. As Ellen later explained, "It wasn't a matter of screening them out. It was screening them in." Many had experienced disappointment and rejection, their paralysis or blindness or cancer taking a back seat to their loneliness. Washington-area psychiatrist Dr. Lucy R. Waletzky (the "R" stood for Rockefeller, making Lucy a fourth-generation member of that family) had created the company after observing that illness had caused survivors and others to "… give up their right to normal social intercourse," as she said in a news-paper interview. "It was as if they are children of a lesser god." When she met Ellen, she knew immediately that Ellen's big heart and personal experience with cancer made her the perfect fit. She was hired.

Because of Lucy's work with cancer patients, she was also on the mailing lists of a number of cancer organizations. It would have been impossible for someone as adept at scouring the country for advocates—as Catherine Logan was—to not have added Lucy's name to the NCCS list. Lucy was so taken by their work, she become a charter member in July 1987, donated $5,000 in October, and ultimately became a member of the advisory board.

The following spring, Ellen learned about NCCS from a syn-agogue acquaintance, Natalie Davis Spingarn, who also told her about the newly formed Greater Washington Coalition for Cancer

Survivorship (GWCCS). It had been founded by a collection of Washington-area NCCS members. GWCCS functioned in much the same way as an NCCS chapter, supporting and educating Beltway survivors with NCCS materials. Natalie was insistent that Ellen become involved in both. Ellen, however, chose to work locally. It made the most sense from a geographical standpoint, and it wasn't long before she became the GWCCS vice president.

In November 1987, NCCS held a one-year birthday celebration. Calling it their second annual assembly, they scheduled it for Friday through Sunday, and chose the theme "Survivorship: Charting the Course." The promotional flyer sent from coast to coast carried this message: "Come help chart the course. Take part in making decisions which will strengthen and give direction to the survivorship movement."

The meeting took place at the Albuquerque Hilton Hotel, where group rates ranged from $20 to $40 per room, and the meeting fee was $25, underwritten (again) by Albuquerque's St. Joseph Cancer Center.

The meeting was dedicated to Grace Olivarez, who had served as board treasurer for less than a year, and had died in September. Her death presented those within the organization a hard truth: a group whose membership includes a large number of cancer survivors faces grief far more frequently than an organization made up of the general population. And when it happens, cancer survivors' thoughts turn to their own mortality.

The assembly began with an open meeting of the board of directors which had grown to twelve. Susie had taken Barbara's place as secretary, while Barbara was now the vice president/treasurer. Another new board member was Julia Rowland. Her reputation in the psycho-oncology field certainly preceded her, and it didn't hurt that her mentor, Jimmie Holland, had already signed on to the advisory board. Just as survivors were seeing the benefits of connecting with one another, for health care providers with an interest in cancer, NCCS offered an educational networking opportunity.

Natalie Davis Spingarn was the assembly's keynote speaker Friday evening. She challenged her audience to do three things: first, "do a better job of speaking for ourselves," second, "make [our] weight felt… to influence the important issues that affect us as survivors," and finally, "do a more effective job of helping one another."

She listed a number of ways that latter point could be accomplished, but the heart of it went back to Fitz's mantra that veteran survivors must lend a hand to the rookies.

The National Cancer Institute (NCI) also participated. It was an exciting sign that the country's largest cancer research body considered the movement NCCS was building the real deal. Earlier that year, NCI's Office of Cancer Communications had initiated a needs assessment. Katherine Crosson spoke in detail about the NCI's interest in survivorship and listed the areas where they were hoping for NCCS member input, including public education, print and audiovisual aids, and funding recommendations. (NCI gave grants to researchers working in specific areas of cancer. This was their first foray into survivorship.)

The agenda for the rest of the weekend, as spelled out in the flyer, was "to give newcomers the opportunity to meet one another, attend workshops with national leaders in the field, and help shape the future of NCCS."

Those workshops developed for the 150 attendees included topics like how to talk to doctors about survivorship issues, how to build local groups, and how to fundraise. As they had in their planning and launch, NCCS took another page from the AIDS movement by also offering a workshop on advocacy and legislation. Attendees listened to speakers explaining how their advocacy to elected officials could impact the spending devoted to survivorship programs. (That power was what Mary Lasker had wielded to increase research spending in the ramp-up to Nixon's National Cancer Act. And it was what she was then wielding on behalf of AIDS research.)

Brad Zebrack, a young Hodgkin's disease survivor, had come to the assembly from San Francisco where he was a middle school teacher. Hodgkin's, so often a disease of the young, had arrived in Brad's life in 1985 when he was twenty-four. He moved to Los Angeles to live with his parents during treatment, and connected with the Wellness Community in Santa Monica. "I was the youngest guy in the room," he said more than thirty years later. "Everyone else was my parents' or grandparents' ages. When I returned to San Francisco, I started going to a support group and was fascinated by the woman who facilitated it."

That facilitator was oncology social work pioneer Pat Fobair. Brad realized her line of work was something he wanted to do, so he researched social work programs, combined with cancer and kids. That profession is called pediatric oncology social work, and Brad began pursuing his degree in the field.

Between Harold Benjamin, Wellness Community founder and a founding member of NCCS, and Pat Fobair, Brad learned about the growing survivorship movement. Like so many other survivors, he, too, had felt disenfranchised after treatment. The NCCS mission was exactly what Brad was seeking. And at nearly the same time that NCCS had accepted Bike America's fundraising offer, Brad had made one of his own. He and his then-girlfriend (and now wife), Joanne, would ride the perimeter of the United States for a full year. NCCS gratefully accepted the offer if it could be put off a year, after the completion of the Bike America ride. So, in the summer of 1988, Brad and Joanne left Oakland, riding the northern tier of the US, and arriving in Portland, Maine, in September. They worked their way down the Atlantic coast throughout the fall, hitting Miami by winter. Next came the southern tier of the country, ridden in the spring. The two arrived back in Oakland in June 1989.

Throughout the eleven-thousand-mile trip—which included twenty-three states and part of Canada—NCCS helped connect them with members and organizations who set up events at hospitals, cancer centers, and within the cancer survivor community.

Brad and Joanne met with survivors and their families, sharing the story of Brad's survivorship.

"I wanted people to know not everybody dies of cancer," he explained. "People can still live a vibrant life after the disease." They, too, raised over ten thousand dollars. And, as importantly, Brad was living, breathing proof of the possibility of survivorship to everyone he met. He was another voice to emerge from the shadow realm, and his involvement with NCCS would continue to grow.

Some years later, after Brad and Joanne had married, they began a process that also smacked of discrimination for so many others. Prior to Brad beginning his treatment, his doctor told him there was an 80–90 percent chance that he would be infertile. That wasn't unusual. Any type of radiation to the pelvic or groin area, along with many chemotherapy drugs, had the same effect on men as it did on women. Brad had the good fortune of being told about his infertility in advance (as opposed to Susie's sudden discovery). His doctor referred him to a Los Angeles sperm bank clinic. In addition, the medical professionals gave him the same canned statement that was repeated to nearly all young cancer patients: if all else fails, you can always adopt. Patients internalized and remembered that message.

Eight years later, Brad and Joanne decided it was time, and their in vitro fertilization (IVF) process commenced. They had set aside ten thousand dollars to begin their family, and used it all in several failed attempts. The couple was resolved to not having children until one night at dinner, when they asked one another, "Is this all there is?" And the adoption discussion began. They had no idea what a judgmental and invasive process they were about to encounter. "Strangers asking pointed questions about you, your habits, and your lifestyle," Brad related. "And then, they ask about your health."

Learning that biological children are not in your future is difficult for anyone to digest. But learning that adoption isn't possible—despite the cheery earlier promise from health care providers—is heartbreaking. Yet that was often the case for cancer survivors. It was protocol for adoption agencies to request medical histories from all prospective parents, along with a letter from a physician. Agencies felt responsible for placing children in homes where the parents were physically and emotionally able to raise them. And while survival rates had certainly improved by the end of the twentieth century, no physician could guarantee a patient was "cured," even after the five-year remission goal line had been crossed. By the time Brad and Joanne began the process, he was more than fifteen years out from his diagnosis and treatment.

There were no standards for adoption procedures, as most adoption agencies are private. Furthermore, many international adoption agencies had such a bias against cancer survivors, they didn't even accept inquiries from them. Just as employment discrimination against survivors was often passive—"We hired someone more appropriate for the job"—adoption discrimination followed a similar route, with long wait times and the excuse that a baby who was a good match just wasn't available. If birth mothers were still in the picture, they too, were hesitant to place their babies with survivors.

Equally frustrating were adoption costs. Again, no standards existed. Many survivors had huge financial burdens from the loss of income during treatments. A significant number of adoption agencies required a large upfront deposit. It was all a sad deterrent to couples. Brad and Joanne had already spent what they had allocated to begin their family on the failed IVF procedures. But they persisted, and their story has a happy ending. Although the birth mother of the first baby they were promised changed her mind after the birth (a decision not related to Brad's cancer), two and a half years later they adopted a beautiful baby girl.

"Survivors, like other Americans, have the right to the pursuit of happiness," Natalie Davis Spingarn, now an NCCS board member, wrote in 1988. Her words were part of the "Cancer Survivors' Bill of Rights" that the American Cancer Society had asked her to write as part of the society's grand seventy-fifth birthday celebration in March. It was a beautifully written outline of what all survivors hoped to achieve, not surprising given Natalie's great talent.

Jill Ireland, the actress, who died in 1990 of breast cancer, read the rest of the Bill of Rights aloud, giving, as Fitz proclaimed in the Spring 1988 issue of the newsletter, "...a tremendous boost." Natalie had taken over editing chores and gave the newsletter a facelift. Now called the *Networker,* it displayed a new NCCS logo, with a sunburst amid the letters. Fitz said the board had deliberated over several logos before choosing this one. Although there is still no written explanation of the sunburst's significance, it could be that, consciously or not, the board realized that their movement was shedding a great light of hope on survivorship.

A second boost came a few months later with the inaugural National Cancer Survivors Day. Merril Hastings, publisher of the relatively new survivor magazine *Coping,* had announced the event's creation at the 1987 NCCS assembly. The *Networker* painted a wonderful portrait of the day:

> Celebrations of achievement of a full life after cancer will mix balloons, music, clowns and mimes with speeches, seminars and the like. From La Jolla to St. Louis to Charlotte, different celebrations will inform the public, and enable survivors, their families, and their friends to enjoy the day.

It was a celebration that would have been unheard of at the beginning of the decade. As Fitz pointed out, "It was not long ago that cancer was a secret...cancer was a stigma, a warrant nobody wanted to have attached to them."

Amid the celebration in Asbury Park, New Jersey, the president of the New Jersey division of ACS proclaimed, "As more and more of us survive cancer, as we are doing, and live normal productive lives, as we are doing, the population as a whole must understand that we are all human beings and that cancer does not make any one of us different."

These two events were milestones in the growing survivorship movement. It was all happening exactly as the NCCS founders had hoped, and at what seemed like an accelerated pace. The third annual assembly of NCCS again took place in November. As had been the case the previous year, 150 attendees made the trip to Albuquerque.

Fitz was reelected to a two-year term as president, saying, "We're no longer simply the glint in the eye of a few zealots; we've matured and jelled." Now it was time to create a larger infrastructure. To that end, the board introduced five committees: Management, Program, Assembly, Networker, and Minority Task Force. Within each were subcommittees, with board members stepping up to work in their areas of interest and expertise. Within the Program Committee, Susie headed the Speakers Bureau/Workshops subcommittee, Barbara took the helm of Advocacy, and Julia was on Research.

The crowd at that third assembly made up quite a tapestry: different ages and ethnicities, surviving dozens of cancer types. But they were of one voice when it came to their sheer joy at being and working together. Texas CPA and board member Larry Moore was spot on when he said, "I never knew having a deadly disease could be so much fun!"

By 1988, NCI was openly talking about survivorship, and that was encouraging. But NCCS was interested in how NCI planned to use the $1.49 billion it had earmarked for survivorship research. Natalie interviewed the NCI official responsible for that enormous sum. Her article for the *Networker* outlined NCI's position. There was interest in looking at interventions that could be built into the medical system which would mean better survivorship outcomes. Of course, that was of great interest to long-term survivors like Susie. And it was a good thing. But then the interview went downhill. The NCI official was not fully on board with the NCCS definition of survivorship. And the organization felt it was more appropriate to focus "survivorship research" on those *living* with cancer, rather than the challenges of life *after* cancer.

In another article, however, NCI's new director, Dr. Samuel Broder, was more encouraging:

As a growing number of Americans survive cancer, they face a number of issues, such as rehabilitation ... psychosocial support, employment and insurability. NCI is committed to help meet the needs and concerns of this growing population.

Chapter 9: "A Streak of Stubbornness and a Loud Voice"

In 1991, 175,000 women are diagnosed with breast cancer, and 45,000 will die of it.

The first *Networker* of 1989 announced that the fourth NCCS assembly would be in the Radisson Plaza Hotel in Manhattan Beach, California, just a few miles south of the Los Angeles International Airport.

"Beyond Survival: Challenging the Stigma—Insurance, Employment, Attitudes." It was clear how important the theme of the November 1989 assembly was to the survivors who attended, all three hundred of them. Julia Rowland later prepared an updated constituent profile, showing that this assembly included more minority participants than previous ones, with one breast cancer survivor coming from as far away as Trinidad. Over half of the participants were survivors, Julia found. They were predominantly well-educated women, and astonishing number of them had survived multiple diagnoses.

Fitz delivered the keynote on Saturday morning, suggesting that survivors cross a river once they have gone through the cancer experience. And they can never go back. But he offered an image of survivorship as starting a new life on the other bank, populated by fellow survivors. At lunch that day, married *L.A. Law* actors Jill Eikenberry and Michael Tucker spoke. The popular television show was now in its third season. Jill had survived breast cancer three years earlier, just as the show's filming began. The couple talked about how cancer affects personal relationships.

With the pride of a father whose child has just made the dean's list, Fitz was eloquent about the assembly's success. "[It] was what it should have been—a great leap forward for the NCCS." New goals for the coming year included quadrupling individual memberships—now at a suggested $20 annually, or whatever an individual could afford—and doubling organizational and institutional memberships—which ranged from $50 to $250 depending on an organization's annual budget. Then came a big announcement. "The board voted a resolution committing the NCCS to moving its headquarters from Albuquerque to Washington, DC, within the next two years," Fitz was quoted in the *Networker*. "It was a hard decision that came after a year of debate ... but the proximity of Washington policymakers and funding sources prevailed in that debate." To ease the transition, Fitz announced that the 1990 assembly would be held in DC, with the Greater Washington Coalition for Cancer Survivorship acting as host.

As the coalition grew, the *Networker's* content also evolved. The quarterly newsletter included more announcements from member organizations across the country, and the list of national resources grew longer. A "bookmart" was added with special discounts for NCCSers. A column called "People Watching" contained bios of survivors within their ranks. And the post-assembly Fall 1989 issue featured "First Timers at the Conference."

The first of the eleven people listed was Ellen Stovall, acknowledged as the director of DateAble, the vice president of GWCCS, and an eighteen-year survivor. Responding to the question "What will you tell your grandchildren about this conference?" Ellen said, "That I met people who really know how to live vital productive lives, because they've had the chance to confront death—some earlier and some later in life." Ellen was also listed as the 1990 assembly chair.

The Civil Rights Act of 1964, signed into law by President Johnson, prohibited discrimination based on race, color, religion, sex, or national origin. But it made no mention of other categories, such as pregnancy, age, or disability.

Although California enacted a state statute protecting cancer survivors in 1980, it wasn't until 1984 that a Federal Cancer Patients' Employment Rights Act was proposed. It was introduced by New York Congressman Mario Biaggi at the urging of one of his constituents, Timothy Calonita. Having been diagnosed with Hodgkin's disease at age eleven, Calonita beat it, only to be told a decade later that his medical history disqualified him from becoming a police officer. This, despite an official admission that he was qualified for the job. His response was to get a law degree, become a prosecutor, and lobby tirelessly to protect other survivors from similar discrimination. As Biaggi put it, "It is the height of hypocrisy for society to promote cures for cancer, only to turn its back on cancer survivors who conquer the disease and hope to resume work."

Three years later, on June 17, 1987, with no bill yet enacted, Calonita addressed the House Education and Labor subcommittee on employment rights, as did Barbara Hoffman on behalf of NCCS and all survivors.

"There is life after cancer. It should be a full life of quality and equal opportunities, not one of narrow prejudices and stunted dreams," Barbara said. The discrimination occurring included outright firing, demotion, physical isolation, and cancellation of medical benefits. "Millions of people are as productive after a cancer diagnosis as they had been before," she went on, including "gold medal Olympic athletes, authors, actors, ambassadors, our current President [Reagan] and members of the 100th Congress."

The last group mentioned was meant to drive the point home. Barbara was testifying before the 100th Congress. Given the percentage of Americans diagnosed with cancer every year, it was highly likely there were a number of survivors in their midst, even if they had never disclosed their diagnoses. The Cancer Patients' Employment Rights Act never made it out of committee, but it gave birth to a new law: the Americans with Disabilities Act (ADA).

Again, Barbara testified, this time in writing, and provided to the Kennedy Committee—a reference to Senator Edward Kennedy's chairmanship of the House Education and Labor subcommittee on employment rights—stories of cancer survivors who had experienced employment discrimination that would have been made illegal by the ADA. In the Summer 1989 *Networker*, Barbara urged readers to "continue your letters and phone calls! They have made a difference; now is *not* the time to stop."

On July 26, 1990, President George H. W. Bush signed the ADA (although it would not take effect until January 1992, with the employment portion going into effect in July 1992), prohibiting discrimination based on real or perceived physical or mental disabilities. It was Barbara's dedicated work, along with that of many others within the NCCS ranks, that helped make the bill a reality.

The next challenge they would undertake would be health care.

––––––––––––––––

With the nation's capital as a backdrop, and more than 450 in attendance, the 1990 assembly was held in November at the Ramada Renaissance Hotel in Washington, DC. It was themed "Speaking Up for Survivorship: An Agenda for the Nineties" and opened, as it had in the past, with a board meeting. After having held the board presidency for four years, Fitz became its chair and Larry Moore stepped into the president's position. The board expanded again, with Ellen replacing Larry as vice president and two other notable additions. One was Dr. Lovell Jones, a PhD at MD Anderson Cancer Center in Houston and the founder of the Biennial Symposium on Minorities, the Medically Underserved, and Cancer.

The other new member was oncology social worker Betsy Clark. Betsy and Barbara Hoffman had met in New Jersey where they were both working on a project about cancer resources. Barbara suggested Betsy might enjoy attending the 1990 assembly. "I thought I was just being invited to a meeting," Betsy remembered with a smile. "But it was really a board interview! Somehow, it just seemed to be a fit, and when they offered, I accepted." NCCS had just added a very important ally to their number.

The assembly's focus was on advocacy: speaking up for ourselves, for others, and for the community. They had scored Senator Paul Tsongas as a keynoter. The senator had been diagnosed with non-Hodgkin's lymphoma in 1983, and underwent a bone marrow transplant in 1986. He would go on to make a run at becoming the Democratic presidential candidate in 1992, and made his survival from cancer an issue in his presidential campaign, when he and two of his doctors, Dr. Tak Takvorian and Dr. George P. Canellos, said he'd been cancer-free since the 1986 operation.

Sharing the keynote position, NCI director Dr. Samuel Broder described national research efforts affecting survivors. He called the formation of NCCS a "life-affirming move." He also asked for each coalition member to be an advocate of cancer research and a messenger of information.

The workshops and panels focused on mind-body connections (with the discussion led by Jimmie Holland), doctor-patient communications, nutrition, and discrimination in the workplace and the marketplace. Lucy Waletzky held a workshop on "Sexuality and Cancer," the perfect complement to the ACS workshop "Look Good, Feel Better." At that point a two-year-old program by the same name was in thirty-eight countries. It assisted women survivors with hair and makeup tips.

Ellen's hard work and attention to detail as the assembly chair shone through, as did her humor and grace. Post-assembly comments were effusive:

"This is great! People are dressed to kill!"

"… Illness doesn't have the power to keep us from looking good and being competent."

"Intensity prevailed. ENERGY! Obvious leadership and organization."

"[A] very classy program."

A photo on the *Networker's* last page summed it all up: Ellen and co-chairs Natalie Davis Spingarn and Alice Cave stood arm in arm, laughing and kicking up their heels.

Most consumers do some research before they make major purchases such as cars or refrigerators. Yet, until recently, few cancer survivors knew how to make comparably informed decisions about their health care [sic] and related issues such as treatment options, insurance benefits, and employment rights.

This cogent observation is found on page three of *Charting the Journey: An Almanac of Practical Resources for Cancer Survivors,* a groundbreaking book from NCCS published in 1990, just in time for the assembly. It came to be known by those who loved it—and there were many—as simply the *Almanac.* The book's introduction, written by Fitz, explains that NCCS realized that cancer survivors were desperate for a comprehensive resource book that addressed all their challenges. He went on:

What was needed, we jested, was a *Whole Earth Catalog* for surviving cancer. We envisioned an almanac rich in information concerned (as traditional almanacs are) with the future, that could be consumed on an as-needed basis to help with decisions and actions.

Today (2021), an Amazon search for cancer survivor books returns over four thousand hits. But in 1990, for the first time ever, the *Almanac* put at survivors' fingertips entire chapters devoted to mind and body resources, helping therapies, peer support, and more. In addition to Fitz's written contributions, he shared co-editing duties with Barbara. She authored a chapter on employment and insurance, and other founding members added their voices.

Patti Ganz pointed out that "sixty years ago, there was little audience for a book about surviving with and beyond a cancer diagnosis. In the 1930s, fewer than one in five cancer patients were alive five years after treatment." But by 1990, there were more than seven million survivors living in the United States, and the *Almanac's* time had come. It was part encyclopedia, part support group, part inspiration. And while its impact on all survivors was huge, it was also an absolute lifeline to those living in rural areas where survivor resources were often nonexistent.

By 1990, the good news was that the long-term, disease-free survival rates for Hodgkin's disease survivors had increased significantly. The bad news was that a number of articles had recently been published about the increased incidence of breast cancer among those survivors.

In December, breast cancer was being called "America's Silent Epidemic." That same year, 1990, Susie became a breast cancer statistic. No one can say for sure whether or not Susie's previous treatments, specifically the radiation, played a part in the development of her breast cancer. "But," as she later said, "I am mightily suspicious since the single tumor was in the field that received an extra radiation boost."

Women younger than age thirty, like Susie had been, who were treated for Hodgkin's disease with radiation were at markedly increased risk for breast cancer. And that risk increased dramatically more than fifteen years after therapy, as Susie also was. She sought other breast cancer survivors and those who had experienced multiple cancers, needing to connect with women who "had been there."

Even worse news was that Susie's Hodgkin's therapies constrained her treatment choices. Radiation was not an option (because she had reached her lifetime limit), and because the risk for contralateral (i.e., in the other breast) disease was unknown, and because all the physicians conferring on her case agreed not to give her any more chemotherapy, she decided—after much deliberation—to have bilateral mastectomies.

"I may have been treated for cancer before," Susie said, nearly a decade later to a group of Pennsylvania oncologists in 1999. She continued:

> But I never had a mastectomy before. I had three drains in my chest and was catheterized. The morning after the operation, a little group of "Doogie Howsers" gathered around me to tell me I could go home that day. I asked for, and got, one more day.
>
> Nurses taught me how to handle the drains and took out my catheter. They explained to my sister, who is an X-ray technician, how to change the dressings. Without my sister, I couldn't have done it. And many patients don't have that support. We're telling people how to be a nurse in twenty-four hours, something it took me four years to learn.

While Susie may have felt alone in this drama, it was also true that in January 1991, her options were still far greater than those of women who had walked the same road before her.

––––––––––––––––––––

Breasts. In one way or another, they've been front and center for centuries (pun intended). They remain hot topics for men, from the locker room to the board room. Women, in turn, recognize early on that their breasts are powerful sexual tools. We agonize over their sprouting. When they do, we worry that they're large enough. And as we age, we worry that they're still perky enough.

Men's breast-ogling is legendary, whether the focus of their attention is on screen, in print or in the flesh. Successful and well-known television journalist Betty Rollin, who had a mastectomy following her breast cancer diagnosis in 1975, put a new spin on that topic. In her book *First, You Cry*, she made this salient observation: "Given *my* shape, 'topless' suddenly strikes me as a very odd way to describe *those* ladies. Imagine if the drooling...men who go to see those shows got an eyeful of a *real* topless dancer."

It is ironic, then, that the segment of the population (men) which has so enthusiastically worshiped the breast was also so willing to unceremoniously remove it when it became cancerous—and without regard for their female patients' physical and mental well-being. In early breast cancer treatment, legions of male surgeons had one goal: preserve life at all costs.

When British surgeon Charles Moore discovered in the 1860s that recurrences of "mammary cancer" seemed to happen most often near the edges of the original surgery, he reasoned that taking more tissue was key. Moore argued that sparing women from further disfigurement was actually a "mistaken kindness."

In the late nineteenth and early twentieth centuries, the man known as the "Father of Modern Surgery," Dr. William Halsted, took the idea of "more is better" even further. He dug deeply into women's chest cavities, removing not just the cancerous breast tissue, but also the *pectoralis major*, the muscle responsible for moving a shoulder and its corresponding hand. He called the procedure a "radical mastectomy," not just because it was invasively over the top (which it was), but because the Latin origin of the word "radical" is "root." His aim was to surgically remove the "root" of the breast cancer.

Some of Halsted's patients still experienced recurrences. Not fully comprehending the science behind cancer's spread, Halsted made his surgery even more "radical," this time in the sense of its aggressiveness. He carved away at women's collarbones and chains of lymph nodes. His students and protégés went further still, removing rib cages and entire shoulder structures.

The result of what came to be called the "Halsted mastectomy" was permanent disfigurement with enormous loss of function. In addition, while removing lymph nodes might have stopped the spread of the disease, it negatively impacted the flow of lymph fluids, which carry away body toxins and deliver infection-fighting white blood cells. Just as damming a river causes the water level to rise, altering the lymph system caused patients' arms to swell from the accumulation of fluid. Halsted referred to the condition that we now know as lymphedema as "surgical elephantiasis," but had no treatment to offer.

Dr. Halsted's motives were almost certainly pure, as he attempted to save his patients from death in this pre-radiation and pre-chemotherapy world. But many of these unfortunate women spent the rest of their lives hidden in their homes, maimed and ashamed.

As medicine progressed—not only with regard to treating cancer, but also with the advent of X-rays and medical tools—it became better understood that positive surgical results for breast cancer had much less to do with how radical the surgery was, and far more to do with whether the cancer had spread before the first cut was made. But even then, a male doctor's perspective of the removal of a breast was very different from that of his female patient.

The world teaches women that breasts make them attractive, and (depending on what's in style at the time) that breasts also make them better mothers. Breasts are not, however, crucial to survival in the same way that lungs and brains and livers are. Thus, amputating them was common in breast cancer treatment, and often without a woman's knowledge or consent.

It was called the "one-step procedure." A woman presented to a general surgeon—early on, there were none who specialized in the breast—with a suspicious lump. Today, the area is anesthetized, and a biopsy is done while the patient is conscious, with results and next steps discussed almost immediately. With the one-step procedure, practiced during the latter half of the twentieth century, a woman was advised that while she was under anesthesia, tissue from her lump would be removed and analyzed. If it was found to be cancerous, her breast would then be removed as well. Thousands of women awoke from the one-step procedure anxiously pawing at their chests to confirm the fate of their breasts. The horror of finding that one or both had been cut off while they were unconscious is hard to imagine. It was this same procedure that Natalie Davis Spingarn had gone through in 1974.

Rose Kushner was determined not to experience that horror, however. A Maryland journalist (and an NCCS Advisory Board member in 1988), she rocked the boat, and she rocked it hard. On June 25, 1974, prior to being anesthetized, she instructed her surgeon to *only* biopsy a suspicious lump, leaving her breast intact. Her surgeon's face loomed over her as she regained consciousness. He angrily pronounced that the biopsy showed she had cancer, and that she would probably die from the delay in treatment. He strode off in a huff, which Rose later reasoned was more because his authority had been challenged than because she actually might die.

Her courage spared her from a radical mastectomy. And in that moment, she gave birth to the "two-step" movement. After Rose fired that first surgeon, she had more tests done, and agreed to a "modified radical" mastectomy, performed by a newly specialized breast surgeon. Only her breast and axillary (armpit) lymph nodes were removed. Muscle and bone were spared, and so was her quality of life. Possessing, by her own admission, "a streak of stubbornness and a loud voice," Rose embarked on "a crusade to tell American women—and through them, American doctors—what I have learned."

In 1975, Rose wrote *Breast Cancer: A Personal History and an Investigative Report*, relating her experiences in an effort to empower women to ask for the "two-step procedure." The *New York Times* praised the book. But the American College of Surgeons censured it, and the American Cancer Society refused to recommend it. Asked why she thought that was the case, Rose said: "Some surgeons think, in good conscience, that women should not know too much. 'It confuses them,' they say, or 'Don't give women more information than they can process.'" Radical Halsted mastectomies and one-step procedures remained the norm until 1979, when two-step procedures and modified mastectomies became equally common options.

Dr. Allen Lichter, former dean of the University of Michigan Medical School, and later CEO of the American Society of Clinical Oncology, wondered why breast cancer had been the only cancer where decisions had to be made in minutes. Every other malignancy, he observed, was treated after a biopsy had been done first. Neither his personal nor his professional research ever produced a sound reason.

"The process just developed," he said, "passed on from father to son doctors." Research was finally done on the physical and psychological damage the one-step procedures caused. Many women who were interviewed for that research reported that their surgeons had told them exactly what Rose's had—"You have two choices: have a radical mastectomy done immediately at the time of the biopsy or die." And it was repeated hundreds of times every day.

"It was the surgeon's choice rather than being done for scientific reasons," Dr. Lichter said. "One hundred percent of the surgeons were men. One hundred percent of the patients were women. I knew Rose Kushner. She caused the situation to explode. Imagine the courage it took for her and other women to say, 'Stuff it. I'm getting a second opinion!' The one-step method was not only scientifically invalid, it was monstrously cruel."

Crueler still was the slow path to making mammography accessible to all. The technology had become commonplace in the 1970s, with the 1976 American Cancer Society recommendation that mammograms should be used as a screening tool for all women. Yet insurance companies refused to cover the cost of the test. States were required to individually change their insurance laws, a decades-long project. When 1990 dawned, a mammogram averaged $60 ($117 in 2021 dollars), an out-of-pocket cost that was prohibitive to many women in the twenty-five states where coverage was still nonexistent. A warrior to the end, Rose Kushner was on the phone promoting legislation to cover the lifesaving tests just days before she died on January 7, 1990, her cancer having metastasized. She was sixty years old.

Rose's powerful voice was not the only one to bring breast cancer, its treatment, and its prevention—a topic previously thought "unfit for public discussion"—to a very public stage.

In 1972, child actress (and later the US ambassador to Ghana and Czechoslovakia) Shirley Temple Black insisted on a biopsy followed by a simple mastectomy. She announced the results of the operation on radio and television, and in a February 1973 article for *McCall's* magazine. The next year, First Lady Betty Ford underwent a mastectomy. Two weeks later, Happy Rockefeller, the Vice President's wife, also had a mastectomy. Five weeks after that, Happy's other breast was removed.

The publicized stories of these high-profile women were unparalleled. They broke the ice for a public discussion of breast cancer, and they made the point that the rich, powerful, and famous were not exempt from the disease. Nor would they settle for a shadowy existence. The spotlight on their cancers and treatments brought such great awareness of breast cancer and self-exams (both the First and Second Ladies had found their lumps themselves) that inquiries about the disease at the National Cancer Institute went from 250 per month to 2,500. Consequently, diagnoses went up as well. Many of them were early diagnoses resulting in lives saved.

This spotlight on Washington, DC, breast cancers, and the apparent ease with which the famous patients recovered, encouraged the ever-growing numbers of women diagnosed with the disease to bravely undergo their own surgeries. Just as Mrs. Ford, Mrs. Black, and Mrs. Rockefeller had come out about their cancers, making the disease and its treatment more socially acceptable, Betty Rollin's *First, You Cry* spoke candidly about the emotions involved in her breast cancer experience: fear, PTSD, a crumbling marriage, poor self-image.

No mention was ever made of how Shirley Temple Black, Betty Ford, or Happy Rockefeller recovered emotionally. But this is certain: every woman who has undergone a mastectomy is reminded of the awful day of her diagnosis each time she undresses (this author included). We have all experienced a sense of loss. And like all those in and out of the public eye in that era, these women were expected to grieve their lost breasts on their own.

It's important to emphasize that the medical community at that point was behaving in the only way it had been trained: believing paternalistically that they knew better than their patients, and that the emotional and psychological impact of the operation, if they even stopped to consider it, was irrelevant. Fifty years earlier, doctors weren't equipped to even discuss a cancer diagnosis with their patients. Now, at least, the disease was more survivable, and a *physical* recovery possible. But doctors were still not trained on how to discuss a patient's *psychological* recovery, even if they considered it. Nor did they understand the psychology of breast reconstruction.

A 1975 *Chicago Sun-Times* article began with these cold words: "After a mastectomy, a woman must learn to cope with the fact that her body has been disfigured to save her life." Five years later, a woman writer made the case that if "a person loses an eye, that eye is replaced with a glass one. So, if a woman loses a breast … why not replace it? The motivation may be vanity—but that's not a neurotic trait. For them, replacing that amputated breast is a necessary part of their physical, social and emotional recovery from a disfiguring mastectomy."

By 1980, there were 108,000 diagnosed cases of breast cancer. Still, that same year, when a woman in Indianapolis asked her doctor about reconstruction, he exclaimed, "My God, woman, how vain are you? I just saved your life!"

Newspaper articles covering reconstruction were rife with quotes from male doctors (only 2 percent of surgical residents were women then). They were always lukewarm on the topic, suggesting that reconstruction was okay for *some* women. No explanation was made as to who "some women" were. And then there was the cost.

In 1980, only the state of California mandated that insurance cover the cost of breast reconstruction. Women in the other forty-nine states had to foot the bill, which hovered around $12,000 in 1980 (about $38,000 in 2021 dollars), on their own.

Ten years later, the year Susie was diagnosed, reconstruction was being done more often at the same time as the mastectomy. Better still, most health insurance plans covered at least 80 percent of the costs. But the type of breast implant was another issue.

After Susie's February 1991 double mastectomy, her intention was immediate reconstruction. Unfortunately, making that decision occurred in the midst of the silicone implant controversy, and her plastic surgeon was somewhat less than pleased when she questioned his judgment about it. His interactions with her were verbally abusive. Finally, Susie told him she needed a break as she was still conflicted about what she wanted to do and was not ready to make a final decision yet. She finished by saying that she might even decide to have no implants at all.

"Well, yes, you could do that," he replied, followed by, "You could always stuff a couple old socks in a bra!" She was so stunned at his insensitivity and rudeness that she left the clinic and never returned. Without criticism or sarcasm, her new doctor helped her review her options and supported her choice. He congratulated her for asking questions and being informed, and hugged her when they had the plan figured out.

Susie's experiences brought to light more issues that survivors had previously been forced to leave in the shadows: second cancers, challenging doctors, overcoming self-image issues, and government and corporate cover-ups. They awaited many long-term survivors, and had been the impetus behind the fourth objective of the NCCS charter: "To promote the study of the problems and the potentials of survivorship."

Between 1985 and 1992, all silicone breast implants got was bad news. They were:

"…masking or mimicking tumors…"
"…linked to digestive disorders in children who had been nursed…"
"…cause[ing] fibrous tissue to grow around the breasts, which, in turn, cause a painful hardening of the breast…"
"…cause[ing] highly malignant cancers in over 23 percent of the animals tested, including large cell lymphomas…"

The idea of new breasts springing a leak and oozing lumps of putty-like silicone into their chest cavities was too much for many women. It was for Susie. Although saline implants were often less discussed, they had fewer issues. If they leaked, the saline would simply be absorbed in the body, so that was the choice she made. But it wasn't patient preference that would end the story for silicone breast implants.

Negative reports about silicone implants had begun as a trickle, but by 1990, they were hitting the news stream like a flood. That year, the Food and Drug Administration (FDA), the federal watch-dog for situations like this, had relegated silicone implants to the "iffy" list of medical devices. Complicating matters further was the way in which the leading maker of silicone implants, Dow Corning, was handling their challenges. Dow Corning's first line of defense was to create a consumer hotline so that concerned patients could get information straight from "the horse's mouth," as it were. Problem was, the "horses" had bad information.

Anxious consumers who called the hotline were told there was virtually no hazard in using the implants. "Scientific data and research show that silicone breast implants are 100 percent safe," they said. "After thirty years of study conducted with patients, there have never been health problems with implants or silicone."

In reality, there was mounting data contrary to those statements. The FDA had begun investigating whether Dow Corning had deliberately withheld information about the safety of the implants even before it began giving out misinformation. Finally, in 1992, an exasperated FDA placed silicone gel breast implants in moratorium in the US, stating there was "inadequate information to demonstrate that breast implants were safe and effective."

In the ensuing years, a number of independent reviews ultimately indicated that the implants did not cause breast cancers or any identifiable systemic diseases. Whether Dow Corning was guilty of a cover-up or deliberately disseminating misinformation, or completely innocent, became moot. The company never recovered, and eventually filed for bankruptcy in 1995 in the face of 19,000 lawsuits.

Chapter 10: Like a Grapevine

In 1992, there are 7.2 million American cancer survivors.

"We will make this a super-panel on cancer. May I call on Dr. Fischinger to begin the proceedings."

By the time Chairman Daniel Inouye, senator from Hawaii, said these words on April 24, 1991, the Senate Appropriations Health and Human Services Subcommittee had already heard testimony regarding polio survivors, kidney disease, tropical diseases, sexually transmitted diseases, and inhumane animal testing. It was now cancer's turn, and the "super-panel" was made up of representatives from heavy hitters in the field: the Association of American Cancer Institutes, the International Council for Coordinating Cancer Research, the National Coalition for Cancer Research, and the American Association for Cancer Research. Speaking for the latter as its president was Dr. I. Bernard Weinstein, who had brought along his own heavy hitter to testify: NCCS Vice President Ellen Stovall. Although Ellen's name was spelled "Stauble" in the official transcript of the day, her words had been very carefully selected for her first appearance before the Senate.

> This December, as we commemorate the 20th anniversary of the Cancer Act, I will also celebrate my 20 years as a cancer survivor.... Seven million people in this country, many of them voters, are living today having heard the bone-chilling words 'You have cancer.'... My mission is to get you to see

in me someone that you know. I could be someone on your staff. I could be your daughter or your wife or your cousin or your mother or your neighbor or your best friend.

What you do not see but what you must know is that there are untold physical and psychological scars that this dreaded disease leaves in its wake. What you must also know is that, while more than one-half of us will win a statistical battle against the odds, we have many war wounds that will never leave us: physical pain and secondary illness resulting from treatment; sterility and sexual dysfunction; and psychosocial stresses.

We cancer survivors are people you know. We are not statistical data to be quantified and pondered by experts. We are your family members and your friends, your children, your grandchildren, and generations to follow.

The quality of our life, no matter how long or short following a diagnosis of cancer, is dependent in large measure on how important this mission is to you and to those you love.

Cancer patients and their loved ones had testified before Congress in the past. But this was the first time the testimony had been in the name of survivorship. Ellen's eloquence and grace were a wonderful lead-in to an NCCS request for *Networker* readers to help in expanding its advocacy efforts. Under the survivorship umbrella, there was certainly no lack of advocacy subtopics, including the dire need for health care reform in America. Of equal importance was access to health care for all, regardless of race or economic status. That was something new board member Dr. Lovell Jones knew a great deal about.

The NCCS founders wanted the organization to be welcoming to all groups, regardless of demographic. Their efforts in attracting minorities weren't achieving the results they had hoped. So, in 1989, Fitz and Catherine had taken a road trip to the University of Texas MD Anderson Cancer Center in Houston to meet with

Dr. Jones. He had been the first African American to be hired by the university's basic and behavioral sciences department, where he began as an assistant professor in gynecology and biochemistry. But more importantly, in 1987, Dr. Jones had founded the Biennial Symposium on Minorities, the Medically Underserved, and Cancer.

A congenial man with a soft voice and kind eyes, and the son of a cancer survivor, Dr. Jones was able to diagnose the NCCS's dilemma right away. They were missing, he told Fitz and Catherine, the "grace note." It was a favorite explanation created by his friend, Dr. LaSalle Leffall. Dr. Leffall had been the first Black president of the American Cancer Society. He was also a friend of the late jazz musician Julian "Cannonball" Adderley.

Listening to music with Dr. Leffall one evening, Cannonball asked his opinion of the "grace note" they had just heard in a song. Dr. Leffall was puzzled by the term. Cannonball explained that a grace note is not really part of the sheet music, but is "a little something extra." One doesn't necessarily notice it when it's there, but without it, the music isn't as rich. When Dr. Leffall later addressed Dr. Jones's first Biennial Symposium, he used the grace note as an analogy to explain the importance of making certain that cancer support be specialized by demographic. That, he said, would give it the necessary depth missing from most generic approaches to the disease and its survivorship.

Dr. Jones shared an important addition to his grace note story with Natalie in the spring issue of the *Networker*. "Poverty exacerbates the problem [cancer burden]; it is one of the reasons, not *the* major reason. To give you a personal example, when my schoolteacher mother, who is not low-income, developed breast cancer, she waited until she had a *massive* lump before she went in for care."

Why did she wait, Natalie wanted to know. "Because of fear," Dr. Jones explained. "She was afraid of the idea of going in. She thought a diagnosis of cancer meant automatic death." Myths and fear hold powerful grips on too many, including the educated.

NCCS was growing, and growth is often accompanied by growing pains. Some of the founding members, many of whom were still on the governing or advisory boards, thought that creating regional or metropolitan chapters was the best way to meet survivors' needs. Each would run somewhat autonomously, and in a manner best suited to their geographical area, much like the Greater Washington Coalition for Cancer Survivorship.

Other members felt the organization could be most effective as a clearinghouse for survivorship resources around the country. For example, if you lived in Fargo, ND, you could call the NCCS office in Albuquerque to locate necessary services closest to you. Still others felt the most important thing the NCCS could do for survivors was advocacy on all levels. The best-case scenario was probably a mélange of all of those things, although attempting to be all things to all people is a difficult feat.

While Catherine Logan certainly understood the need for more research and its related funding, along with advocacy, her heart was in working directly with survivors. The telephone and post office were all she needed, along with the immense support of her assistant, Deb Ash. Three years earlier, in December 1988, Deb had been going to graduate school part-time and working in a bank. But she wanted to do something more meaningful, something she could really care about. She had answered Catherine's newspaper classified ad for an administrative assistant. Catherine offered her the position and Deb took it on the spot, soon falling in love with all the organization stood for.

As it was for Catherine, a great deal of Deb's time was spent answering phone calls. A woman from Colorado phoned to discuss the feasibility of divorcing her husband. That way, she could fall below the poverty level to receive cancer treatment through a government program for indigents. They had kids, the woman told Deb, and if she was no longer married, their family funds wouldn't be depleted by her disease.

Another day, Deb spoke to a St. Louis man who asked what information NCCS might have about cancer not being contagious. Every night after he left his office, he explained, a secretary scrubbed it down with Lysol so no one else would "catch his disease." He only found out about the cleansing ritual because he had returned one night for some forgotten papers. How can this happen in America, Deb wondered. It was then she realized what a sheltered bubble she had been living in. It was only when she came face-to-face with cancer survivors that she saw how much they were struggling.

Deb was inspired by Catherine's quiet passion and practical mind. But the longer they were together, the more Deb saw that Catherine's calm surface belied the intensity beneath it. "She was like a duck," Deb said. "They appear placid on top of the water, but all the while, they're paddling furiously below."

Catherine believed absolutely in the "veterans guiding the rookies" concept that Fitz had voiced in the early days of NCCS. That was just another way of expressing her personal passion and mission. "Peer support is the real foundation of the survivorship movement," she said. "Peer support groups led by survivors have intrinsic value on their own and are not just fallbacks when professional psychosocial services are not available."

It saddened Deb to have to leave the team in August of 1991 when she relocated to Washington, DC. The experience with Catherine in Albuquerque forever changed her. "NCCS was like a grapevine," she recalled later. "Suddenly, the organization was growing in all directions, reaching survivors in all corners of the country. I was so proud to have been a part of it."

As any viticulturist (the professionals who cultivate grapes for wine) will tell you, for grapevines to grow upward—and thereby be most easily maintained and harvested—they must be secured and trained to some type of support. Viticulturists use stakes and wire to create an arbor. The NCCS would soon discover the power of public policy on which to begin training its grapevine.

"Cancer Survivorship in Action: Activating and Advocating." It was the perfect theme for the 1991 NCCS assembly, its sixth, held October 31–November 3 in Denver. Both Colorado's governor, Roy Romer, and its first Congresswoman, Pat Schroeder, were featured speakers. The 350 attendees gladly paid $89 a night at the Sheraton Denver Tech Center to be a part of it.

Congresswoman Schroeder was the co-chair of the Congressional Caucus for Women's Issues. She was well known for making women's health one of her top priorities, so her participation in a plenary panel about breast cancer came as no surprise. In her session, the congresswoman pointed out the lack of research and funding for women's health. Then, using the one-in-nine statistic for breast cancer diagnoses, she brought down the house when she emphatically exclaimed, "You can bet if I walked up the Hill and told one of every nine men that he was going to lose a testicle this year, there'd be lots of research money!"

As with previous assemblies, the variety of workshop topics made certain there was something for everyone. There was also a new one on the menu: "The Late Effects of Cancer Treatment," subtitled "You're cured, what more do you want?" Not surprisingly, Susie led the session, joined by Ellen, who shared a story about her twenty-year-old son. She had been a cancer survivor his entire life. He had asked why, since she no longer had cancer, she was still involved with cancer issues. Ellen responded to him, "My involvement with NCCS is an affirmation of the fragility of my existence. And it is a way of exorcizing my anger and pain."

The flip side of the anger and pain that cancer causes is the odd and wonderful way it has of drawing people close together in a very short time. Just as it had for Susie, NCCS had breathed new purpose and passion into Ellen. Given their similar ages, their shared cancer diagnoses (with nearly the same diagnosis dates), and their passion for survivorship advocacy, it wasn't long before the two women recognized they were soul sisters. Long-term survivorship issues were the passions that drove them. But Susie and Ellen, along with all those involved with NCCS, also recognized the changes needed in what Governor Romer had called in his assembly presentation the "network of inaction," a.k.a. the American health care system.

At the nation's National Cancer Survivors Day events the previous June, the NCCS had circulated petitions calling for health insurance reform. The petition-signing continued through the assembly itself, with a plan to present the signatures to appropriate officials in Washington. But something even greater developed: a policy paper.

"Finding the most appropriate cancer treatment is only half the battle," *Los Angeles Times* health writer Shari Roan wrote in her multipart newspaper series, *"Cancer: The New Battlefront."* She continued, "Patients often face a second battle in persuading their health insurers to pay for their care."

This sad fact was supported by a 1991 Gallup survey, co-sponsored by the National Cancer Institute, in which two hundred oncologists were questioned about providing their treatments of choice to their cancer patients. More than half of the doctors reported that their patients were unable to receive the treatments the oncologists really wanted to administer because insurers refused to pay for them.

News of health care coverage issues was not at all new. Determining who might pay for what goes back centuries in American history. Let's begin with a fact rarely considered today. Until the mid-twentieth century, medical care was pretty much a pay-as-you-go deal. If you couldn't pay, you didn't get treatment, with a few exceptions. Those exceptions became the stepping-stones for today's concept of health insurance. The first prepaid medical care plan in the United States was signed into law on July 16, 1798, by President John Adams. The "Act for the Relief of Sick and Disabled Seamen" assessed twenty cents per month from every seaman at American ports to cover costs for the care of their sick colleagues and for the building of seamen's hospitals.

Another early health care coverage plan came seven decades later when, after the Civil War, the federal government established the Freedmen's Bureau. The bureau constructed forty hospitals, employed over 120 physicians, and treated well over a million sick and dying former slaves. The hospitals were short-lived, lasting only from 1865 to 1870, although the Freedmen's Hospital in Washington, DC, remained in operation until the late nineteenth century, when it became part of Howard University.

The closest model to the current American health care system came into being in the early twentieth century. It was called sickness insurance, and consisted of generally inexpensive policies available to employees of the same company. They were small in scale and administrated locally to keep overhead low. Since most workplaces had a vibrant gossip line, everyone knew everyone else's business. And that prevented people who were already ill from buying in.

While Britain passed the National Insurance Act 1911, which introduced a limited national health insurance program for its citizens, Americans were already associating insurance with employers. (The British National Health Service wasn't created until 1948.) That, in turn, paved the way in the 1930s for the birth of third-party health insurance. As the Great Depression had choked the financial throat of America, President Franklin Roosevelt revised his pending Social Security Bill to include publicly funded health care programs. But the Congressional battle that followed caused Roosevelt to remove health care from the bill.

In the meantime, hospitals began offering their own insurance programs, the first of which was called Blue Cross. Physician groups, too, began selling health insurance policies to employers, who then offered them to their employees and collected premiums. Blue Shield was the first of those.

During World War II, shipbuilder and industrialist Henry J. Kaiser created a plan in which doctors bypassed their traditional fee-for-service. Instead, they were contracted to provide medical services for Kaiser's company employees on construction projects up and down the West Coast. After the war, Kaiser opened up the plan to the public as a nonprofit organization called Kaiser Permanente, still in existence today. But it wasn't until the election of Lyndon Johnson, and his Great Society programs of the 1960s, that public opinion shifted toward the problem of the uninsured, especially the elderly. Everyone would one day be elderly, so supporters of health care reform were able to avoid the public's fears of "socialized medicine," considered a dirty word because of its association with communism.

In July 1965, Congress enacted Medicare, under Title XVIII of the Social Security Act, to provide health insurance to people aged 65 and older, regardless of income or medical history. Medicaid was a part of Title XVIII, too. Today it serves as the nation's primary source of health insurance coverage for low-income populations.

With each decade of the second half of the twentieth century, more and more individuals received insurance coverage from their employers, and that was a good thing. But tapping into that coverage for a catastrophic illness, like cancer, often took more effort and courage than actually fighting the disease. Suddenly, health care reform became the first arbor to support the NCCS grapevine. In 1991, the organization presented its "Policy Paper on Insurance Reform."

Seven crucial areas were covered, which the NCCS board called "minimum ingredients" necessary for reform. They included: no more discrimination based on health status; acceptance of preexisting conditions; coverage for anti-cancer drugs; coverage of investigational treatment; coverage of mental health and rehabilitation services and therapies; coverage of preventative health care; and amendments to the Employee Retirement Income Security Act. Each area was followed by an NCCS recommendation.

The paper was officially presented at the assembly in Denver, acknowledging the enormous financial burden of cancer treatment.

That year, even with insurance, twenty-eight million Americans would still be left bankrupt by a catastrophic illness.

December 27, 1981: "War on Cancer Makes Little Gains." It was a less-than-enthusiastic headline in the *Los Angeles Times*, heralding the ten-year anniversary of Nixon's exciting "Christmas gift to the nation." The article that followed wasn't much cheerier:

> The big killers—cancers of the lung, breast and colon—still take the lives of 200,000 Americans each year. Even today, one of the most persistent myths about cancer is that someday a single cure will be found that will eradicate the disease....

At the war's fifteenth anniversary in 1986, doctor-turned-statistician John Bailar III had bravely done to the war on cancer what Dorothy's Toto did in *The Wizard of Oz:* pulled back the curtain to expose truth.

"The public has supported [cancer research] very generously for decades," Bailar said in an interview, "and I think the public has a right to know what they're getting for their money—not much. It isn't zero, but it isn't much."

In May of that year, Bailar and colleague Elaine M. Smith had authored an article in the prestigious *New England Journal of Medicine* titled "Progress Against Cancer?" Their research was in exceedingly stark contrast with the generally optimistic reports from the American Cancer Society and the National Cancer Institute. Using cancer death rates as a measure of the war's progress (Bailar called death "the most fundamental measure of clinical outcome"), their research showed that cancer death rates rose from 170 per 100,000 in 1950 to 185 per 100,000 in 1982 (the latest year for which figures were available for the article).

In recognition of the war's twenty-year anniversary, on December 23, 1991, the *Washington Post* featured a piece titled "Cancer: A Statistical Minefield." The article echoed the thoughts Bailar had had five years earlier.

> Claims of progress in the war against cancer show more about what statistical measure is used than about actual inroads against the enemy. Higher five-year survival rates reflect not so much improved treatment as earlier diagnosis. One doctor reflected: "The biology of the disease is the same—it's just that the survival clock starts ticking earlier."

Another piece in the same *Post* issue was written by author and journalist Malcolm Gladwell. He called the war on cancer "a failure," but went on to say that it is "a failure so unexpectedly fruitful...it will be widely considered one of the great success stories of biomedical public policy."

The fruits harvested over the twenty-year war, Gladwell said, included fewer radical mastectomies and less intensive radiation therapy. He ended the article with this observation: "Researchers also began asking more profound and innovative questions about the fundamentals of human biology." Those questions had launched the Human Genome Project the year prior, something never imagined by Nixon's scientific team in 1971.

In her article "Search Persists for Magic Weapon in Cancer War," Abigail Trafford summed up the war's twentieth anniversary pointing out that cancer was no longer "the premier political disease."

> AIDS has pushed cancer to the side of the national debate. While cancer kills far more people, AIDS is newer, more lethal and growing faster. In the competition for funds, AIDS has garnered dramatic amounts of research funds while cancer's share has remained flat for a decade.

We can be quite sure that Trafford wasn't challenging which disease was more important or less horrific at its end. Rather, she spoke eloquently to a sad fact of media and politics: whatever is newer and shinier has more words—and more money—devoted to it. AIDS is also contagious and strikes the young, while cancer was finally being recognized as not contagious and often striking older people. What had changed the most by 1991, according to Trafford, was the culture of cancer. "No longer is it an illness so shrouded in fear and pain that no one dares to say the word." That may have been so in some circles. But for the majority of America's cancer survivors, the people living between the more socially advanced and forward-thinking coasts of the country, the shrouds remained.

Those within the NCCS knew all about the shrouds. The most pressing challenge was educating the public that cancer doesn't end when treatment does. Whether the war on the disease produced a cure today, tomorrow, or never, the country's millions of survivors would still be survivors, still facing challenges they never expected.

"The science of survival attempts to understand the disease itself; the art of survival attempts to understand the human experience of that disease."

So reads one of many powerful concepts Susie wrote in the 1992 *Oncology Nursing Forum* article "Myths, Monsters, and Magic: Personal Perspectives and Professional Challenges of Survival." In point of fact, there is probably no more beguiling crossroad than the one where science and art meet, regardless of the topic being referenced. In the case of surviving cancer, the myths, monsters, and magic at play cast an even more intriguing light on the science-art crossroad.

From the moment of the termination of her own treatment, Susie had struggled with the quality of her compromised life. "Quality of survival," she wrote in the article, is in the eye of the beholder. If the beholder is a physician, the factors defining quality survival are likely to be biomedical in nature, have scientific parameters, and be measurable. If the beholder is a social worker or psychologist, these factors encompass psychosocial components and are humanistic in nature.

If the beholder is a nurse, there tends to be a great capacity to blend biomedical and psychosocial factors. And if the beholder is a patient, the factors defining quality of survival include all of the above, along with personal, social and cultural values.

The myths Susie referred to were the absurd fairy tales of previous generations: that cancer was a death sentence; that cancer was contagious; that patients "cause" their cancers. The monsters, she said, came in various sizes and ferocities, depending on one's Achilles heel. For some people, for example, information helps slay their dragons. For others, information *is* the dragon. And the magic? Susie's definition of magic in this context was the perfect example of why she had become one of the country's leading survivorship advocates.

The sense of empowerment experienced by so many of today's survivors of cancer inspires individuals to investigate possibilities. Even if we cannot change our destiny, we can change the way we react to it. We can mobilize our internal strengths to seek out the the kind of information and support that each of us needs.

Every experience in Susie's twenty-year survivorship had not just been about finding her own quality of life, but about guiding other survivors to find theirs. She continued,

Survivorship is about the quality of our lives with or without cancer, about healing the visible and invisible wounds, and about feeling satisfied that we have made the right choices and are doing the best we can.

After all, isn't that what any of us can do, whether it's cancer or any other life challenge that plagues us?

Like a ship appearing on the distant horizon, the thought of researching survivors and the lives they were living had been a barely perceptible notion when NCCS was founded. But the embryonic survivorship movement would not be silenced. If science could identify long-term issues, it would raise the awareness of both the positive and negative effects of survival. That would better prepare the new legions of survivors who were hoping for decades of quality life. Developing follow-up for long-term survivors, including guidelines for continued care, could also be researched. Additionally, studies could be done about decreasing the adverse effects of treatments by employing the "less is more" theory: just enough treatment to eradicate the cancer, but not so much as to cause more severe, long-term effects.

In truth, survivorship topics far outnumbered the manpower and dollars allocated to them. It was time to bring the ship from the horizon to the shore. It would be a win-win for both camps. Research on survivors' health challenges—both physical and psychosocial—would allow the oncology community to mold future treatments. Their new discoveries would benefit the lives of current and future survivors.

This was why the NCCS board decided they must move to Washington, DC. The city was geographically located in the thick of things—between the NCI, where cancer research was done, and Congress, where cancer research was funded. The bonus was that research and funding would also garner press coverage. And that in turn would drive, and hopefully help pay for, more research. It was a perfect circle of life for the growing survivorship movement.

The first hurdle was affordable office space. The financial burden of the Albuquerque office had been modest. But Washington, DC, was expensive. The Silver Spring, Maryland, organization management firm they had hired offered NCCS unused space in their building, along with some other office services. It wouldn't be forever, but it was a great start.

Meanwhile, Catherine Logan faced a horrible dilemma. She greatly loved the organization she had helped found, and she appreciated the idea of having chapters around the country. But she also loved the Native American jewelry she created in her spare time and the serenity of riding her horses. She wanted to be surrounded by the New Mexico mountains, with a clear, blue New Mexico sky above. The city was not for Catherine. She chose to remain in Albuquerque and to rebrand Living Through Cancer as People Living Through Cancer. Her dedication to the NCCS survivorship movement, however, would not end. Nor would the organization's appreciation for all she had done. Catherine would serve as the 1992 National Cancer Survivors Day chair, and NCCS created an annual award, the Catherine Logan Award for Service to Survivorship, in her honor. It would be given each year for outstanding contribution to cancer survivorship.

Realizing the big shoes someone would have to fill, an executive director search team screened more than one hundred applicants before, eventually, Fitz told Ellen she'd be perfect for the job. Ellen laughed at him. Fitz told Ellen they should stop wasting time and just put her name up before the board. She argued. He won. In the spring of 1992, Ellen Stovall became the new executive director of NCCS.

That March, she was invited to address the President's Cancer Panel, a three-person federal advisory group. Then, newly elected President Bill Clinton appointed her to the National Cancer Advisory Board. Created as a requirement of the 1971 National Cancer Act, the board meets every two years to make a report to the US President and Congress about NCI's progress in its fight against cancer. The seventeen-member assemblage includes scientists, physicians, and other cancer-related specialists. Not only did Clinton recognize Ellen's survivorship chops, she was the *only* layperson on the board. And she came out of the gate at a dead run.

"The survivor community has not been as successful in pressing the two largest cancer research bodies—the American Cancer Society and the National Cancer Institute—to significantly direct more monies toward psychosocial and behavioral research," Ellen announced at her first meeting. On behalf of NCCS, she recommended that NCI coordinate a coalition of consumer groups to advance research into survivorship issues, something that would soon become a reality.

It was dubbed "The Year of the Woman." For the first time ever, on Tuesday, November 3, 1992, a total of five women were elected or reelected to the US Senate. It was groundbreaking for women, but what had happened six weeks before the election was lifesaving for them as well. That was the day Fran Visco's efforts paid off and funding for breast cancer research was tripled.

In 1987, Fran was a Philadelphia corporate litigator with a two-year-old son. And then she heard the terrifying words, "You have breast cancer." She was thirty-nine years old. Gathering information about her disease and treatment options, she was shocked when she learned how little money was being spent on breast cancer research. Fran refused to accept the status quo. Four years after her diagnosis and treatment, she and a group of other breast cancer survivors founded the National Breast Cancer Coalition. Like NCCS, it was a tapestry of more than forty grassroots organizations devoted to women's health. Their battle cry was clear: "Silent no more!"

Breast cancer diagnosis statistics were rising, from one in twenty women in 1940 to one in nine in 1991. Additionally, more women were dying of the disease every year and no one knew why. It was only logical that with more research, the puzzle might be solved.

Like Fran, the women who were being diagnosed with breast cancer in the '80s and '90s had come of age in the 1960s. They had marched in Vietnam War protests and, just like many NCCS founders and volunteers, had watched the rise of the civil rights, women's, and more recently, gay rights and AIDS movements.

They also saw the enormous disparity in research funding. In 1991, $132 million was allocated to breast cancer, while $1.262 billion was earmarked for HIV/AIDS. "I do not want to take money from AIDS research," Fran said in an interview. "But the numbers underscore how ignored breast cancer has been." True, Nixon's war on cancer had greatly increased research money twenty years earlier. But the amounts had stagnated and hadn't kept pace with the times.

For quite a while, Congress—nearly all male—had trivialized and minimized women's issues. Newly reelected Colorado Representative Pat Schroeder expressed it correctly. Speaking to breast cancer survivors at an October 1991 event, and referring to her fellow lawmakers, she said, "They do not fund what they do not fear. They do not fear breast cancer. And they do not fear you."

It was time to shake things up. Fran's idea was to tap into one of the nation's biggest coffers: the Pentagon. With no large-scale military actions going on at the time, Fran asked the question no one else had thought of. Rather than stockpiling their annual budget allotment that year, why couldn't some of the Department of Defense dollars be used for breast cancer research?

To gather attention for their mission, she and her troops began a letter-writing campaign called "Do the Write Thing." Their goal was to send 175,000 letters to Washington during the month of October. Each letter's purpose was two-fold: to put a human face on the devastation of the disease, and to flat-out ask for the money. The number of letters was significant as it represented one for each woman who would be diagnosed with breast cancer in 1991 (including Susie). They far exceeded that number, sending nearly 600,000 letters.

"If they want to get reelected," Fran said, referring to the members of Congress facing voters that year, "they'd better listen to us and do something about it." The "it" was their request for an increase in research funding, and lawmakers got the message.

On Tuesday, September 22, 1992, in an 89-4 vote, "... the most generous federal financing yet for research into breast cancer" was passed, according to an Associated Press article. The more than $400 million allocation would take effect in the next fiscal year, beginning eight days later. The nearly threefold increase would come from two sources: $210 million from the Pentagon, and $196 million from the Health and Human Services Department.

It was a big win for breast cancer, but it was also a big win for other cancers. Although childhood cancer groups had been in existence for two decades, the success of the breast cancer groups led to a proliferation of disease-specific—and body part-specific—advocacy organizations. In addition to peer-to-peer support, these groups, too, were on the hunt for more recognition for their diseases. With more recognition came more funding, and that brought more research for early detection and better treatment.

One thing was certain. Being a "squeaky wheel" was the way to success. Rose Kushner and others had challenged their surgeons about Halsted and one-step mastectomies. The women of the National Breast Cancer Coalition had challenged stagnated research funding. Now, with a purpose "in defiance of disease and in affirmation of life," as their *Almanac* proclaimed, NCCS was challenging how the world saw cancer survivors.

By the 1992 assembly, NCCS had five hundred institutional members on the roster and two thousand individual members. Those figures were double what they'd been the year before. Cancer survivorship had come of age as a national movement. The assembly, with the theme "Life: Celebrate the Challenge," was held at the Omni Hotel in Charlotte, North Carolina. Former Massachusetts senator Paul Tsongas was again the keynoter, as he'd been for the 1990 assembly.

The seventh NCCS assembly, in 1993, would be Susie's first as president. Thirteen years after Mount St. Helens erupted in 1980, survivors would gather just 185 miles away in Seattle. In some ways, the most destructive volcanic eruption in US history was a perfect analogy for the growth of the survivorship movement. The November assembly's theme would be "The Quest for Quality Survivorship," with the goal "to assist survivors in gaining access to information and resources that will enhance their quality of life."

Susie began the 1993 assembly edition of the *Networker* with her President's Letter:

[S]ometimes we get so bogged down in our goals that we fail to notice our accomplishments. Yet NCCS has achieved much since October 1986, when we gathered for the first time in Albuquerque, NM.

At that meeting, we identified diverse needs, along with many creative programs targeting these issues. Everything was scattered, hit or miss, sometimes duplicated, and lacking national coordination. Resources and support were adequate in a few areas, but minimal in others. A collective voice expressing the concerns of people with all types of cancer was absent. As survivors and supporters, we decided to advocate for ourselves and to develop a national survivorship agenda.

She ended her letter with a call to arms. "Our agenda is challenging. We need your help. Get involved. Share your ideas. Together, we can strengthen and energize the survivorship movement."

Chapter 11: Tickling the Dragon's Tail

In 1994, one American is diagnosed with cancer every 30 seconds.

In a soft, friendly voice, Sandra Day O'Connor, the first woman to ever serve as a Supreme Court Justice, announced to her audience, "I am a survivor."

Once the standing ovation subsided, she continued, "I was told I had a potentially fatal disease. Now *that* gets your attention!"

It was 1994, six years since she had been diagnosed with breast cancer. It was also the first time she had spoken publicly about it, as if she was chatting with gal pals over coffee. She talked about the fear and the emotion. She talked about having to make rapid treatment decisions, which for her meant a mastectomy. She talked about her hair falling out, and a stylist—who was later a cofounder of the "Look Good, Feel Better" program—taking her under his wing and fitting her with wigs. And she shared it all at the NCCS Assembly at the Washington Court Hotel in Washington, DC.

Justice O'Connor's surgery had been Friday, October 21, 1988. The court was in recess until the 31st, and she released a statement that she would be back on the bench on that date. Everyone in the audience who had been through cancer treatment—particularly one involving major surgery—snickered at her optimistic prognostication. But. a tough cowgirl at heart, Justice O'Connor made good on her promise and returned to work. Supreme Court Justice or not, however, her cancer experience was as difficult as anyone else's.

"I thought if I got sick, I went to my doctor, the doctor said what ought to be done, and that was the end of it. Right? Wrong!" The medical system, she said, was fragmented and disjointed. "Moving from doctor to doctor with separate appointments and separate approaches and one doctor not hearing what the other said increased the uncertainty and increased the trauma." She was describing *every* cancer patient's frustration. Her ideal scenario, she told the audience, once the necessary diagnostic tests were completed, would have been to "have a consultation with all the experts who've already looked at these things... the surgeon, the radiologist, the oncologist, the plastic surgeon, the nurse, a psychologist, and so on, everybody there to help you through the process of what to do."

When Justice O'Connor had finished speaking, Susie told the five hundred assembly attendees, "Advocacy has never been so crucial. Our presence is vital on both the local and national levels. We must continue to help lay the groundwork for true health care reform. Together, we *are* making a difference." After Justice O'Connor's appearance at the NCCS Assembly, "...Tom Brokaw (NBC), Peter Jennings (ABC), and Dan Rather and Connie Chung (CBS) all closed their news shows with the footage of O'Connor's address," reported the Winter 1994 *Networker*. "Thus, with one forthright speech... Sandra Day O'Connor catapulted the concept of survivorship to a whole new level of public awareness."

It was no secret that survivorship and its advocacy needed a louder voice. And insomuch as it was so important on a personal level, Ellen Stovall was the perfect voice to take the lead, proclaiming, "We have to figure out a way to work together, so the voice of advocates can be heard!" A giant step in that direction came in 1993, when NCCS convened the Cancer Leadership Council. It was not only designed for patient advocates to have a seat at the national health policy table, they *built* the table! Ellen had guided the concept from acorn to oak tree.

The council originally consisted of NCCS and other cancer patient-centric organizations, including Cancer Care,

Candlelighters Childhood Cancer Foundation, Susan G. Komen, National Alliance of Breast Cancer Organizations, Us TOO (a prostate cancer support group), and Y-ME (a breast cancer information and support organization). (As of 2021, there are now thirty groups on the council.) Following its purpose of developing positions on health policy matters of consequence to people with cancer, the council had two major goals. The first was to discuss survivorship issues, and then make recommendations to the American Society of Clinical Oncology, NCI, and others. Second, in light of the debate on reform of the health care system, everyone on the Cancer Leadership Council was driven to make certain the concerns of cancer survivors were heard. Their initiatives would guarantee survivors access to high-quality and specialized care.

Equally exciting was the March 1994 release of NCI's *Measures of Progress Against Cancer.* In it, NCCS was credited with playing a major role in the rapidly growing survivorship movement to enhance survivors' quality of life. According to the report:

Over the last decade [1982–1992], a strong infrastructure has also emerged to advocate for research, health care and social reform on behalf of cancer survivors. This is clearly seen in the establishment and growth of the National Coalition for Cancer Survivorship and its increasingly sophisticated efforts to push for changes that improve the opportunity for cancer patients to successfully reestablish a normal life during and after their diagnosis and treatment.

Probably most thrilling of all was this statement in the report: "As defined by the National Coalition for Cancer Survivorship, *a person is a survivor from the time of diagnosis through the remainder of life.*"

The venerable National Cancer Institute had endorsed the concept that was at the core of NCCS, something that burned brightly in the hearts of each of the founders. Their Albuquerque meeting had shaken up the long-accepted view of the cancer continuum and dispelled myths. And they had done it in just seven years.

Justice O'Connor's presentation was the icing on the cake. Themed "Seasons of Survivorship," (with Fitz's iconic 1985 article as the inspiration), the assembly was subtitled "Quality FOR Life." The emphasis on "for" as opposed to the usual "of" was certainly the aspiration of all survivors. Ellen and Susie co-presented a workshop with the same title. As twenty-two-year survivors, they were both well-suited to lead the discussion, as described in the program.

> ... survivors are increasingly concerned about their quality of life through and beyond their individual cancer experiences. As survivors strengthen their voice in the political arena, develop mutual aid networks and share information, the passivity of the past has given way to a new activism. As we approach the new century, we can work together to help shape a vision of the future that incorporates technologies of caring and curing with, ultimately, the complete prevention of cancer altogether.

This assembly was their most successful to date, and was co-chaired by Betsy Clark and Julia Rowland. Julia had left the board of directors several years earlier, but remained very much involved in the organization, continuing to devise and analyze the results of assembly attendee surveys. For NCCS to grow in meaningful directions, it was important to know who attendees were; their connection to cancer (survivor, co-survivor, health care provider, etc.); their diagnoses, backgrounds, education, and professions; and about their assembly experience.

Julia's findings from the 1993 assembly reminded NCCS of the importance of reaching all populations. Seventy-eight percent of those attendees had been women, and only 6 percent identified themselves as members of ethnic minority groups. Board member Dr. Lovell Jones was keen to address that. "Unless people, especially people of color, see individuals who have survived this disease, it's hard to combat the myth that cancer is a death sentence. That's why support groups are so important."

An invitation in the 1994 assembly program posed an intriguing question. "Do you ever wonder how health policy is made or if anything you can contribute to the process could make a difference? Come to the first NCCS Town Hall and participate with survivors, health care providers, politicians and community leaders to make **your** voice heard on the *cancer survivorship issues that matter most to* **you***!*"

Susie opened the town hall, declaring, "It's time for us to go to the people!" One hundred survivors and loved ones packed into the room to speak about their personal struggles with cancer and the issues they faced every day. The NCCS board used the assembly town hall as a testing ground, with the hope that more could be held around the country. When moderator Ellen Tobin, president of Health Surveys and Marketing, asked, "What's the worst thing about living with cancer?" a virtual tide of stories flooded the room.

Issues ranging from access to quality care and psychosocial support to long-term side effects and cancer's effect on the whole family were tossed about. It was more than the board had hoped for, and exactly what they needed to create a "how-to" town hall kit. The kit included a video of that inaugural gathering, complete guidelines, and a survey template for participant feedback. It was cutting edge in 1994, but cutting edge was what NCCS was all about.

There was one more thing: for several years, the board of directors had discussed doing something really big to call attention to the issues of cancer survivorship. Some years earlier, Betsy had taken a sabbatical from her college teaching position to organize a "congress" on thanatology (the scientific study of death and the losses brought about as a result). "It was quite successful," Betsy later commented. So much so, she and Ellen thought they could use that same model for a survivorship congress, and the board agreed. The announcement of the First National Congress on Cancer Survivorship, which would be held as a part of their tenth gathering the following year, was made on the last day of the 1994 assembly.

Betsy and Julia would co-chair the congress. The two were equally hopeful for what the congress would achieve. Summing it up in a *Networker* article, Betsy explained, "It's the first time that people with all types of cancer will have the opportunity to mobilize and be heard on a national level."

Julia continued the enthusiasm. "The capital is the perfect place to do this, where we can bring survivorship issues to the attention of members of Congress. When a constituency group says 'we demand change,' the political leadership responds... It's an important opportunity to set an agenda for priorities that need to be addressed in cancer treatment and care. And no one can do this better than survivors themselves."

The inaugural town hall provided perspectives that would help define the congress agenda, including identifying "priority issues to guide the cancer community's public policy efforts through the year 2000."

The primary issue involved the tense and ongoing health care debate.

When Bill Clinton ran for president in 1992, a cornerstone of his first-term agenda was health care. Once in office, President Clinton set up a Task Force on National Health Care Reform, chaired by First Lady Hillary Rodham Clinton. The Task Force's goal was to come up with a comprehensive plan to provide universal health care for all Americans. In a speech to a joint session of the US Congress on September 22, 1993, Clinton proposed a bill that would provide a "health care security card to every citizen. That card would irrevocably entitle him or her to medical treatment and preventative services, including for pre-existing conditions." Also included was a mandate requiring employers to provide health insurance coverage to all of their employees. The resulting Health Security Act was a complex proposal of more than one thousand pages. It drew objections from senators and representatives on both sides of the aisle, and the bill died a year later.

As had been the case when President Franklin Roosevelt had proposed his health care plan sixty years earlier, Americans still eschewed anything smacking of socialism. Regardless of moniker, forcing "sameness for all"—in this case, health care—just wasn't palatable. But for cancer survivors, accepting or rejecting universal health care wasn't so black and white. Politics aside, they had become accustomed to clouds of fear and doubt when it came to health care insurance. Just a decade earlier, a cancer diagnosis caused insurance policies to evaporate. And having a history of the disease checked the box of a preexisting condition, precluding a new policy.

Without health care insurance, those diagnosed with cancer could never afford the new, effective, and very expensive treatment modalities. Sometimes even with insurance, cancer's financial burden was so great it overwhelmed survivors' ability to pay. (Today, we call it the financial toxicity of cancer.) Such was the case of a 1994 assembly attendee who brought gasps from the audience at Saturday morning's town hall. In the midst of the health care discussion, she explained that there was only one financial way out for her. "I am declaring bankruptcy on Monday."

NCCS board members and staff saw clearly that having a voice at the health care table was crucial. It would be an important goal to come from the Congress on Cancer Survivorship. And given her critical involvement in President Clinton's quest for health care reform, it was announced at the end of the 1994 assembly that First Lady Hillary Rodham Clinton had accepted the invitation to serve as the congress's honorary chair.

In her gracious, written message, Mrs. Clinton said:

> I am grateful for your efforts to promote awareness and offer support and hope in the battle against cancer. Almost all of us have a friend or family member whose life has been threatened or lost because of cancer....

I commend your participation in this creative forum and encourage your continued commitment to those who are fighting to overcome this threatening disease.

Awareness…battle…life threatened or lost…overcoming this threatening disease. Even with all her education, the First Lady was unable to wrap her mind around the fact that she *wasn't* chairing an event to create awareness of cancer or keep people from dying from it. She was chairing an event to support the ever-growing number of lives that had been forever altered on countless levels as a result of their diagnosis and treatment. It was no wonder that the NCCS team felt paddling the river of survivorship was always an upstream effort.

And like so many before her, Mrs. Clinton spoke of "the battle." It had been the case for decades, with President Kennedy contemplating a "war on cancer," and President Johnson watching his watered-down "war on cancer" stumble through Congress. President Nixon finally succeeded in declaring "war on cancer," although not for truly altruistic reasons. For all three of those presidents, the drive to cure the disease existed beneath the shadow of the Vietnam War. But Vietnam wasn't the first war to cast its shadow over cancer. That distinction went to a war the country desperately wanted to prevent.

———————

As the 1994 NCCS assembly was occurring in Washington, DC, Mary Dickson was recovering from a hysterectomy in Salt Lake City. It didn't matter that Mary had never met any members of, or even heard of, the National Coalition for Cancer Survivorship. What mattered was that Mary's personal history made her a part of the survivorship population, and, like millions of others, she was the reason NCCS was working so diligently to bring justice to cancer survivors. Nine years before her hysterectomy, Mary had been diagnosed with thyroid cancer. After her thyroid and surrounding lymph nodes had been removed, she was given radioactive iodine to drink. The memories of her hospital experience are not fond.

"On the door of my room was a sign: 'Caution! Radioactive Material,'" she describes two decades later. "Stamped on my hospital bracelet was the same symbol. *I* was the radioactive material. Every day a radiologist opened the door to my room and pointed his Geiger counter at me to see how 'hot' I was.

"Knowing it wasn't safe to enter the room, the nurses shoved trays of food under my door. I did nothing but drink water in a desperate attempt to flush out the radiation. I was isolated in my hospital room for four days until the reading on the Geiger counter was low enough that I could be around people again. When I left the hospital, they destroyed my clothes and everything I had touched."

Mary had been told not to get pregnant for at least a year after her treatment. She never did get pregnant, and after years of trying, gave up. Doctors told her that tumors in her uterus and on her ovaries were to blame. She worried what else might show up in years to come. Thus, the hysterectomy. Mary's cancer was not the result of bad luck or poor lifestyle. Mary was a "downwinder."

The newspaper stories in late January 1951, made Americans pause.

A brilliant "sunburst-like" blast from the Atomic Energy Commission's Nevada testing range was seen and heard by hundreds in four states today.

The AEC [Atomic Energy Commission] merely announced in Washington that 'one of the periodic tests' of atomic explosions had taken place. The commission said January 11 that such tests would be held.

The third atomic blast in four days jolted this desert gambling town [Las Vegas] early today as atomic scientists apparently continued 'tickling the dragon's tail...The Atomic Energy Commission continued to say nothing about its experiments.

What did these articles all mean? They meant that one of the greatest cover-ups the US government would ever engineer was beginning, involving weaponry many times more powerful than either of the atomic bombs dropped on the Japanese cities of Hiroshima and Nagasaki. The horror those explosions rained down ended World War II in the Pacific. But even their developers were horrified at the pervasive damage they caused. The power they unleashed alerted the world to the threat of atomic weaponry. They also ushered in the nuclear arms race, one of the most frightening periods in human history.

With fascism contained, communism was now the great enemy. When Russia tested an atomic bomb in September 1949, it became apparent that the United States had to keep its atomic arsenal at the ready. More bombs of greater intensity were in production, but where to test them? Officials of the Atomic Energy Commission (created in 1946) and others initially counseled President Harry Truman against testing within the country's continental boundaries. Additionally, General Dwight Eisenhower, the former World War II Supreme Allied Commander of the Allied Expeditionary Force in Europe, was concerned about the fear it would spread among the population. That fear was justified. Even in the early stages of development, scientists suggested that radiation from the bombs would have a carcinogenic effect, no matter how low the level of exposure.

After the US became involved in the Korean conflict in 1950, national security concerns were louder than the scientific voices. Finding test areas was now of the utmost importance. The "AEC Decision Documents" of 1950 made certain requirements clear:

For the protection of the population existing near the test site, favorable meteorological conditions...are necessary to permit firing.... It is recognized that the problem of radio-logical safety is most critical in site selection. Not only must high safety factors be established in fact, but the acceptance of these facts by the general public must be insured by judicious handling of the public information program...By such means as these, and taking advantage of more sparsely populated areas, it is believed certain continental sites would permit a substantial improvement in predicted safety....

The AEC concluded that its overriding responsibility "above all is to expedite the weapons development program."

So, on December 18, 1950, President Truman approved testing of nuclear devices at what came to be called the Nevada Test Site. Between January 1951 and October 1958, on a 1,300-square-mile stretch of vacant desert land—about the size of Rhode Island—121 atomic bombs were detonated above ground. Following a three-year test moratorium, another 102 explosions "tickled the dragon's tail." This colorful euphemism was what atomic physicists called their trick of creating low-order nuclear fusion, burst-like tests, without provoking a full-scale explosion, which would have destroyed half of the continent.

Testing only occurred when the prevailing winds were not blowing toward Las Vegas (one hundred miles to the southeast) or Los Angeles (three hundred miles due south). On the days when Mother Nature cooperated, the radioactive clouds floated on easterly winds. Their deadly dust fell on ranches and farms, small Mormon communities, and the Havasupai, Yavapai, and Navajo reservations. Geographically, visible dust settled in southern Nevada, northern Arizona, and southern Utah. Those who scratched their living from the desert soil, according to an AEC document, were "low use populations." They were also fiercely patriotic, even without the government pamphlets making it clear that to question the tests was akin to embracing communism.

Despite what they saw and felt coming from the NTS, the AEC assured those impacted that the "effects of the 'fallout' on anyone in the US equals that of a luminous-dial watch," and that "fear of food contamination is refuted." Most important of all in its communiqués, the AEC attempted to convince American citizens that "the Nevada tests are being conducted for a humanitarian purpose—to determine the best ways to help civilian defense—and not to develop stronger weapons of war." This was the opposite of the purpose outlined in the 1950 "AEC Decision Documents."

More absurd still was the fact that the same officials who oversaw the creation and detonation of the bombs, and the uranium mining going on all over the Navajo reservation in order to make those bombs, were also those responsible for monitoring contamination and protecting citizen health. And the Atomic Energy Commission answered to almost no one.

It wasn't long, however, before stories began to circulate among those who were living downwind from the testing site. Sheep, grazing on grass dusted with fallout from the bombs, quickly developed burns on their muzzles and produced lambs with horrific physical defects. Suddenly, the men who had herded those sheep, along with the women who hung laundry on outside lines in downwind communities, developed cancers at alarming rates. Additionally, families experienced significant financial losses, and even financial ruin, as entire herds were wiped out and the sick became unable to work or died.

The "low use populations" began asking questions. They took a closer look at the objects they came in daily contact with. Shockingly, some of the highest levels of contamination were discovered in milk. As with the sheep, cows consumed the grass, absorbing radioactive elements into their milk, whose consumption was at an all-time high in the decades of the 1950s and 1960s. Hundreds, maybe thousands, of healthy children were stricken with cancer and died before anyone started to connect the dots. What they didn't know at the time is that radioactive pollution insinuates itself into human genes, where it can have effects for generations.

In a horrible irony, in January 1952, the Federal Civil Defense Administration (FCDA) produced a cartoon, featuring Bert the

Turtle, instructing schoolchildren to "duck and cover" under their desks at school to keep safe from the radiation that would come from a nuclear attack on the US "If you are not ready, if you do not know what to do, then it [an atomic bomb blast] could hurt you in different ways," Bert the Turtle counseled. "It could knock you down hard, or throw you against a tree or a wall. It is such a big explosion, it can knock down walls and knock signboards over or break windows all over town ... Duck and cover underneath a table or desk, or anything else nearby."

Bomb drills occurred in the nation's schools with the same frequency as fire drills, as children dove under their desks for protection. The FCDA designated and supplied community buildings to be used as "fallout shelters" in the case of a bomb falling on US soil. But the fact was, the bombs were already falling at the Nevada Test Site. And thanks to *Popular Mechanics* magazine, citizens could purchase plans to build their own bomb shelters, while newspapers were full of suggestions on how to stock them. Government films and booklets showed individuals and families contentedly cohabiting in public and private shelters, playing games, knitting—and calmly smoking—as if they were tucked safely in their own homes.

A further, albeit later, insult occurred in July 1971. Then-AEC General Manager Robert E. Hollingsworth sent a memo in support of the war on cancer bill making its way through Congress. "In our view," the memo read, "H.R. 8343 would greatly strengthen the national effort in cancer research. Accordingly, we favor its enactment." Mr. Hollingsworth had been with the commission since its 1947 inception in various management positions. He was described by one of the commission's chairmen as "... a veteran AEC employee who knew the organization and its personnel intimately." While Hollingsworth may not have been aware of the extent of the death clouds caused by the NTS testing, he would certainly have been aware of the stories that had come from the downwind communities during the testing.

It took the United States government until 1979, seventeen years after the last aboveground test at NTS, to really listen to the thousands of voices of those living downwind of the blasts. Sifting through thousands of AEC documents and interviewing dozens of those at ground zero, Congress released its findings in a 1980 report titled "The Forgotten Guinea Pigs." The sickening picture it paints was summed up by one of the congressmen on the committee: "The greatest irony of our atmospheric nuclear testing program is that the only victims of the US nuclear arms since World War II have been our own people."

A year later, Congress realized reparations had to be made. But it took until August and September 1990 for the Radiation Exposure Compensation Act (RECA) to be passed in the House and Senate, respectively. Even then, it was slow going. Filing procedures for compensation were still not in place by February 1991. Nothing was clear.

Who would be covered? Someone who could prove they had lived for at least two years in what was deemed the downwind area, originally including only parts of Nevada, parts of southern Utah, and the "Arizona Strip," an area north of the Grand Canyon and west of the Colorado River. School yearbooks, phone books, church records, and city directories all became lifelines to compensation for these "downwinders."

What would be covered? Cancer, to be sure, but only a very specific set of cancers, as decided upon by the National Academy of Science. Their list of nineteen seemed arbitrary. Non-Hodgkin's lymphoma was covered, but not Hodgkin's; colon cancer was covered but not prostate; ovarian cancer but not other gynecological cancers; pharynx cancer but not cancer of the larynx. Lung cancer was excluded if someone had smoked. Given smoking's popularity in those decades, how could a doctor tell whether it was smoking or radiation exposure that had caused the cancer? More questions ensued.

How would they file? The standards were extremely rigid, confusing to many, and forbidding for those, like some Native Americans, for whom English was challenging and fewer records were kept. The Navajo language doesn't even have words for radiation or cancer.

And what was the compensation? Downwinders within the general population were due $50,000 each. On-site participants, including the military personnel who marched or parachuted in during simulated war situations, would be paid $75,000. Uranium miners would receive $100,000. There were four thousand uranium mines in the Four Corners region—the spot at which Arizona, Colorado, New Mexico, and Utah all come together. It is now ruefully referred to by the inhabitants as the "National Sacrifice Area." The red tape was so thick that many died before receiving compensation, leaving their heirs to continue wading through the bureaucracy.

Children, particularly girls, were most susceptible to the effects of radioactive iodine, one of the primary by-products of nuclear fission. It is easily absorbed by the thyroid gland, and thyroid cancer became common among adults who had been exposed to radiation as children. And although the Nevada Test Site was 341 miles southwest of Salt Lake City, and according to all governmental documents the city would not have been affected, besides Mary Dickson, fifty-four of her childhood friends and neighbors became sick or died.

Their illnesses varied, including brain tumors, leukemia, lymphoma, and cancers of the thyroid, breast, ovaries, pancreas, lung, liver, and stomach. Maladies like lupus, multiple sclerosis, autoimmune diseases, and rare blood disorders also plagued them, along with miscarriages and birth defects. Mary's sister, Ann, died after suffering nine years with lupus. And her younger sister, Donna, was diagnosed with a rare stomach cancer.

The famous were affected, too. According to a former AEC researcher, radioactive fallout can concentrate in "hot spots" such as canyons, which act as a natural reservoir. In 1954, the movie *The Conqueror* was being filmed in Snow Canyon, near St. George, Utah, about 137 miles from the test site. Two especially "dirty" bombs dropped radioactive fallout in the canyon. By 1980, 91 of the 220 cast and crew had contracted radiation-related cancers, and at least half of them died from their diseases. The list includes John Wayne, Agnes Moorehead, and Dick Powell.

A National Institutes of Health report in 1997 caught up with what many already knew. The fallout region and the number of people affected was actually greater than the government admitted to. One American was diagnosed with cancer every thirty seconds that year. How many might have been spared were it not for all those "safe" bombs being detonated in the name of national defense?

In his 1999 book, *Under the Cloud: The Decades of Nuclear Testing*, Richard Miller agreed, writing that "distance from the test site was of small importance. Towns and cities across the entire continent were at risk." Whether from the direct fallout that floated in the clouds on the prevailing winds, or from the vegetation consumed by animals, everyone in America became a downwinder during those decades.

"No one can prove that exposure to radiation *didn't* make us sick," Mary says. "Growing up in Salt Lake City in the 1960s, I don't remember hearing about nuclear testing. We heard about the 'Red menace,' and godless Communists, but didn't hear about cancers or strange tumors or fallout. We drank our milk and ate our vegetables, assuming that, as the Mormon hymn told us, all was well."

Even though RECA was highly *under*-publicized, and millions of citizens—like Mary Dickson—were completely excluded, the response was overwhelming. The money that had been allocated ran out in ten years. For five months, those whose cases were approved were given IOUs. Then, in June 2000, despite the lack of funds and without allocating more money, RECA coverage was expanded, encompassing more cancers and more citizens. It still did not, however, offer the breadth of compensation truly owed.

As of September 2018, more than $2.254 billion had been paid out. To be sure, the money is nice. But a combination of anger and sorrow grows in the hearts of the victims of the testing. They had trusted that their food would be safe, and that their government would protect them against atomic bombs. And although the sun sets on RECA compensation on July 11, 2022, as of this writing, the US government has been silent about issuing last calls for filings.

It is a cruel additional burden facing American cancer survivors. As if the demons of survivorship weren't already bad enough—the discrimination, the PTSD and other psychological issues, the loss of fertility, and more—survivors must also be vigilant about whether or not they, too, were part of some "low use" population.

Susie's term as NCCS board president was coming to a close, and the position would next be filled by the very capable Betsy Clark. Like so many others within the organization, Susie's speaking and writing about survivorship would continue for decades. It was her personal mission and passion. In her last *Networker* president's letter, Susie talked about recent events that had bolstered her conviction that NCCS was making a difference.

> I recently returned from the annual Oncology Nursing Society Congress, where I was amazed to hear survivor or survivorship mentioned in every session I attended…a number of presenters even defined survivors as we at NCCS do….
>
> But even more important than the growing acceptance of the word was the influence of the survivors themselves. Survivors were members of panels, plenary sessions and special dinner sessions, and while our presence was often subtle, it was substantial….
>
> We survivors are role models and living proof that early detection can save lives; that access to treatment can extend lives; that we can still be productive members of society, even with a chronic illness; and that we can remove social barriers that hinder our recovery.

Ellen, too, was spreading the NCCS message, spending hours on phone interviews. She explained to one newspaper that NCCS had lobbied the White House for better health insurance for cancer "sufferers" (the writer's words, certainly not Ellen's). Their intention was to ask for restrictions on insurance companies that rejected people with preexisting health conditions or charged exorbitant rates. Ellen went on to explain that job discrimination was persistent among workers with a history of the disease, affecting close to 25 percent of them. "There's still a kind of leprosy phenomenon out there," she accurately pointed out.

From the original twenty-three to the thousands now in their fold, the NCCS board, staff, volunteers, and members were persistent and dogged; sometimes pushing, sometimes dragging the survivorship movement along. It's difficult to maintain enthusiasm when those outside of your world still don't understand. "You get the pat on the back for taking chemo and going bald," Ellen said. "Surviving is one of those issues that make people yawn."

But they never gave up.

Chapter 12: Illumination

In 1995, America has 8 million survivors, twice the size of the US population when the United States Congress met for the first time in 1787.

At the 1993 NCCS assembly, Denver support group facilitator and two-time Hodgkin's survivor John Anduri told the audience: "This is the most inclusive minority group!" He pointed out that cancer was an equal opportunity disease, not discriminating by age, race, religion, ethnic background, sexual orientation, or any other personal feature.

The cancers faced down by NCCS founders and fans had been physically and emotionally arduous. But as mostly Caucasian heterosexuals, their experiences were a world away from those in other ethnic or social groups, including indigent, undereducated, and culturally diverse peoples.

Although NCCS was illuminating cancer's fourth realm, its disenfranchised survivors were often still living in the shadows, even in the latter part of the twentieth century. That weighed heavily on the minds of those involved in the survivorship movement. In 1995, two things would happen to help this cause. First, the NCCS board created the Task Force on Multicultural Groups and the Poor, which they asked board member Dr. Lovell Jones to chair. Second, during the fifth Biennial Symposium on Minorities, the Medically Underserved, and Cancer (the meeting Dr. Jones founded) in April 1995, an Intercultural Cancer Council (ICC) was created. The ICC was a coalition focusing on changing cancer-related policies controlled by Congress and other government bodies. NCCS was invited to become a charter member. With a growing list of cancer-related policy changes they were working on, the organization certainly had experience in the area.

It was important to understand why the disparity in the cancer experience existed in the first place. Partially to blame were the tragic sagas of many minority populations woven into American history. Layered on top of them was the one-size-fits-all approach to research, disease, and treatment. Just as cancer was once thought to be a single disease, humans were originally thought to be homogenous, too, and so were clinical trials.

Researchers, the vast majority of whom were white, chose Caucasian men as test subjects, considering them to be the "norm" study population. Women of childbearing age were routinely excluded from drug trials (unless the drug was specific to women), to protect a potential fetus. However, it was also thought their hormonal fluctuations and monthly menstrual cycles would skew test results. Yet those very fluctuations, along with other factors, cause women to metabolize drugs differently than men, something hugely important to know for dosing levels. Researchers excluded minorities in part because, it was assumed, they would be unable to see a clinical trial through to the end. Historically, minorities tended to have more inflexible employment situations that would not allow time off for the trial treatment, and more transportation challenges to get to that treatment.

These practices cut out a significant percentage of the population. So despite an explosion in the capacity to prevent, diagnose, and treat cancer, a large swath (more than half) of the population was not benefiting from the fruits of scientific labor. The irony was that women and minorities were diagnosed with cancers (whose treatment drugs were the very ones tested in clinical trials) and experienced survivorship challenges just as frequently as the "norm" study population. It was not until 1993 that the FDA lifted the ban, allowing anyone to participate in early-phase research.

The stories of health care disparities in America are complicated and ongoing. They could fill volumes.

In 1951, Henrietta Lacks, an African American woman from Baltimore County, died of cervical cancer. She was a thirty-one-year-old mother of five. She might have become just another statistic: poor, barely educated, with little knowledge of disease and her own body. But instead, Henrietta Lacks became famous.

During her treatments, samples were taken from her cervix without her permission or knowledge. The cells eventually became known as the HeLa immortal cell line, still used in biomedical research today (2021). As Rebecca Skloot explains in her award-winning book, *The Immortal Life of Henrietta Lacks,*

> Scientists had been trying to keep human cells alive in [laboratory] culture for decades, but they all eventually died. Henrietta's were different: they reproduced an entire generation [of cells] every twenty-four hours, and they never stopped. They became the first immortal human cells ever grown in a laboratory… Like guinea pigs and mice, Henrietta's cells have become the standard laboratory workhorse.

Even after scientists learned Henrietta's identity in 1970, her children weren't made aware of their mother's place in biomedical research until 1975. Stories such as this are an inexcusable stain on research history. They also fuel medical mistrust.

In Native American culture, medicine as a concept isn't mistrusted, but the use of unfamiliar protocols in an unfamiliar setting certainly is. The best way to understand the feeling native people might have when brought into a metropolitan hospital and told they must be treated for cancer would be to reverse the scenario. Picture, as a non-indigenous person, being taken to a traditional healer at a pueblo for treatment. Receiving unfamiliar procedures, drugs, and other therapies, the majority of which are being explained in a nearly foreign language, would terrify even the most courageous.

Members of the LGBTQ community struggle with a different kind of mistrust. Many have been the recipients of bigoted slurs at some point in their lives. Being in the position of needing lifesaving cancer treatment, and "coming out" to a medical team by bringing one's same-sex partner to appointments, is a 50-50 proposition. Are their doctors and nurses homophobic? Will their prejudice adversely affect the course of treatment?

Medical mistrust is just the tip of the proverbial iceberg in a discussion of health care disparities. In the cancer world—as in many health venues—three other issues greatly impact how well a person will fare with undoubtably the most frightening diagnosis they could ever receive. Racial and sexual bias, cultural differences, and poverty impact all aspects of life, but never more crucially than when mortality is in question.

From medical bias to overt racism, there are so many layers and levels, it's hard to wrap our heads around it. Racism is as odious a human disease as cancer itself, and inexcusable on any level. But another issue could be the lack of diversity training in health care, often resulting in poor cross-cultural communication between doctors and patients. Even in 2021, medical schools rarely teach students the history of medical racism, a large umbrella also covering experimentation on those who are less educated, withholding care because of personal bigotry, and simply lacking compassion for people whose appearance or belief structure isn't familiar. But training alone won't dissolve the biases that centuries have honed. The most overt examples are more publicized, but many others simmer in the stew.

For example, in the mid-1960s, a US Public Health Service (PHS) venereal disease investigator named Peter Buxton stumbled across a PHS medical study, the Tuskegee Study of Untreated Syphilis in the Negro Male (informally referred to as the Tuskegee Syphilis Study or the Tuskegee Experiment), that had been underway since 1932, a time when there was no cure for syphilis. Some six hundred African American men, primarily sharecroppers, were recruited into the study, run by Dr. John Cutler, with the promise of free medical care. Many had never visited a doctor before. Doctors from PHS, which ran the study, told the participants they were being treated for "bad blood." Some 399 of the men had latent syphilis, and a control group of 201 were free of the disease.

According to the Centers for Disease Control and Prevention (CDC–US Public Health Service Syphilis Study at Tuskegee), the men were monitored but only given placebos, despite penicillin being available as a treatment for syphilis by 1947. What's worse, PHS researchers convinced local physicians not to treat the participants. Perhaps the most bitter irony of all was that the research was done at the Tuskegee Institute (now Tuskegee University), where Booker T. Washington was the original principal.

As a result, twenty-eight men died from syphilis, a hundred more died from related complications, at least forty spouses were diagnosed with the disease, and it was passed to nineteen children at birth. Buxton struggled to expose the story and it wasn't until 1972 that it was broken by the Associated Press wire service. There was public outrage and the study was finally shut down.

In 1997, President Bill Clinton apologized for the study, calling it "deeply, profoundly, [and] morally wrong...." Because of examples like the Tuskegee Experiment, many African Americans have developed a deep and lingering mistrust of public health officials.

In a 2016 study, even with all the treatment advances, early detection, and prevention publicity, African Americans had an 11 percent greater risk of developing cancer than non-African American. And even today (2021), five times as many Blacks as Whites die from the disease. Yet a 1949 study found Black and White people suffer from cancer equally. Still, African Americans are diagnosed at later stages and are more likely to be mistrustful of treatment. Many reasons exist for these statistics, one of which is what happens the minute a Black person walks into a doctor's office or treatment facility.

Marion Kelly, now the Director of Community Affairs for Mayo Clinic Arizona, has worked for more than three decades in health care administration. Over the years, he has watched some of his colleagues make biased assessments based on who they *think* they see sitting in front of them. He worries that thoughts of "they don't have," "they can't," and "they won't" occur far more often when the patient is a minority. He's not suggesting those patients receive less than optimal treatments. But unfounded judgments impact the way a patient is treated, and cause a cascade of emotions from the patient, ranging from anger to shame. The result is additional stress, a negative opinion of the health care system, and a fatalistic attitude toward their prognosis.

When Darryl Mitteldorf, a New York social worker and founder of Malecare.org, hears members of the medical community tout that they treat all patients the same, experience has caused him to translate that as "I treat all patients as straight, WASP patients." As with other minority populations, the LGBTQ community, within which Darryl works, has very distinct needs. For many, health care is not affordable or a priority. This results in not being diagnosed with any disease, including cancer, until it has become advanced. Intimacy discussions with straight doctors are strained at best. Very few clinical trials are created specifically for the LGBTQ community.

For Lee Magnuson, the memory of his partner, David (not his real name), is forever clouded by bias. David began having chest pains in 1987. When he presented to a doctor, he was diagnosed with lung cancer. And then came an even more shocking diagnosis: his blood work revealed that he was also HIV-positive and at the end stages of AIDS. As a Black man, David had experienced racial discrimination. But that had in no way prepared him for the treatment he would receive as an AIDS patient. By this time, fear of AIDS had overtaken fear of cancer. An orange "Biohazard" sign hung on David's hospital door. The staff members who were willing to treat him did so in full hazmat suits. Others were not so brave. They refused to take his vital signs or take out his garbage.

It broke Lee's heart to see David suffer such neglect. And because David's family would never have understood his homosexuality, the couple agreed that when his death came—which it did six months later—his family would be told it was from cancer, and only cancer.

The seismic tremors of events like the Tuskegee Experiment continue to reverberate in odd and disturbing ways. In his 2016 book, *Black Man in a White Coat: A Doctor's Reflections on Race and Medicine,* Dr. Damon Tweedy recounts being a Duke University medical student in the late 1990s. He walked into the hospital room of a Black patient. The patient sneered: "C'mon, man, we both know what the deal is. I'm sure you did good in school and everything, but they're passin' you off on me. We both know you're here to fill a quota."

The patient insisted on seeing a doctor who was in medical school "because he was smart and not just a number." He finished with, "Go tell your boss I don't want no black doctor...I didn't come all the way to Duke to see no black doctor unless he's some kinda expert. I could have stayed home if I wanted to see a country ass doctor. I ain't gonna be no guinea pig."

A different kind of reverse racism happened to Mary Lavato, a New Mexican jeweler, mother of three, and member of the Santo Domingo Pueblo. Diagnosed with leukemia in 1987, Mary was the first Native American to receive a bone marrow transplant to combat her disease. The transplant was successful, but her anti-rejection drugs caused severe sun sensitivity.

Mary returned to New Mexico from the hospital in Los Angeles wearing a wide-brimmed hat and sunglasses, weak but glad to be alive. Her tribe vilified her, accusing her of trying to look like a white woman. She couldn't make them understand why she had to protect herself against the powerful, high-altitude sunlight. A more direct hit came when Mary went to the pueblo post office. She greeted an elderly woman she knew. The woman looked at Mary, and then grabbed her granddaughter's hand, saying "Don't touch her. She might be contagious."

Mary went home and cried. Her ostracism cast her into a deep depression, until the night her deceased parents visited her in a dream. According to Mary, they told her she had a responsibility to her children and to her people. And the idea of a pueblo cancer support group was born. It took three years and three changes in tribal government for the idea to become a reality. With the help of Catherine Logan's Albuquerque organization, Living Through Cancer, Mary was able to file for grants and eventually founded A Gathering of Cancer Support, endorsed by the Santo Domingos and two other New Mexican pueblos.

Mary became the "grace note" (as Dr. LaSalle Leffall expressed earlier) for Native American cancer support, while also becoming a partner and contributor to NCCS. Her petite frame and smiling face became a fixture at NCCS assemblies. But even more than thirty years later, cancer remains the leading cause of death for Native American women and the second leading cause of death for men among the five hundred different tribes in the United States. Each tribe has their own language, and there is very little cancer material available in any of them.

Low numbers of Native American cancer cases in the 1980s and 1990s were attributed to potential DNA safeguards. The truth was that their cancer cases were not being reported. While indigenous North American people are very familiar and comfortable with their traditional healing methods, Western medicine is not understood. Many believe taking body specimens—blood, skin, or tissue—takes a part of their spirit. Unless they know where those samples will end up, they're loathe to give them, whether for clinical trials or for diagnostics. And insomuch as hair is a sacred connection to their families and the Creator, hair loss as a result of chemotherapy is often unacceptable, regardless of the fact that it might save their lives.

Cancers involving private body parts (colon, rectum, prostate and reproductive organs) are particularly difficult to diagnose and treat in cultures where Western medicine is not understood. In most of Africa, women die of cervical cancer at a much higher rate than breast cancer because of human papillomavirus (HPV). Even though a successful vaccine was approved in 2006, many African women refuse to be vaccinated. They feel to do so would be an admission that they're participating in promiscuous behaviors.

HPV is also a problem in Miami's Little Haiti. Dr. Erin Kobetz of the University of Miami's Sylvester Comprehensive Cancer Center discovered that cervical cancer was four times greater in that community than any other type of cancer. "The Haitians worried that the speculum used in a Pap smear would stretch their vaginas," Dr. Kobetz explained. "It would make them less attractive to sexual partners on whom they are economically dependent. And most Haitians are Catholic and believe that whatever they have, God will fix. Or not. And while no one admits to believing in voodoo, they're afraid not to give it credence nonetheless. Those beliefs trump Western medicine."

Hair is important to Haitian women, too. Those with long hair are thought to be the most sexually attractive. Losing hair as a result of chemotherapy is not an option. In other paternalistic cultures, women refuse surgeries because they don't want to be disfigured, and thus less desirable.

Other cultures see Western medicine as an interference. For traditional Asian women, health concerns are far down on their priority list. Family and earning a living to support that family come first. Many women never go beyond a trip to their neighborhood herbalist. Consequently, cancer is their number one cause of death.

For both men and women of many societies, colonoscopies are feared because of their likeness to anal rape. Prostate exams don't take place for the same reasons. Unless a woman discovers an abnormality in a partner's testicle, and can then get him to seek medical attention, it goes untreated.

Exacerbating mistrust, racism, and cultural barriers is poverty. Poor people tend to have a diet higher in fat and sugar, and eat more processed foods and fewer fresh foods. They exercise less, smoke more, and consume more alcohol. Because they tend to have less education, the information highway doesn't always run by their doors. The internet, cable television, even newspapers are less available. Health information is sometimes conflicting, sometimes confusing. Those who do have information, don't have enough. And often out of fear, they don't want more.

Dr. Harold Freeman witnessed this early in his career. At the Harlem Hospital Center in 1967, Dr. Freeman was shocked to learn that the majority of his patients (nearly all African Americans) had hopelessly advanced cases of cancer. His mission became to determine the cause of the higher mortality rates of these African Americans, and to reduce race- and income-related disparities in health care. In 1979, he established two free breast and cervical cancer screening centers in Harlem to improve the chances of early detection. Later, he became president of the American Cancer Society from 1988 to 1989 and was the driving force behind their initiative on Cancer in the Poor. Dr. Freeman went on to become the chairman of the President's Cancer Panel.

"Poverty does not respect race," he said at the 1994 NCCS assembly, where he was presented with the Public Leadership Award. "Any group with inadequate income, housing and education will suffer a higher death rate, whether they're white Appalachians, black New Yorkers, or any other group." He closed his remarks with what would become his signature rallying call: "The penalty for poverty should not be death."

The poor are also more likely to experience competing discourses. People in the upper half of the socioeconomic scale are accustomed to the message that everything's fixable, even something as frightening as cancer. But if you grew up on the streets of Chicago's South Side, that message competes with what you see and hear in your neighborhood: a trip to the hospital always seems to be one way, and cancer always kills.

Those messages are not surprising when we take into account that many of the poor who finally arrive at the hospital with cancer (usually after an emergency room visit first) do so at an advanced stage of the disease. That means treatment will be more aggressive and lengthier. If they have jobs, they'll begin missing paychecks, their families will suffer, and their standard of living will drop even farther.

The notion that every cancer journey is different was never far from the minds of the NCCS board and staff. Their initial battle had been to bring survivors and survivorship out of the shadows. But could that truly be a reality for everyone?

The *Networker* had become part news relate-*or*, part motivate-*or*, part inspirate-*or*. Its layout always included special sections for advocacy, NCCS news, and announcements from individuals and organizations across the country. There was also a section labeled "Appreciations." It was a careful and intentional spin on what might otherwise have been called "Memorials." The section recognized fellow survivors' deaths *and* appreciation for their contributions to the survivorship movement.

The Summer 1995 edition included a notable tribute to Ellen Hermanson, a forty-two-year-old metastatic breast cancer survivor, and, among many other things, an NCCS fan and the first executive director of the Judges and Lawyers Breast Cancer Alert. Ellen Stovall wrote,

> For many of us at NCCS, the loss of Ellen's wonderful friendship will be the most sorely missed. Her beautiful smile, art of self-deprecation, engaging wit and sense of humor will all stay with us always...And for her fellow survivors, their loved ones, friends and family, the words she wrote for them, and tens of thousands of others, to guide them, inspire them, and educate them, are a testimony to her own passion for survivorship and to this organization that she loved so much...We shall miss you, Ellen, and we will treasure the time you had with us.

Her words would be echoed two decades later.

The first town hall to be held after the inaugural one at the assembly was in Albany on June 3, 1995. It was part of the "Cancer Survivorship Initiative," co-chaired by Betsy Clark. The hot and humid weekend also included a National Cancer Survivors Day celebration. When Ellen Stovall shared her observations of the weekend in the next *Networker*, she said,

> I heard what we hear in our office every single day, a thousand times a month: a lot of "c-words." We heard *cancer*. We heard *courage, care, compassion, competition, consensus, contacts, confidence, Congress, clinical trials, counseling.*
>
> What we need to hear are *coordination, community, collaboration, and coalition.* Because without them, the others won't happen ... NCCS wants to work with you and your community. We hope you want to work with us. Together, we can transform the survivorship movement into a unified force that will make a profound impact on US health care.

Ellen was familiar with health insurance challenges. After her second round with Hodgkin's disease in 1983, her husband, John, left his architectural firm to start his own business. They were forced to look for private insurance for the family. Ellen called ten companies before finding one that would take her as a cancer survivor. Even then, she had to pay out-of-pocket for her oncologist follow-up visits. That very topic was a main focus of the First National Congress on Cancer Survivorship. And when the congress convened at the Washington Court Hotel, on Saturday, November 11, 1995, the survivorship movement, and NCCS, would take another giant leap forward.

The NCCS brought together three hundred delegates, representing the many faces of survivorship. Cancer survivors, their family and friends, health care providers, health educators, health writers, scientists, business leaders, government officials, community leaders, and the media were all in the mix. They were chosen in a variety of ways. Nearly all major cancer organizations had opted in for the congress, and were issued delegate invitations. Others were selected from among the attendees of each of the ten NCCS town halls that had occurred during the previous twelve months. And to ensure that no state was unrepresented, all fifty governors were asked to personally appoint two people, one a survivor and the other an individual influential in state health care.

Their common interest, of course, was survivorship. Among the actions that would be taken, three were paramount: First, to communicate to participants, the media, and the public at large the need for a health care system that would provide access to quality cancer care for all Americans, even those with preexisting conditions. Second, to set public policy priorities for the survivorship movement. And finally, to create an action plan to address those two priorities.

Susie and incoming board president Betsy Clark co-chaired the steering committee, while Julia and Betsy co-chaired the program planning committee. Although Susie's term as president of the NCCS board had come to an end, she happily joined Betsy in welcoming the congress attendees. Then Fitz explained how the program would reflect his "Seasons of Survival" model of survivorship. The honorary committee co-chair, Dr. Harold Freeman, encouraged the audience to take action in making a difference in survivorship within their communities. Twenty-seven committee members made up the honorary committee, coming from both houses of the US Congress and representing both political parties. Some of them were survivors themselves.

Over the ensuing days, the congress was peppered with "firsts." For the first time, the American Society of Clinical Oncology joined an NCCS event by co-sponsoring the Saturday night reception, giving delegates and oncologists a chance to mingle and share ideas. A "futuristic" introduction to the resources available on the internet was sponsored by NCI. And for the first time, death was discussed in a general session titled "Learning a New Language: How to Talk about Death and Dying," moderated by Betsy.

Sunday morning began with "A Celebration of Hope." The nonsectarian gathering was a mosaic of gospel music, meditation, and a moving candlelighting closing, in which survivors passed the "flame of hope" from one to another. Hope was an important cornerstone in the survivorship movement, and NCCS was founded on it. Ellen had spoken of hope eloquently in a paper she and Betsy wrote in 1991: "With communication comes understanding and clarity; with understanding, fear diminishes; in the absence of fear, hope emerges; and in the presence of hope, anything is possible."

Betsy had focused on the concept of hope for decades, and produced an NCCS booklet in 1995 titled "You Have the Right to Be Hopeful." In it, she wrote poignantly,

> Hope is a way of thinking, feeling and acting. In fact, hope is a prerequisite for action. Hope is flexible, and it remains open to various possibilities and the necessity to change the desired outcome as the reality changes. These aspects of hope emphasize how important hope is for living with an illness as serious as cancer. Finally, it should be noted that hope is a phenomenologically positive state, and by definition, hope can never be false.

To emphasize that last point, there is a single sentence on the back page of the booklet: "There is no such thing as false hope." Much to Betsy's delight, as well as to the delight of those within NCCS, hope would blossom into something more tangible.

In the early '70s, John Feight had been an unfulfilled ad executive and part-time artist looking to do something meaningful. He began volunteering at a local hospital in suburban Atlanta, and one day decided to paint a mural on a blank wall. As he was working, a four-year-old patient tapped him on the shoulder and said, "I want to paint." That moment inspired him to ultimately paint in hospitals across the country, and eventually around the world.

Ellen heard about John in 1982. Along with murals, John painted ceiling tiles. Remembering her own agony, staring at the ugly ceiling above her cobalt machine, she contacted him and asked him to come paint at that same hospital in Georgetown. In just a few weeks, the ceiling was transformed. Instead of dull acoustic tiles, Jonathan Livingston Seagull sailed against a cerulean sky, soaring over a calm sea. John then went to work on ceilings at Ellen's hometown hospital in Honesdale, Pennsylvania.

In 1994, Ellen called on her—now—friend John Feight again. By this time, John had founded the nonprofit Foundation for Hospital Art. During the assembly that year, a "Paint-In" had occurred as a part of their "Celebration of Cancer Survivorship Through the Arts."

As Ellen described it, "...the Washington metropolitan community will come together with Assembly registrants to...paint on ceiling tiles (that's right, ceiling tiles) that will transform ordinary ceilings in extraordinary places!...It is a true 'happening.' Don't miss it!"

The celebration was a huge success.

As they were planning the congress, the NCCS board was searching for a symbol they could use for outreach and community awareness campaigns. In a perfect circle, three things came together: the NCCS sunburst logo (designed and introduced in 1988), John Feight, and hope, the cornerstone of survivorship. Thus, the Ribbon of Hope was born. In a *Networker* article, Betsy described the ribbon as a "traveling 'work in progress.'" It was, she said, "...a symbol of the cancer survivorship movement's hope and life force."

The "Ribbon" would actually be multiple lengths of yellow ribbons, sent around the country and the world for cancer survivors and their supporters to sign. When all the ribbons returned to NCCS, they would be displayed like a radiant sun, symbolizing hope and new life. And the whole project would get off to a strong start at the congress, where everyone lined up to sign it—attendees, board members, members of the US Congress, and celebrated speakers. Although First Lady Hillary Clinton had accepted the invitation to be honorary chair of the event, she was unable to attend. But she was the first to sign the ribbon after the congress, when an NCCS delegation met with her at the White House.

Throughout the congress's three days, Susie, Ellen, Betsy, Julia, Fitz, and others in the movement took turns emceeing and introducing speakers at plenary sessions. In between, delegates attended the variety of workshops. The shining star of the congress actually wore four stars, as in four-star general Norman Schwarzkopf. "Stormin' Norman" had not only led troops during Operation Desert Storm in 1991, but he had also survived prostate cancer in 1993. As lunch was being served, Susie told the delegates that NCCS had always been about veterans helping rookies, an apt analogy given that it was Veteran's Day weekend, she was a veteran, and General Schwarzkopf was in the house.

"Toughing it out alone wasn't the answer," Schwarzkopf told the audience. "To learn how others survived was the first key to my survival." He ended his presentation by saying that the work of NCCS, that of voicing the needs of the nation's cancer survivors, was "a mission I'm proud to be a part of."

The congress was subtitled "Mobilizing for the 21st Century." The new century was an enticing unknown, just five years away. Like fresh snow on an open field, it spread out pristine and unscathed.

Over the previous twelve months, the town halls had gleaned a list of chief cancer-related issues from the grassroots membership. The input from over one thousand "boots on the ground" survivors with firsthand experiences was profound. Three primary areas of importance emerged: quality cancer care, psychosocial issues of cancer, and physiological long-term and late effects of cancer. Questionnaires went out to experts around the country in each of those areas. The material was summarized in drafts of briefing papers, which were then distributed to the congress delegates when they arrived.

To further flesh out those three areas, concurrent and interactive working groups were held Monday afternoon. Delegates could attend whichever one most concerned them. The working groups were led by individuals with experience and passion for their assigned area. Board member, oncology nurse, and Hodgkin's survivor Debra Thaler-DeMers led the Quality Cancer Care group, while Betsy and Julia steered the Psychosocial Issues of Cancer group. Susie led the Physiological Long-Term and Late Effects of Cancer group, as she was, once again, one of the longest-term survivors at the event. Each group was responsible for delineating its top five priority principles, presented as brief bullet summaries of larger principles for which NCCS could advocate and which would become NCCS position papers.

The final evening of the congress began with an opening address by the new director of NCI, Dr. Richard Klausner, who had stepped into the position just three months earlier. It's unclear whether his words were written before he arrived at the congress or were a result of what he experienced that weekend. Either way, they made the hearts of everyone associated with NCCS flip.

"Survival is increasing," Dr. Klausner said. "And we're going to need to begin shifting our thoughts from only thinking about how do we attack cancer, to how do we achieve the highest quality of life for cancer survivors."

Dr. Klausner got it! Cancer doesn't end with treatment. Blasting this message from the rooftops had been an enormous goal of NCCS from the beginning. It was the perfect launch for the rest of the evening. The briefing papers that had been constructed that afternoon were summarized. And then the Speak Out was introduced, to debate the question, "What should quality care in the year 2000 look like?"

When the first congress on cancer survivorship closed, it did so with a Declaration of Principles, voted upon by the delegates, that gave a unified voice to the nation's nearly eight million survivors where previously there had been none.

Chapter 13: The Office

In 1996, 25 years after Nixon declared "war on cancer,"
there are 9.8 million survivors in America.

Dr. Richard Klausner was officially sworn in as the National Cancer Institute chief in August 1995. A few weeks later, Ellen Stovall met with him. "Cancer survivors have a friend in Richard Klausner," she reported back to NCCS after the meeting. "He brings to NCI an extraordinary scientific mind, strong leadership skills, and an inclusive attitude toward cancer survivors." Dr. Klausner and Ellen had a mutual respect for one another that became an important friendship. And being on a first-name basis with the head of NCI had its privileges.

"Rick, I think you need to read this," Ellen told him in May 1996. She handed him the fruits of the NCCS Congress. It was a white paper called "Imperatives for Quality Cancer Care: Access, Advocacy, Action and Accountability."

It began with the Declaration of Principles:

Principle 1: People with cancer have the right to a system of universal health care. This access should not be precluded because of preexisting conditions, genetic or other risk factors, or employment status.

Principle 2: Quality cancer care should be available in a health care system whose standards and guidelines are developed in consideration of treating the whole person with cancer. Health care plans must regard the cancer patient as an autonomous individual who has the right to be involved in decisions about his or her care.

Principle 3: Standards of cancer care should be driven by the quality of care, not only the cost of care, and should include participation in clinical trials and quality-of-life considerations.

Principle 4: All people diagnosed with cancer should have access to and coverage for services provided by a multidisciplinary team of care providers across the full continuum of care. Health care plans should be held accountable for timely referral to appropriate specialists when symptoms of cancer or its recurrence may be present.

Principle 5: People with cancer should be provided a range of benefits by all health care plans that includes primary and secondary prevention, early detection, initial treatment, supportive therapies to manage pain, nausea, fatigue and infections, long-term follow-up, psychosocial services, palliative care, hospice care, and bereavement counseling.

Principle 6: People with histories of cancer have the right to continued medical follow-up with basic standards of care that include the specific needs of long-term survivors.

Principle 7: Long-term survivors should have access to specialized follow-up clinics that focus on health promotion, disease prevention, rehabilitation, and identification of physiologic and psychosocial problems. Communication with the primary care physician must be maintained.

Principle 8: Systematic long-term follow-up should generate data that contribute to improvements in cancer therapies and decreases in morbidity.

Principle 9: The responsibility for appropriate long-term medical care must be shared by cancer survivors, their families, the oncology team, and primary care providers.

Principle 10: The provision of psychosocial services must be safeguarded and promoted. Persons diagnosed with cancer should receive psychosocial assessments at critical junctures along the continuum of cancer care to determine availability of needed support and their ability to seek information and to advocate on their own behalf.

Principle 11: Psychosocial research is integral to comprehensive cancer care and, as such, psychosocial outcome measures should be included in all future clinical trials. The importance of this research and its application and transfer to oncology care plans should be recognized and encouraged.

Principle 12: Cancer survivors, health care providers, and other key constituency groups must work together to increase public awareness; educate consumers, professionals, and public policy makers; develop guidelines and disseminate information; advocate for increased research funding; and articulate for and promote survivors' rights.

The points seem so obvious to us now. We can't imagine *not* having survivors' rights. But in 1996, those were not the status quo. Following the principles were the finalized versions of the briefing papers hammered out by each of the congress working groups.

At the time that Ellen had given him the report, Dr. Klausner was heading to a health care meeting in Italy. He tucked the file into his briefcase to be read later. The "later" came on his return flight, and the report's contents—coupled with what he had witnessed at the congress—began a tsunami of events. When Dr. Klausner landed in Washington, DC, he was so enthused about what he had read that he called Ellen and, not realizing how late it was, woke her up. "We need to do something about this," he said.

In the ensuing days, he went to each NIH ally in Congress and announced, "I'm going to create an Office of Cancer Survivorship. We need answers about survivorship and we need *you* [directed to whomever he was talking to at the time] to support the science that's going to provide us with the information about what happens to people after cancer treatment."

Six months later, on October 27, 1996, a ceremony occurred in the White House Rose Garden. "Today I announced that this Friday, November 1, the National Cancer Institute will open its new

Office of Cancer Survivorship," President Clinton told the assembled press. "The office will support much-needed research that will help cancer survivors deal with the problems they face, even after their cancer is cured."

While the word "cure" was becoming increasingly passé in the cancer community, the event was a thrill. An NCI statement, released the next day, further spelled out the new office.

> The research priorities of the past 25 years have focused on cancer prevention, early detection, and treatment [two of the cancer empire's realms]. The efforts to meet these challenges must and will continue. But we must also recognize that recovering from cancer and living as a cancer survivor are in themselves challenging. For this reason, Richard D. Klausner, M.D., director of the NCI, has established within the NCI the Office of Cancer Survivorship.
>
> ...The new OCS will explore the physical, psychological, and economic well-being of individuals who are cancer survivors. Klausner has named Anna T. Meadows, M.D., to head this office. Meadows has engaged in research related to cancer survival and has the enthusiasm and experience to bring the issues of survivorship into focus.

Dr. Meadows was a brilliant and highly respected pediatric oncologist. Her appointment would be interim while a full-time director was sought. The press release continued, "In establishing the OCS, Klausner has recognized the growing number of cancer survivors and the need for a 'home' within the NCI for research related to survivorship. The overall goal of the NCI is to reduce the burden of cancer on all Americans. This new office will be a part of reaching this overall goal by exploring, on a national level, the important issues facing cancer survivors and their caregivers through excellent scientific research."

Decades earlier, Margaret Mead had said, "Never doubt that a small group of thoughtful, committed citizens can change the world; indeed, it's the only thing that ever has." There could be no better description of what NCCS had accomplished. The nearly sixty-year-old National Cancer Institute is government's primary agency to address cancer. While it had accomplished great feats in the war on cancer, by its very nature up to that point, it had been somewhat siloed from the day-to-day lives of the patients its work served. The NCI was focused on saving patients' lives. Now it had started to ask the question: What happens *after* those lives are saved?

The research that would come out of this office would be life-changing for the ever-growing population of cancer survivors.

Prior to his OCS announcement, the president had also added his name to the Ribbon of Hope. Seated at the Resolute Desk in the Oval Office, Betsy Clark, as NCCS board president, and Ellen Stovall, as its executive director, were among the dozen people convened behind him. The combined length of the ribbon's individual sun rays now measured more than 750 feet. While the first lady had been the first to sign the ribbon after the survivor's congress the previous year—and with many VIP signatures following hers—President Clinton's gold ink signature brought the total to more than 10,000.

In 1992, two years after her diagnosis of indolent non-Hodgkin's lymphoma and just months after completing treatment for her first recurrence, Dr. Wendy Harpham attended her first NCCS assembly. Having shuttered her solo practice of internal medicine, Wendy had the same questions any survivor has. Who am I now? What am I doing? She knew she wasn't cured, and was struggling to figure out how to make cancer a part of her life.

Wendy had been so impressed by her first experience with NCCS that she was among the 1993 assembly attendees who gathered in Seattle. As NCCS president, Susie's welcome address during the opening ceremonies moved Wendy. "She was poised, funny, confident, and hopeful," Wendy said later. "I thought, 'I want to be her!' I was in awe. I saw Susie as someone who was plowing the road, plowing through the bramble of survivorship. She was using her experience to make survivorship better for others."

Wendy was hooked on NCCS, and fell easily into the survivorship movement. She had already published her first book, *Diagnosis: Cancer: Your Guide to the First Months of Healthy Survivorship*. It was written to encourage survivors to focus on quality of life from the very beginning. As a physician, Wendy knew she had a unique perspective from both sides of the stethoscope. She knew she had a voice that physicians would hear, too.

The side effects of her treatment were making it difficult for her to practice at the time, so Wendy thought she would write and speak about survivorship until she could get back to working full-time. A series of recurrences and persistent aftereffects made that impossible. As often happens with cancer survivors, Wendy's life took a different path, allowing her to reach thousands more people than she otherwise would have. Publishing five more books, she also began writing a regular column for *Oncology Times*. An observation shared in one of those columns offers a beautiful and poignant example of Wendy's artistry with words: "Illness doesn't make life uncertain. It simply exposes the uncertainty of life."

Wendy wasn't the only person inspired by Susie's passion for survivorship. The fact was, Susie inspired everyone. "The collective spirit of those in NCCS helped me find my voice, gave me courage to speak out on behalf of cancer survivors," she later reflected. "[They] propelled me into the arena of advocacy. I have been accused of being an overly obsessive 'professional cancer survivor,' to which I say, 'So be it!'"

At forty-nine, and despite yet another diagnosis—this time early-stage bladder cancer, found after a 1995 traffic accident caused a broken pelvis—Susie was in high demand. She was the veteran many turned to at their darkest moments. She spoke from coast to coast as an oncology nurse, a cancer survivorship consultant, *and* a three-time survivor. Her tone and focus varied depending on the audience, but the topics remained constant: the myths surrounding cancer, the veteran-rookie connection, and her greatest passion and personal mission, educating about late effects of treatment and long-term survivorship issues. While she continued to support NCCS in every way, she was now speaking to a very broad audience.

Organizations, oncology conferences, hospital events, and the National Cancer Institute requested that she share her personal and professional relationship with the disease. Pharmaceutical companies, including Glaxo, Amgen, Eli Lilly, and Schering, invited her to speak at their meetings and conferences, helping to teach every attendee, from the researchers to the sales reps. It was crucial for them to understand what cancer was like from the patient's perspective. Hardly anyone had a better grasp of what survivors, their health care teams, and the world at large should know about living decades after a cancer diagnosis. But the group that probably got the most Susie face time, after NCCS, was the Oncology Nursing Society.

She was frequently a part of their meeting agendas, on both regional and national stages. Since its founding in 1975, ONS ranks had grown to such a point that focus groups were created to bring like-minded nurses together into small communities within the larger organization. The Nurse Survivors Focus Group was exactly that. Created in 1983, it fulfilled the special need for oncology nurses with histories of cancer, like Susie. In addition to supporting their personal needs, these nurses' unique perspective of the cancer experience from both sides of the hospital bed made them a valuable asset in all things oncology. Their mission was straight out of a Joni Mitchell ballad: "I've looked at life from both sides now."

Susie chaired the Nurse Survivors Focus Group from 1988 to 1990, and steered the birth of its offspring, the Survivorship Focus Group. That in turn became the Survivorship Special Interest Group in 1992. "The Nurse Survivors Focus Group originally began as a peer support network," Susie wrote as the SIG coordinator in their first newsletter. "But interest in survivorship has increased over the past few years. The need to open up to the general ONS membership became apparent and we elected to formally establish ourselves."

Susie's term as coordinator was to be just a year, but applicants were slow in stepping forward. "Remember, without leadership participation, we can't survive," another of her newsletter messages read. "And 'survival' is the name of our game. So write to me. Call me. Communicate in any way, shape, or form! I'm waiting...."

The Survivorship SIG included nurses Susie had worked with in one way or another over the years. Her friend Lois Loescher was one of those, the same nurse from her U of A years who had so vigorously supported Susie's enthusiasm after the founding NCCS meeting. And their names all kept reappearing with different titles.

"Those of us who faithfully attend the SIG meetings every year [at the ONS congress] seem to be rewarded with recycled leadership positions!" Susie wrote. After a two-year hiatus, she had returned as coordinator, and then served four more years as the newsletter editor.

Educating her nurse colleagues was important too, particularly those who hadn't had cancer. "Many oncology nurses continue to view survivorship as a stage of survival (i.e., the time when patients have completed their therapy and are in remission or are considered cured)," she explained in the May 1994 *SIG Newsletter.* "But this view is limited, and it suits the needs of the medical profession more than it does those of the consumer population. Because of my involvement with NCCS, I will continue to represent the viewpoint that survivorship is a process of living through and beyond the experience of cancer and not necessarily an outcome."

Recognition from Susie's oncology-nurse peers spoke to their love for her. They honored her twice in 1995 with both the Quality of Life in Long-Term Survivors Award and the Excellence in Cancer Nursing Research Award. They were ideal honors for a woman who had devoted nearly a quarter of a century to her fellow survivors.

Susie unleashed her experience and wisdom via the written word as well. She wrote chapters in medical books, and articles for professional journals and consumer publications alike. "My passion continues to fuel my professional mission," she said in an article for the *American Journal of Nursing.* "As I wrote in *Cure* magazine, addressing my fellow long-term survivors: 'Our time has finally come!' Survivorship and long-term survivors are on the oncology radar screen."

NCCS recognized that many survivors were willing to take on advocacy roles, but didn't know how to take the first step. So, within their Town Hall Meeting Guide was a chapter called "Blueprint for Advocacy." Designed to help ordinary survivors feel comfortable and confident in the realm of advocacy, the eight points urged them to: champion themselves, get involved, learn more, network, make an action plan, build alliances, go regional, and see the bigger picture. The hope was that survivors—no matter what age, education, or cancer—could each do their part in helping the survivorship movement grow. Ellen had been the primary author of the chapter.

As it did for Susie, advocacy played a monumental role in Ellen Stovall's life mission. This was the result of two significant events: first, her desire to be a part of the MOPP clinical trial in 1971, and her inability to do so because she had just given birth, made her an ardent advocate for quality cancer care. And second, at her Georgetown Hospital support group, the young man she met whose mother sterilized his dishes to prevent his leukemia from spreading to the rest of the family, made her realize the importance of advocating for others who were unable to do so for themselves.

Ellen didn't just give lip service to advocacy. She dissected it, analyzed it, and amplified its applications and possibilities. She viewed advocacy as divisable into three distinct, yet equally crucial, types: personal or self-advocacy, advocacy for others, and national or public interest advocacy. Ellen and Betsy fleshed it all out in a 1996 article co-authored for the ACS journal *Cancer Practice.* As they so clearly explained, "In cancer survivorship, advocacy is a continuum."

Personal advocacy lies in the ability of survivors to take charge of their own cancer. It empowers them, a feeling which is often lacking during a cancer experience. Understanding diagnoses and treatment, speaking to health care providers, locating resources, and being proactive in all aspects of their lives falls into this type of advocacy.

The next type of advocacy is for others. This form is best described as survivors sharing their own experiences (the veteran helping the rookie) and advocating for changes at a community level. Ellen and Betsy went on to explain, "One of the easiest and most satisfying ways to advocate for others is to speak at the local community level... to educate them about the complex interpersonal and psychosocial issues that dominate survivors' lives after a diagnosis of cancer."

Last in the continuum is public interest advocacy. These advocates participate at the cancer survivorship movement level, with a goal of effecting change in public policy. They are professional survivor advocates. All those involved with NCCS were perfect examples. From ensuring appropriations for survivorship research, to bearing public witness at the local, state, and federal levels, to contributing to the body of knowledge about life after a cancer diagnosis, decades worth of public interest advocacy is what has changed the lives of millions of survivors.

Ellen and Betsy also cogently realized that a specialized skillset was crucial to advocating, regardless of the type. While most people might have had some skills in each of these areas prior to their diagnoses, honing them would make their advocacy less stressful and more successful. Regardless of where they fit in, advocates, they wrote, needed to be adept at information-seeking, communication, problem-solving, and negotiation. And in this, too, the veterans led the rookies.

"Survivorship became what I did," Ellen once said. But advocacy was what got her blood pumping. "I'm not very patient about watching Congress or government," she told a reporter in 1995. "There are major things that don't happen more quickly because of bureaucracy...Action is needed at local, regional, and state levels where health care reform is taking place." And Ellen Stovall acted.

On behalf of NCCS and America's cancer survivors, she became a frequent face on television and a familiar name in newspaper articles. She spoke to Congressional committees, and at conferences for NCI, AACR, and ASCO. She had been transformed from a housewife and mother with no experience in politics or public speaking into a seasoned presenter. Politicians loved her. And so did everyone else. No one had a bad word to say about Ellen. Everyone admired her tireless and passionate work.

Ellen never took her foot off the advocacy gas pedal. She closed a joint NCI/ACS survivorship symposium with words that underscored exactly that.

> ...the cancer advocacy community, represented by scores of organizations that were founded by and for cancer survivors, stands ready and eager to tell you our stories of survivorship with the belief that, while grateful for the blessings of survivorship, for the increasing length of days, months and years added because of new and improved therapies for cancer, that this diagnosis is filled with many punishing and adverse consequences as well as joy for living each day.

On October 3, just three weeks before the birth announcement of the Office of Cancer Survivorship, NCCS opened its annual assembly. The celebration garnered little press, but the more than 350 attendees didn't care. They were there to celebrate the organization's tenth birthday, and doing so in the very location it had all begun: Albuquerque. The anniversary assembly logo proclaimed "A decade of service to the cancer community," and the assembly's theme reminded attendees that NCCS was the only national organization "Of, By and For Cancer Survivors." They had come a long way from the small conference room at the Barcelona Court Hotel with giant notepaper taped to the walls.

The assembly was presented jointly with Catherine's local organization, People Living Through Cancer, and took place at the combined sites of the Albuquerque Convention Center and the nearby Doubletree Hotel. Susie, Barbara, and Fitz opened the assembly with a Thursday evening reception featuring memories of their original meeting. Joined on stage by Betsy, Ellen, and Natalie, they expanded on the history at Friday morning's plenary session, "Where We've Been…Where We Are…Where We're Going."

The birthday party was filled with excitement. The first NCCS public service announcement debuted, featuring General Schwarzkopf. Betsy presented Susie with the President's Award for "bringing a message of hope to countless survivors throughout the country." The presentation was made at the beginning of the twentieth town hall. These gatherings of survivors, health care professionals, and community leaders had become an essential component of NCCS.

Barbara Hoffman received a President's Award for "her tireless work combating cancer discrimination and her advocacy efforts in employment, legal, and insurance issues related to cancer survivorship." It was the perfect segue into the announcement of the new *Cancer Survivor's Almanac.* Edited by Barbara, this edition included recently emerged topics like loss and grief, advocacy, and cancer's effect on the family, plus changes in laws covering insurance and employment rights.

The survivorship movement's strongest voices—Natalie, Betsy, Catherine, Ellen, and Susie—weighed in with chapters on their special interests. Susie's contribution was "Cancer Survivorship: Defining Our Destiny." In addition to many of the other salient points that were closest to her heart, she ended the chapter with this tribute:

Survivors and their caregivers, both personal and professional, have laid the groundwork for survivorship. One of their greatest gifts to today's survivors is knowledge, for knowledge is power. No cancer journey is easy. But with information, understanding, support, and resources, cancer survivors are dispelling myths and improving the quality of their lives with, through, and beyond cancer.

The full display of the Ribbon of Hope made a shimmering backdrop for the entire assembly. By this time the yards and yards of yellow ribbon had traveled the United States, where signings had taken place at the centennial Olympics, NFL games, National Survivors Day celebrations, cancer awareness events like Relay for Life and Race for the Cure, and at hospitals and treatment centers. Artist and NCCS friend John Feight was the ribbon's travel agent, taking it as far as Japan and Europe.

Betsy described it in the *Networker* as "...a bright symbol of progress...that has helped the public to recognize that cancer no longer automatically equates with a death sentence." The ribbon was also an extremely successful public awareness campaign, highlighting the survivorship movement and the fact that hope was, and has always been, the cornerstone of it all. NCCS would even go on to create and sell Ribbon of Hope kits that included enough ribbon for about two hundred signatures. Just as so many other NCCS family members had been drafted to help with projects, Betsy enlisted her mother and children. They spent days cutting ribbon from big spools for the kits, which were then sold for a nominal amount, allowing communities across the country to contribute to the growing numbers of names.

While Catherine hadn't been able to hold their original 1986 gathering the same weekend as the International Balloon Fiesta, the tenth assembly succeeded in doing so. It was the twenty-fifth occurrence of what is billed as "the most-photographed sporting event in the world," and registration to the assembly included a 5:15 a.m. bus trip to Balloon Fiesta Park. At dawn on Sunday morning, 850 hot air balloons prepared to launch into the first rays of sunlight peeking over the Sandia Mountains. Prominent among them was the brand-new NCCS balloon. It was bright gold, with a band of navy blue on which the NCCS sun ray logo was displayed. This giant Ribbon of Hope (as it was named) also carried a lucky assembly attendee, whose name had been drawn in a lottery the day before. Suddenly, a rush of sound … energetic shouts … and the most meaningful balloon in the array rose majestically with the others into the purple sky.

As the nine before it had been, this assembly, too, was a rousing success. It was also the last for NCCS. Bringing together survivors from across the nation had wonderful benefits, with just one drawback. And it was a big one. Despite an impressive list of sponsors and donors—who that year had given generously in celebration of NCCS's decade of success—the increasing assembly costs to both the organization and those attending were too great a hurdle to overcome. Nonetheless, the voices of the survivorship movement would continue to build, and one day be heard even more powerfully.

Twenty-five years after it was declared, twenty-nine billion dollars later, and two years after his death, Richard Nixon's war on cancer was still being waged. And cancer survivors were getting tired of progress that was measurable only in inches. As Ellen Stovall told an Associated Press reporter, "The war on cancer got stuck and there's no will to unglue it."

NCI's Dr. Klausner was frustrated as well, and on two fronts. "For too long we've made false promises. We don't know when we're going to cure cancer," he said in support of the survivors. And then in support of the research, "… But we cannot confuse the frustration with not curing it, with the conclusion we're not making progress."

There were recently approved drugs that blocked nausea, blood infections and other chemotherapy side effects. Scientists were unlocking genetic mysteries, in the hopes that if they better understood the structure and behavior of the myriad types of cancerous cells, they could attack them with more precision and improved results. Yet discouraging statistics rose to cast shadows on all that effort. The July 4, 1996 Associated Press article in which Ellen was quoted reported that twenty-five years ago, cancer killed 162 of every 100,000 Americans. By 1990, the mortality rate had jumped to 174. "Congress," the article read, "repeatedly asks the nation's top doctors: why are there significant new drugs to fight AIDS, but nothing as exciting for the cancers that strike millions more Americans?"

Despite being irritatingly titled "Victims Desperate for Cancer War Victory" (why did journalists insist on using the word *victim*?), the article posed a very good question.

As he had at the war's fifteenth and twentieth anniversaries, Dr. John Bailar weighed in again on the silver anniversary, saying that preventing cancer by fighting smoking, sun exposure and other controllable risks may be the best option for a disease now considered too complex for a magic bullet. And then he delivered this disheartening message: "I am simply no longer convinced that there are a lot of wonderful cures waiting to be found."

Making an even more discouraging point, the article reported that only 2–3 percent of cancer patients participate in clinical trials of potential new treatments. This was bad for science. If the trial pools weren't large and varied enough, they would be less effective at proving whether something did or didn't work. So where were people going to buy a new chance at life? The internet, although still young, was rife with bogus "miracle cures" that ran the gamut. Laetrile, made from apricot pits, had been banned by the FDA in 1981, yet it was still available at Mexican clinics. Essiac tea, a Native American formula discovered in 1922 by Rene Caisse (Essiac is her name spelled backward), was marketed in newspaper and magazine ads from coast to coast. Even more extreme offerings included bee venom, coffee enemas, and a variety of herbal concoctions. These untested, unapproved, and unsubstantiated treatments were often accompanied by the conspiracy theory that chemotherapy drug manufacturers were deliberately blocking a cancer cure to ensure ongoing company profits.

Ellen's exacerbation with the war on cancer was evident on a different level. In the Winter 1996 *Networker,* she wrote,

> ...the ten million troops who have survived cancer, who live among us and who have 'returned home' to tell the tale, need more than medals and parades to herald their hard-fought battles. Medals tarnish; parades become faint memories. In fact, if we do no more than salute our fellow survivors, we all have failed them.
>
> For those of us with cancer, the war never really ends...Cancer exacts an incalculable toll on our physical, psychological, and financial well-being.
>
> Platitudes from well-meaning individuals, about how grateful we cancer survivors should feel just to be alive, wear thin as our leaders keep focusing on "curing" cancer rather than helping people live and die as well as they can in the wake of this terrible diagnosis.

The war needed a different goal. The troops needed more rallying. The message needed to be louder.

Natalie Davis Spingarn had written thousands of words before she was diagnosed with cancer in 1974. And she had written more still by 1987, when she was a thirteen-year survivor. By the time she arrived at her first NCCS assembly that same year, she had also done a good deal of public speaking at previous events (most notably to promote her first book, *Hanging In There*). She had been asked to be NCCS's first assembly keynoter, and she had expected that the assembly would be no different than her other speaking engagements had been. Instead, as Natalie wrote for a 1996 *Networker* article,

I found a gathering of extraordinary people who had been through the trials of the cancer experience and come out punching. I found them the teachers, and myself the learner. Bowled over by the guts and optimism of the Cathy Logans and Susie Leighs I met in Albuquerque—people who hoped for the best but pragmatically prepared for the worst—I hopped aboard the NCCS bandwagon, and onto its board of directors.

By her own admission, she was "hooked on survivorship," and proud of the advances NCCS had made over the past decade. "To say we've come a long way is an understatement," Natalie continued. "We need to increase our participation wherever survivorship decisions are made."

Humans have battled against cancer for a very long time. As mentioned early on, the first written description of it exists on an Egyptian papyrus. The word cancer itself would not be used until 1,300 years later, when Hippocrates, the "Father of Medicine," used the Greek word *karkinos*—crab—to describe a tumor he discovered in a cadaver. With its swollen blood vessels sticking out all around it, Hippocrates wrote that it reminded him of a crab dug into the sand, legs spread in a circle. And the word stuck.

Around the same time, the translations of a Greek historian tell the story of Atossa, Queen of Persia. She is recorded to have had "a boil form on her breast which, after it burst, began to spread and increase." It's assumed the queen had suffered from inflammatory breast cancer, which was excised using tools and methods of the time.

So, when Natalie said, in 1996, that we had come a long way, she was not referring just to cancer treatment. That journey now included the recognition of what life *after* treatment could and should look like. The mission statement crafted a decade earlier by the NCCS founders spoke to that directly:

...to communicate that there can be vibrant, productive life following the diagnosis of cancer; that millions of survivors share a common, transforming experience that has impacted their lives with new challenges and enhanced potentials; and that these survivors, their families and supporters represent a burgeoning constituency and a powerful, positive force in society.

Chapter 14: The March

In 1998, 1,228,600 Americans are diagnosed with cancer.

Susie was angry. According to American Cancer Society projections for 1998, cancer would kill in the neighborhood of 565,000 people that year. That was more than 1,500 people every day. And *that* was the equivalent of three-and-a-half jumbo jet crashes every day.

"Where is people's anger about this?" she asked the *Arizona Daily Star* reporter who was interviewing her. "How much outrage would there be if we had three-and-a-half plane crashes a day?"

By this time, Susie had lived more years with a cancer history than she had without it, and her anger was understandable. She could quote sad statistics all day long. The five wars that had been fought since the beginning of the twentieth century had so far cost around 496,000 American lives. More than that were dying of cancer *every* year. While cancer deaths could fill jumbo jets each day, in the same 24-hour period, 69 Americans were murdered and 110 died of AIDS. It was not that those deaths were any less important. But each of those causes garnered more public outrage, more attention from politicians, and more money to combat them than did cancer.

"My God!" Susie proclaimed. "Who doesn't know someone with cancer?"

Considering that, in 1998, 4.5 percent of all Americans would get cancer, because of the disease's staggering implications, every family member, friend, and coworker would also be impacted. The final calculation, then, was that nearly everyone in the nation was affected by the disease.

To assist General Schwarzkopf in winning the seven-month (August 1990–February 1991) Gulf War, the US government spent $61 billion. In the twenty-seven years since the war on cancer had been declared, $30 billion had been spent on cancer research, with $2.3 billion of that going to the National Cancer Institute. Meanwhile, annual cancer care costs were roughly fifty times that—$115 billion. In other words, for every $10 the government collected in taxes, one penny went to cancer research.

Referring to the $10, Ellen stated in another newspaper article, "That's the cost [at the time] of one movie ticket and a small bag of popcorn to see *Titanic*, a ship which ironically lost in one day the same number of lives we lose every day to cancer."

It was a crazy conundrum. Millions of people being diagnosed with cancer... millions of people dying from cancer... millions of cancer survivors, no longer hidden in the shadows, but still not living quality lives nor being acknowledged by the public at all. The figures just didn't add up.

Americans had used their First Amendment right "peaceably to assemble, and to petition the Government for a redress of grievances" to great success in recent decades. The civil rights movement of the 1960s, the women's rights movement of the 1970s, and the gay rights movement of the 1980s all raised awareness of injustices. When the Million Man March occurred on the Mall in Washington, DC, in 1995, it planted a seed in Ellen's mind.

The seed was still germinating when, in early February 1997, Ellen attended her first National Cancer Policy Advisory Board meeting. The twenty-member board had been created by the National Academy of Sciences at Dr. Klausner's request. The group, he felt, was meant not to replace but rather to supplement other advisory bodies already in existence. And because he valued Ellen's work, he made certain she was among the twenty members. Only one other patient advocate was on the board, the rest being distinguished cancer researchers and care providers.

"I've been taking the pulse of a few key people in the cancer community," she had written in an email to Betsy Clark on February

23, 1997, "...and trying to figure out the best way to reach people to disseminate our materials AND raise consciousness of the public at large about survivorship and NCCS. I believe I have found the answer to the latter and it's a biggie! We need to talk."

Ellen's idea was a march on Washington, with General Schwarzkopf in fatigues leading an army of survivors, advocates, members of the oncology community, and more. Together, they would wage a new war on cancer. NCCS would also bring other advocacy organizations whose stakeholders would participate. The country and the world would see a sea of humanity, all connected to cancer survivors. And their collective voice would ring loud in the ears of Congress, the men and women responsible for doling out cancer research funding. After all, Ellen told Betsy, if Louis Farrakhan could get a Million Man March, what's the big deal?

Others around the country were also acutely aware of the way Nixon's war—and attention to cancer—had stagnated. Unbeknownst to Ellen or Betsy, those folks were percolating on some kind of a big splash as well. One of them was prostate cancer survivor Michael Milken, the financier who had founded CaP CURE, the Association for the Cure of Cancer of the Prostate, a disease he had survived. Two years earlier, he had participated in the NCCS Congress. Ellen saw him on April 6, 1997, and mentioned the march idea to him. She and Betsy had taken the idea to the NCCS board, too, and they all agreed to work on feasibility details behind the scenes, but not to make any announcement till their proverbial ducks were lined up. And then fate intervened.

On April 7, 1997, Dr. Klausner was unable to take part in a cancer panel to air on *Larry King Live*. Ellen was asked to step in, with the rest of the panel being made up of actor Robert Urich (a synovial sarcoma survivor who connected remotely from Los Angeles), ABC news anchor Sam Donaldson (a melanoma survivor), talk-show host Morton Downey Jr. (a lung cancer survivor), television journalist Paula Zahn (who'd had four family members diagnosed with cancer a decade earlier) and Milken.

The program began innocently, with Ellen, Milken, and Donaldson lamenting the meager cancer research dollars and the fragmentation of its organizations. During the commercial, Donaldson declared, "We need a march!"

"Ellen's in charge of marches," Milken said, in an offhanded way. The concept spread like wildfire around the studio and by the time they were back on the air, King proclaimed in his booming voice, "We have an announcement!"

Ellen was a deer caught in headlights. This was just, as yet, an idea. No strategic planning had been done. She certainly didn't want to ignite the vulnerable survivorship population for something that NCCS couldn't deliver. She had promised her board she would keep the idea under wraps. Now it had been broadcast to King's million-strong audience. She was horrified. And she was angry, after the show telling King, Milken, and Donaldson—in no uncertain terms—that they had no idea what they had just done.

While they were all still in the same city, Ellen, Milken, and Donaldson, along with Ellen Sigal, who had founded Friends of Cancer Research the year before, met at the Madison Hotel to hammer out the dozens of questions. How much could a march cost? (The answer, they would learn, was millions.) Who could find a campaign and logistics wizard? Who could drum up political assistance, celebrities, and scientists? And what about the cancer community? Each of the brainstorming-session participants stepped into the arena that best suited them, with Ellen taking on the cancer community component. Suddenly "a march" became The March (always presented with a "T" capitalized). And as had been the case throughout NCCS history, dominoes seemed to just fall into place.

The vision was reminiscent of the 1990 Earth Day Celebration. The March would occur in Washington, with smaller marches occurring simultaneously all across the country. Milken consulted his Rolodex for organizers and funders. He was able to contact the very fellow who had organized the original Earth Day Celebration, Walter McGuire. McGuire had an event proposal in their hands a few days later. And shortly after that, at the AACR annual meeting, the two Ellens (Stovall and Sigal) fortuitously met Richard Butera, the president of the Sidney Kimmel Foundation for Cancer Research. Kimmel was Butera's best friend, the CEO of Jones Apparel, and very rich. The two men had also recently put their heads together to find a way to wake up voters about cancer research funding. The March was exactly the kind of thing they were considering.

As soon as he heard about it, Kimmel was so inspired, he immediately wrote a personal check in the sum of $500,000. He apologized it wasn't for the entire $1.5 million he had pledged, but $500,000, he said, was the max his bank allowed per check. In addition to making good on the other $1 million, he pulled in more donors to cover the cost of a massive ad campaign.

For complete transparency on all levels, the NCCS board and staff recognized immediately that they needed to separate themselves from The March. Ellen became the event's president. Betsy left her position as social worker for a year and stepped down from the NCCS board presidency to become the full-time chief operating officer of NCCS. Susie stepped back in as president of the board. The March had its own board, stacked with high visibility people. And as technology was taking an ever more important place in society, The March had a dedicated website, too. They opened an office in Washington, DC, on K and 17th Streets Northwest in an old campaign office space. The March staff set up folding tables throughout from which to work, and it was conveniently located right around the corner from the Firehook Bakery. The takeout meals flowed from breakfast through dinner, with lots and lots of coffee as the day of The March drew closer.

NCCS staff members were pulled over to work on the event, including Donna Doneski. In early spring 1996, she had grown weary of her job working for a software firm. She had mentioned it to her friend and hairstylist, Diane, some time ago, and Diane now called to ask Donna if she was serious about changing jobs. Donna said she was. "Then I've got something for you," Diane told her. Ellen Stovall, also Diane's client, was overwhelmed by her work at NCCS and looking for an executive assistant. Donna called Ellen on a Friday morning and Ellen asked her to come in that afternoon. The two hit it off just as Diane thought they would, and Donna started the job two weeks later, becoming Ellen's right-hand girl.

Although Donna's title was Director of Community Operations, she became a "Jane" of all trades at NCCS. She was in the green room the day The March bombshell dropped, and at the Madison Hotel meeting the next day. Going forward, she kept a running list of any celebrity who ever mentioned cancer, to pull them in. And she connected with others who had done big events to learn from them.

The official launch of The March came on a return visit to *Larry King Live* six months after the bombshell announcement. This time, October 23, 1997, Ellen, Milken, and Donaldson were joined by supermodel Cindy Crawford, whose younger brother had died of leukemia when they were children; tennis star and children's cancer advocate Andrea Jaeger; and figure skating champion Scott Hamilton, who had completed treatment for testicular cancer six months earlier. Following a year-long marketing and P.R. campaign, The March—subtitled "Coming Together to Conquer Cancer"—would be the culmination. It would take place on Saturday, September 26, 1998.

Donaldson closed the first segment of the show with a quote from Ronald Reagan: "When you can't make them see the light, make them feel the heat." When they came back from the commercials, King announced that they had a "very special caller," General Norman Schwarzkopf. Asked if he was going to march, Schwarzkopf said yes, and challenged all Americans to be there with them. He had already signed on as co-chair, along with Sidney Kimmel. Still on the air, Ellen asked the general if he could have taken back the Persian Gulf with a $2 billion defense expenditure, NCI's purse for the war on cancer.

"No," the general answered emphatically. "With $2 billion, that wouldn't have been a war, that would have been a minor skirmish!"

A "skirmish" was not acceptable to those within NCCS. Things had to change. The March team started by bringing in powerful troops, including the same press secretary who had handled the communications for a National Organization for Women (NOW) March. The DC event had attracted 400,000 people. Ellen's brother was well-placed in media; he was tapped to help with national exposure. Plus, Ellen's good friend, P.R. expert Rosemary Wussler, immediately stepped up to volunteer. Her father, Robert Wussler, was President and CEO of Affiliate Enterprises, a company owned by ABC Television Associates, thus beefing up their television exposure.

The preparation was enormous. The responsibility was enormous. But the results would be enormous, and lifesaving. As Ellen explained in a Dallas interview, "We're spending a few million dollars to increase the cancer research budget by billions of dollars."

Between the *Larry King Live* appearance, the advertising campaign that began the next day, and contacting nine hundred organizations across the country—every one they could find with the word "cancer" in its name—it was the right combination to amp up the excitement. They attracted big names in oncology as well, including Dr. Donald Coffey. By his own admission, Dr. Coffey had been transformed from a quiet scientist and researcher at the Johns Hopkins Oncology Center to a loudmouthed advocate when he became president of AACR. He discovered that out of every hundred research grants then approved by the NCI—the proposals that had met the rigorous standards of scientific "peer review"— only about twenty-three could actually be funded.

"That's bad," Coffey said, "because we don't have all the answers yet. We don't know where the next breakthrough is coming, and we are discouraging a whole new generation of scientists from ever trying for one.

"People are angry and frustrated," he continued, "they believe that there has been a war, and it has failed. This hasn't been a war on cancer. This has been a skirmish." Exactly General Schwarzkopf's impression of the paltry cancer research budget.

Coffey believed so much in what NCCS was forging, he became the lead scientist supporting The March. He invited his fellow oncology professionals to join him. And they did. When March day finally arrived, Dr. Coffey and about 250 of his peers crammed into five buses at the Johns Hopkins Medical School campus to make the trip to Washington.

It wasn't all smooth sailing, however. While the decision to become involved was a no-brainer for the AACR, along with the Oncology Nursing Society and the ASCO, other groups were not as anxious to jump on board. This was not a new challenge for NCCS, but rather a frustrating one they had dealt with since their inception. Regardless of cancer type, survivorship posed similar challenges across the board. Other organizations' success in garnering more influence and more money would produce more long-term survivors. They, in turn, would need support in their survivorship, which was where NCCS would step in. But some in the cancer world, where there was fierce competition for influence and dollars, didn't always see NCCS as complementary to their work.

For some organ-specific cancer groups, helping to gin up March donations would compete with their own fundraising efforts. In addition, they didn't relish having another entity, in this case The March, take even a sliver of their autonomy. They didn't want their messages to be watered down with someone else's agenda.

"It's like nailing Jell-O to the wall," Ellen said, regarding their efforts to bring the other organizations to The March table. "It's time this community came together."

The *San Francisco Examiner* observed: "Cancer advocacy is nothing new. What's different is the attempt by The March organizers to marshal the country's eight million cancer survivors into one supergroup."

There were also naysayers who felt that NCCS was too young, too small, and too poor to pull off such a massive event. Fortunately, the results of an early planning meeting with the National Park Service never became public. The Park Service representative told Betsy Clark and Rosemary Wussler they needed to reserve jumbotrons immediately. After all, she told them, there were only eight in the entire nation (at the time). Betsy later admitted to Rosemary and Ellen she didn't even know what a jumbotron was, let alone why they needed some.

But naïveté is often the seed that sprouts greatness. The ship had sailed, and March Madness had begun.

At 3:00 a.m., four years earlier on May 20, 1993, Betsy stood in the dark parking lot of an AMC theater in Albany, New York. Terrified she'd be arrested for nefarious activity, she was actually waiting for an unmarked car to pick up an envelope. Inside was a proposal for a research project grant that was due at NCI by 5:00 p.m. that day. The group of ten who had worked on the proposal—which, in addition to Betsy as principal investigator, included Ellen, Susie, and Barbara Hoffman—hadn't calculated how long final sign-offs from various institutions would take. They were up against a wall with not enough time to mail it. Betsy was waiting for an unmarked car to pick up an envelope with the grant documents and drive them to DC, thus the clandestine meeting.

The premise of the research project, titled "Survival Skills Training for Cancer Adaptation," was a new intervention model they had developed. Called Cancer-Related Self-Advocacy, it would turn out to be an important means of adaptation for survivors to manage the enduring and complex ways that cancer had transformed their everyday lives. The project would begin with a randomized trial of 480 women and men, who were one to five years out from diagnosis, and divided into age groups. The intervention included six weekly two-hour training sessions on self-advocacy. The research team would use several quality-of-life scales and other measurements to assess the trial members' well-being and functioning.

Ten months later, in March 1994, the group was notified that their project would not receive a grant. Of the sixty-four proposals submitted that year, theirs was the tenth best. But NCI only had enough money to fund six. Later, through cancer gossip channels, they learned that one of the stumbling blocks for some of the reviewers was the NCCS definition of the term "cancer survivor." The reviewers couldn't wrap their heads around the idea that people diagnosed just a year or two earlier could actually be considered survivors. While it was one of the very first things NCCS had addressed at its conception, many in the field were still not on board.

But sometimes in life, as the saying goes, when one door shuts, another opens. Pharmaceutical giant Genentech was looking for a public education program. Not long after the NCI rejection, Genentech approached NCCS and asked if they had any projects that needed funding. It was like asking a kid if he wanted Santa to come on Christmas morning. The research group rewrote the NCI grant as a project and submitted it. Genentech awarded them an unrestricted educational grant, with the assurance there would be no product endorsement expected in return. Then came Christmas morning: Genentech offered to send NCCS a check for $335,000, and take care of production, marketing, and distribution of the project on top of that.

Titled "The Cancer Survival Toolbox: Building Skills that Work for You," the project proposed a program that could teach everything necessary to survive cancer well. And "well" was the key. It was what they had all been espousing since day one. Nicknamed The Toolbox, it would be easy to access and provide what they all believed was lacking as a survivorship focus: quality of life, as well as quantity of life.

From the beginning, the team envisioned that The Toolbox would be created by those on the frontline of cancer: survivors—having them at the table kept it real and showed that self-advocacy could be learned from other survivors—and professionals, including oncology nurses and oncology social workers. To bring aboard the latter, the team invited ONS and the Association of Oncology Social Work to be partners. The core team of The Toolbox developers included Susie and Betsy (representing NCCS), P.J. Haylock and Debra Thaler-DeMers (representing ONS), Carol Marcusen and

Kathy Walsh (representing AOSW). Throughout the project, other specialists were brought in as needed.

The initial program consisted of six major advocacy skills every cancer survivor would need. (These were akin to what Ellen and Betsy would write about a few years later in their advocacy article.) The skills included communicating, finding information, making decisions, solving problems, negotiating, and standing up for your rights. The program was professionally recorded on two-sided cassette tapes. The team felt the audiotape format was best, as it allowed survivors to listen to the tapes at home, in their cars, or in treatment centers. They could be listened to several times and survivors could pick and choose those portions they felt they needed at any given time. And while the The Toolbox was designed for those newly diagnosed, it would be helpful to any survivor still interacting with insurers, employers, or their health care team. The Toolbox's debut was scheduled to coincide with The March.

While a package of cassette tapes may not seem like a big deal today, it was a very big deal in 1998, and the first of its kind for survivors. To put it in perspective, that same year, gasoline sold for a dollar a gallon. And 1998's most important technology debuts included the iMac computer, the MP3 player, and a mobile phone with a full keyboard that allowed for a new form of communication called texting. The ocean of information accessible today with a few keystrokes on laptops or smartphone apps was not even on the horizon then.

In the ensuing years, with additional funds from Genentech, The Toolbox was translated into Spanish and Chinese, and added to with new modules about finding ways to pay for care, topics for older adults, caring for the caregiver (any unpaid person who helps a cancer patient), and dying well. The original Toolbox team still feels today it was one of their most significant professional achievements. Ironically, Genentech's financial assistance far, far exceeded the dollar total of the original NCI grant proposal. And that, in turn, allowed The Toolbox to reach hundreds of thousands of survivors and health care professionals, helping them to understand the great importance of self-advocacy in cancer survivorship.

As Susie later explained in an interview at an ONS Congress, "When you're diagnosed, you have to learn a new language and make decisions at one of the most vulnerable times of your life. You don't know how to navigate this entire system." That was precisely why The Toolbox was so important.

But there was another loud, equally important statement that would be made by The Toolbox debut: cancer survivorship was not a return to one's previous life. "The transition to post-treatment is a really, really scary time for most cancer survivors," Susie continued in that same ONS interview. "In the past we heard, 'We've given you curative treatment, we hope you're going to be fine.' But there was nothing in that post-treatment phase. We help patients when they're first diagnosed, we support them through their experience. Now we've got to continue to support them."

"My name is Ellen Stovall and I am one of this country's more than eight million cancer survivors," Ellen's June 1998 article in *The Oncologist* began. It was part memoir, part economics class, and part recruitment poster for The March.

> Why come to Washington, DC? Because this is America. Because historically when Americans have had enough— enough segregation, enough oppression, enough injustice— they've come to Washington, DC. They come to testify, to bear witness, to stand vigil, to protest, to raise their voices, to let their lawmakers know what is unacceptable to them and to say, 'NO MORE.'
>
> ... Science continues to make great progress against the more than 100 diseases we call cancer. In 1998, we are turning hope into action. We need you to stand with us and say, 'NO MORE. No more waiting, no more patience, no more

silence, no more cancer.' THE MARCH ... Coming Together to Conquer Cancer. Join us.

As the weeks slid closer to the big day, Terry Campbell, now the *Networker* editor, made one last request of the pre-March newsletter readers.

If you have a job to do, the key to getting it done is to show up. Show up, and you have a chance to accomplish your goal. If you don't show up, your odds of success hover around zero.

On September 26, we have a job to do ... The job is The March: Coming Together to Conquer Cancer ... Here's the deal: cancer kills. Those it does not kill, it generally beats up pretty badly. And who cares? The people with the bruises. And those people—meaning us—are the people who must take action to spare those we love, and generations to come, from the ravages of cancer.

... One way or the other, we've got to show up. It's up to us. We have to show Congress, and the nation, that we mean business. Let's do this thing!

That same newsletter outlined in full the elements of The March weekend. Events would begin on Thursday, September 24, and run through Saturday. It also had a map to familiarize readers with the National Mall, the center of it all. It was almost showtime for the biggest gamble the NCCS ever made.

A mile and a half from the White House, at Dupont Circle, the Luxury Collection Hotel was a proud beacon of swank history. For seventy years, her 250 Georgian-style rooms had provided beds and pillows on which some of Washington's most famous heads had slept, including Senator Henry Cabot Lodge Jr., Republican from Massachusetts and member of the famous Lodge family;

President Dwight D. Eisenhower; President George H.W. Bush; and the Al Gores, both senior (Congressman and Senator), and junior (Congressman, Senator, and Vice President). It was at this grande dame of the hotel world that the National Coalition for Cancer Survivorship kicked off The March weekend.

Celebrated in the hotel's magnificent ballroom on Thursday evening, September 24, 1998, the Ribbon of Hope Awards Dinner was captained by an able master of ceremonies, Sam Donaldson. Gospel-singing great Cissy Houston, mother of Whitney, prepared the audience—a collection of survivors, caregivers, dignitaries, and advocates—for a night of high emotion. Joining Donaldson were fellow cancer survivors General Schwarzkopf, Hamilton Jordan (a Jimmy Carter staff member), and Scott Hamilton (who took time from Olympic training to participate) along with survivorship advocates William Bennett (political pundit), Andrea Jaeger, Dr. Richard Klausner, and Dr. Harold Freeman. The auspicious group presented trophies to the recipients of the Catherine Logan Award for Service to Survivorship and the Natalie Davis Spingarn Writer's Award.

There were two new awards as well. The National Public Leadership Award was presented to Senator Connie Mack, and his wife Priscilla, both cancer survivors and both ardent advocates of early detection, to which they attributed their successful treatments. The second honor, the National Private Sector Leadership Award, went to Dr. Donald Coffey. His outspoken criticisms of the nation's cancer policy and his high esteem of NCCS made him the perfect choice.

Next in the spotlight were ten "Everyday Heroes," ordinary people who had exhibited extraordinary courage in facing humankind's deadliest adversary. They came from every ethnicity and walk of life, including a Baltimore Orioles outfielder, an advocate for Native American survivors, and seven-year-old Morgan O'Brien. The second grader was a two-time leukemia survivor who had plastered March buttons and bumper stickers all over her home state of Maryland. Little else could top the inspiration of the recipients' stories.

But NCCS had one more surprise in store for the evening. At the conclusion of the dinner, the attendees were given goody bags. Amid the fancy chocolates and other swag was a priceless gift: an inaugural copy of the Cancer Survival Toolbox.

On Friday morning, Susie, Ellen, Betsy, and the rest of the NCCS board and staff had long to-do lists. The final March set-up was going on at the National Mall just a mile away from the J.W. Marriott on Pennsylvania Avenue where they were all staying. The main stage had been positioned along Third Street, practically at Congress's doorstep. That was, after all, the whole purpose: to create an event so large, the men and women inside couldn't ignore it.

Heading east from Third Street, toward the Washington Monument, the Mall would overflow with displays, learning and networking opportunities, and activities. Sponsors and advocates had reserved their spots from which to hand out information. A special tent called "Meet the Experts" would give attendees a chance to chat with oncology professionals from all disciplines. At the Wall of Courage, attendees could leave a message in honor or memory of someone loved. Its fifty-three panels represented each American state and territory. A Children's Patchwork Playground would not only provide entertainment for younger attendees—both survivors and supporters—but it would also be the location for the debut of the National Childhood Cancer Awareness Quilt. Stretching the length of a football field, each of its almost 4,000 handmade squares had been created in memory of a child who had died of cancer. The Ribbon of Hope was on display, too, not far off the Mall at the National Postal Museum. Its golden resplendence was now over 5,000 feet long, with more than 150,000 signatures.

NCCS would have a cancer education tent as well, where attendees would receive free copies of the newly minted "Cancer Information Guide." Computer stations would allow visitors to navigate the new website, "CanSearch." The NCCS boutique would be open, too, selling tee shirts, posters, buttons, note cards and beautiful scarves. The gauzy confections were designed by artist Margaret

Roberts, whose two sisters died of cancer, and who had been recognized as an "Everyday Hero" the evening before.

The March activities would stretch for nearly half a mile. Dotted throughout were concession stands, first aid stations, courtesy stations (dispensing free water and sunscreen), and lost person booths. It would be part state fair, part memorial garden, part political rally. The enormity of it was meant to deliver a single, strong message to Congress and the Clinton administration: "You must do whatever it takes to end this devastating disease. We are watching, and we will hold you accountable."

Although the day had begun early for the NCCS crew, it would end late, and with a bang. The board of directors had arranged for The March celebrities and dignitaries to attend a reception at Vice President Gore's residence. Security screened the attendees at the Marriott, after which they took a fifteen-minute bus ride to One Observatory Circle, on the northeast grounds of the US Naval Observatory. Following the reception, the bus then took the invitees to a remarkable event unfolding at the Lincoln Memorial: the Rays of Hope candlelight vigil.

One of The March's goals was to challenge the nation to face the reality of cancer. That goal was brought to the forefront at this vigil. The Lincoln Memorial is not far from where the names of more than 58,000 Americans who died in the Vietnam War are etched into polished black granite. In similar style, The March Honor Roll scrolled across large video screens at the vigil. The tens of thousands of names belonged to parents and children, siblings and friends that the nation had lost to cancer.

The vigil of hope and remembrance began at sunset and included powerful words from Reverend Jesse Jackson, who implored all in attendance, "We are going to succeed in turning our pain into power." Scott Hamilton, Andrea Jaeger, and other well-known survivors spoke as well. And the honorary vigil chair, Queen Noor of Jordan, provided the perfect tone of grace and strength. Her husband, King Hussein, was receiving treatment for non-Hodgkin's lymphoma at the Mayo Clinic in Rochester, Minnesota. Between his treatments, the royal couple had planned to visit their children who were attending colleges in Washington. Their daughter, Princess Iman, explained she wouldn't be able to see them on Saturday. She was joining the war on cancer, she told her mother. Her passion about the event persuaded her parents to become involved. The king would die five months later.

With 14,000 flickering lights (open flames weren't allowed), the stirring melody of "Amazing Grace" floated through the air, played by the celebrated jazz flute player and cancer survivor, Herbie Mann. Individuals representing communities across the nation came to the stage, stating for whom they lit candles. And when Ellen came to the podium, she invited everyone back for The March the next day, promising that NCCS would continue to fight, continue to testify, to bear witness, to protest, to raise its voice, to stand vigil and to say, "No more."

The Washington weather had been perfect for the Ribbon of Hope dinner and the candlelight vigil, with clear skies and highs in the upper 60s. But on March day itself, Mother Nature had a different idea. When the NCCS crew arrived on the National Mall just after dawn, dressed in March branded tee shirts, the temperature was already 66 degrees with 90 percent humidity. It would rise to a steamy 86 by afternoon, making it 105 on the heat index.

As the morning wore on, couples, families, individuals, and small groups began arriving. They were, in turn, joined by busloads. Some attendees carried photos of parents who had died of cancer. Others had photos of their children. They were a diverse array of regular people representing cancer's deadly swath through every racial, socioeconomic, and generational subset.

The throngs walking the National Mall that bright September day came from across the country. But Dani Grady should have won the prize for the greatest physical effort to get there. A survivor of advanced-stage breast cancer, she had left San Diego on July 20, making a 3,600-mile, ten-week, "Conquer Cancer Coast to Coast" national bike tour. Michigander Brad Zebrack (no stranger to survivorship, NCCS, and awareness bike tours, having done his own with his wife a decade earlier) joined her as she rolled through Detroit. And when Dani arrived at The March that Saturday, it was to a hero's welcome on stage, lifting her bike high over her head. When she and Brad took their seats on the stage, Brad realized he was not only sitting next to one of the main entertainers of the day, but his musical hero as well: Graham Nash of Crosby, Stills, and Nash. He felt like a starstruck teenager.

From Des Moines, Iowa, to Tampa, Florida, and from Trenton, New Jersey, to Sacramento, California, concurrent rallies were occurring all across the country. As on the National Mall, crowds of survivors, caregivers, advocates, and health care professionals used September 26 as a rallying point to send a message of hope and determination. Given the estimated annual cost of cancer—$92 billion in medical and supportive care and $12 billion in lost productivity—the needs on both a state and national level were clear. And they echoed the published mission of The March on Washington: "More federal funding for ALL cancer research; increased access to quality cancer care for ALL people; a renewed commitment from ALL of our elected officials to conquer cancer." The day so inspired the nation that even college football got involved. At the annual rivalry between Michigan and Michigan State that year in Ann Arbor, the half-time show included a special March tribute.

In Washington, DC, as the temperature climbed, so did the attendance, until it reached an estimated 200,000 people. Around noon, Ellen stepped up to the podium, centered on the enormous stage, to begin the program. "...Look around you," she said. "Embrace the sorrow cancer has created. Feel the strength and the determination and the hope and courage of the survivors and their families. We are the faces of cancer. We are real. And we are not going away.

"Today we defy the politics that deliberately divide us; the politics that dare to put a price tag on cancer; on the millions of lives touched by this horrid disease. Today we say no...more...cancer!"

Ellen was followed by sports heroes, politicians, well-known clergy, celebrities, and journalists. The Queen of Soul, Aretha Franklin, lent her powerful voice. Joining her were a general, Schwarzkopf; another queen, Noor; and the Vice President, Al Gore.

When the quiet man in a suit and tie—his attire more noticeable because of the heat—took the stage, the crowd hushed. Unbeknownst to them, if it hadn't been for the influx of cash from that man, March co-chair Sidney Kimmel, the day might never have taken place.

Modest and humble, he told the audience, "This March is both a historic moment in our nation and a turning point in our battle against cancer. It must represent the final chapter in the war against cancer. We're here in Washington to tell our government in one very loud, very strong voice that America will no longer tolerate anything but the strongest commitment to make cancer our top health care priority."

And then, pointing his finger over his shoulder at the Capitol, "Good God! What the hell are you waiting for?" The crowd roared in agreement.

It is often said that the first and last things people hear in a speech or at an event are the things best remembered. The historic march, Coming Together to Conquer Cancer, concluded with words and music from cancer survivor David Crosby and his longtime musical partner Graham Nash, as they performed their familiar "Teach Your Children." Released nearly thirty years earlier, the song's original focus was on the generation gap. But the words have taken on even greater meaning with the passage of time.

Chapter 15: Lost in Transition

In 2005, there are 10.8 million survivors in the United States.

When Ellen looked back on The March, her thoughts went to the initial vision of it that had come into her mind on a January day in 1997.

"I can recall the weather on the day it took hold, and with equal clarity, the similarity the weather bore to my disposition. It was very gray, dark, drizzly, and cold," she said in an *Oncology Times* editorial. "…After what seemed to be an unrelenting stream of phone calls and emails…that brought news of more diagnoses and more deaths from cancer, I thought to myself, 'How much good are we doing here?'

"…What distinguished that day from others was the fact that with these familiar feelings came a flood of memories and one phone call that planted the seed of The March…That call came from my friend and NCCS Board President, Betsy Clark, who was letting me know that her beloved sister, Eleanor, had died after years of suffering the diagnosis of multiple myeloma.

"All I could think of," Ellen said, "was 'too soon…no more.' It became a mantra."

The stark contrast between "gray, dark, drizzly, and cold," and the bright sunlight and heat of the actual day of The March, twenty-one months later, was almost as if the event itself had brought about the change in weather and spirits. The March had been spectacular on so many levels that, in the weeks and months afterward, it would have been easy for the hard-working NCCS survivorship advocates to exhale a collective, "Whew—we did it!"

The March had demanded that Congress approve doubling the NCI budget. The March had given birth to poignant new slogans like, "I found a cure for cancer: RESEARCH!" and "If you want to silence a killer, make some noise!" And The March had provided the setting for the Vice President of the United States—whose sister had died of lung cancer—to proclaim, "We want to be the generation that wins the war against cancer."

Ellen's vision had not been a march to cure, but a march for hope, building on that concept's importance in all NCCS work. The first question in those early post-March days, then, was whether the vision would reality. Part of it certainly did. Several days following The March, Congress voted for a 16 percent increase in funding for NIH. It was the largest increase to date, and part of a five-year plan that would eventually double the NIH budget. Some of that would trickle down to the NCI and the Office of Cancer Survivorship.

Two years earlier, Natalie Davis Spingarn had written words that provided the second post-March question:

"Our NCCS work is a new endeavor ... Our advocacy of patient interests and patient rights—in the hospital and clinic, the community and on the national scene—is a difficult, more subtle undertaking. If we do not undertake to lead it, who will?"

Rather than a jubilant exhale, then, all within the NCCS fold asked themselves, "If we do not keep The March momentum going, who will?" Thought had been given to that question even before the NCCS army had executed the historic event. Those thoughts became an article in the issue of the Networker newsletter immediately after The March. Titled "Now what? Next Steps in Your March against Cancer," it put recommendations into digestible bites.

The article began with steps a single person could take to prevent cancer and steps that would help them to understand a diagnosis. It then led readers to consider actions that could be taken at a community level. The article ended with what an ordinary person could do that would have an impact on a larger stage by educating local, state, and national elected officials about cancer survivorship. These were a slightly repackaged version of the types of advocacy Ellen had written about years earlier. Repeating them as often as possible followed the age-old advertising tip: the more times a person hears something, the more likely it is to sink in.

In the same Networker issue, Donna Doneski wrote a stirring perspective on the "what next" question:

The March was never intended as a day for the troops to march into Washington, DC, to cheer speeches and rhetoric of important leaders, and then in a week, to forget the reason we all came together.

That hit the bullseye they were all aiming at. Donna continued, referring to her own work in the lead up to The March:

For inspiration, I found myself reading the collected speeches of heroes like Robert F. Kennedy and Martin Luther King, Jr…Change, revolution, and activism were watchwords for the baby-boom generation. I'm a gen-Xer. But what I have learned from The March is that 'activism' is really moral courage. We must champion the issues facing survivors and their families now, for the same reason Robert F. Kennedy advocated for social change in the 1960s, "not because it is economically advantageous, although it is; not because the laws of God command it, although they do…We must do it for the single and fundamental reason that it is the right thing to do."

In the case of cancer survivorship, the "right thing" had many components. More money for cancer research would allow for more survivors. More programs and support for survivors would equate to better quality of life for them. Better quality of life for a population that was growing by more than half a million people each year would mean a healthier national economy as a result of fewer lost workdays and less cancer discrimination. And a healthier national economy was, of course, a win for the entire nation.

"I never look back to The March with regret," Ellen said later. "I think it pushed many of us to see what was possible for cancer advocacy. It's much more satisfying to work with others collegially than to work alone—and this was an important legacy of The March for those willing to learn it."

When asked about the achievements that grew from, or as a part of, The March, her answer was honest. "Very few cancer advocates are willing to take on the health care system. They want to eradicate cancer…it sells better…it's something people can understand…The cure we seek is not just for cancer itself, but for the health care system that finances and delivers that care, so that whatever we accomplish scientifically or medically will also be available to those who need it."

The tangible achievement associated with The March also had the greatest longevity: The Toolbox, which debuted at the Rays of Hope dinner. "The Toolbox is a breakthrough in self-advocacy," Susie said in post-March presentations. "It goes beyond the requisite disease information and actually teaches cancer survivors how to use this information in their own best interests." That was important for all survivors, and particularly for those who lived in small towns and rural areas without convenient access to the greater resources of large hospitals or cancer centers.

Susie merged this new theme with her other inspiring presentations, and took them on the road. From Allentown, Pennsylvania, to Racine, Wisconsin, and from Davenport, Iowa, to Palm Springs, California, she spoke to groups of oncology doctors and nurses, as well as survivors, introduced as a "nationally recognized survivorship consultant." It wasn't a surprise when NCI selected her—from a pool of 136 nominees—to become one of the first members of its Director's Consumer Liaison Group (DCLG). Brad Zebrack was also selected, the two joining thirteen other consumer advocates.

Eleanor Nealon, founder of the NCI's Office of Liaison Activities, had created the DCLG. She had begun her career at NCI in 1981 as a speechwriter, and was diagnosed with breast cancer two years later. (She would die of the disease in 1999.) Eleanor worked her way up to a director's position, and was a true friend of the survivorship movement. She was also one of the original "Everyday Heroes," recognized at the Rays of Hope dinner a few days before The March.

The DCLG pioneered the idea of including cancer survivors in the review of science and cancer research. Survivors also provided input around what, from a patient perspective, was important to improving the survivorship experience. This strong collaboration between NCI and the cancer advocacy community gave DCLG members the opportunity to participate in ways that were significant. For Brad, that included the establishment of the Consumer Advocates in Research and Related Activities (CARRA) program. CARRA was a staffed effort to identify, recruit, and prepare patient advocates to be involved as consultants in NCI activities.

Susie's DCLG work was to make site visits to NCI-designated cancer centers around the country. While many hospitals provided outstanding patient care, the NCI-recognized cancer centers were a breed all their own, and a part of Nixon's original National Cancer Act. They were required to meet rigorous standards for transdisciplinary, state-of-the-art research, as well as to deliver cutting-edge treatments to patients. (As of this writing in 2021, there are a total of seventy-one such cancer centers in thirty-six states and the District of Columbia.) In addition to the prestige of the designation, the centers also received NCI funding, and that's where Susie came in.

The centers were (and are) required to create massive, highly detailed reports on their research on a regular basis, in order to keep or renew their NCI grants. Committees of experts like Susie, from both inside and outside NCI, visited the centers, whereupon scientists and researchers presented their work in person and answered the experts' questions. As cancer advocacy groups became more prominent, NCI felt a patient advocate was an important addition for the two-day site visits. And Susie was a perfect choice, with her knowledge of cancer from both sides of the hospital bed and a flexible schedule that allowed her to travel the country.

Like pieces of a jigsaw puzzle fitting together, it is striking the way each of the movement's major players connect. Each came with his or her personal skills and personal relationship with cancer. None of them had planned a future in advocacy as they trooped through their individual treatments, or watched those they loved do so. But the rich portrait they created as an ensemble was more than the sum of their individual parts.

Susie's passion for long-term survivorship issues, was matched by Ellen's volunteering heritage and impressive contact list of Washington insiders and media power brokers. Added to that was her passion for advocacy and her ability to not only never take no for an answer, but to also be able to turn the no into a yes, with a little persuasion and a smile. She was equally comfortable speaking to survivors on the telephone in her office and testifying before Congressional committees.

Although by this time Fitz had stepped down from the board to be, as he put it, "an ordinary NCCS citizen," his ability to clearly articulate all that survivorship entailed had been the movement's foundation. He continued writing survivorship articles in his engaging and inimitable style. Betsy, whose board presidency was coming to a close, provided eloquent speeches and writing on the topic of hope, one of the foundational pillars of the survivorship movement. Her work brought a comforting aspect to the challenges survivors faced.

Barbara tirelessly worked within the legal system to fight survivor discrimination, including in the areas of employment, insurance, and now medical leave. The laws she advocated for or against made certain that survivors' rights as citizens and humans were respected. Still growing like a grapevine—although now a much sturdier one—the NCCS projects expanded to include the medically underserved; bringing in the family; chronic pain; chronic fatigue; and death, dying, and grief. As had been the theme of the 1994 assembly, their work was all about quality "for" life for their fellow survivors. It was never an easy job.

The phrase attributed to Hannibal of Carthage as he crossed the Alps in 219 B.C. could easily be applied to the survivorship movement: "We will either find a way, or make one." And those affiliated with NCCS were certainly up to the challenge.

It was unseasonably balmy as dusk deepened into darkness on Saturday, September 25, 1999. The crowd on the steps of the Lincoln Memorial had begun to grow. Emblazoned against the monument were the fifteen-foot-high golden letters that spelled out H-O-P-E. By the time night descended, NCCS's second annual Rays of Hope candlelight vigil was underway. A crowd of 20,000 gathered, with newsman Sam Donaldson again emceeing. He opened the event with a video retrospective highlighting moments from The March the year before.

This vigil placed special emphasis on childhood cancer survivors. Donaldson introduced ten of them, who were joined by WNBA Washington Mystics star Nikki McCray. Her words about the courage and inspiration the young survivors exhibited would become more personal in the future. (Nikki's mother would be diagnosed with breast cancer in 2007 and die of a recurrence in 2018. Nikki herself would be diagnosed with the same disease in 2012.)

Next came a taped message from Vice President Gore, affirming his support for doubling cancer research funding. Once again, Sidney Kimmel, the champion of The March and the previous Rays of Hope vigil—both financially and verbally—told the gathered throng, "We are here—and we will continue to be here—until cancer no longer plagues our world." He ended by asking, "Mr. President, can't you hear us?"

Then, NCI director Dr. Richard Klausner introduced the event's Honorary Chair, Her Majesty Queen Noor of Jordan. Together with her daughter, Princess Iman, the queen lit the Candle of Hope in honor of her husband, King Hussein, who had died in February. A single, soulful violin played "Amazing Grace," hovering in the night air. Then a reluctant speaker took the stage. The words of Johnathan Stovall, Ellen's son, moved the crowd as he expressed his wish that no child should ever know the pain of having a parent with cancer. Then those on stage and off committed themselves to standing vigilant in their quest to end the suffering. And they promised one another to return the following year.

They did, on September 23, 2000, gathering again on the steps of the Lincoln Memorial.

It was only when a new kind of cancer—terrorism—invaded the nation's capital the next year that the event was cancelled. The 2001 Rays of Hope vigil was to have been held at the Ellipse, a part of the President's Park, just half a mile south of the White House. NCCS had planned to begin the vigil set-up on September 12. But the sunny morning before, all of America was horrified when two hijacked jets hit the Twin Towers in New York City. Thirty minutes later, another jet slammed into the Pentagon. And a half an hour after that, a fourth jet crashed into a field southeast of Pittsburgh. Its target is believed to have been either the Capitol or the White House.

This new day that would "live in infamy" (as President Roosevelt described December 7, 1941, when Japanese forces attacked the America naval base at Pearl Harbor) had a complicated impact on the War on Cancer. After September 11, 2001, the nation's attention was understandably focused on finding and destroying those who perpetrated the attacks, as well as constructing preventative measures against future attacks. But some of the troops in the cancer trenches were concerned about its impact on their fight. In the October 2001 issue of *The Oncologist*, NCI Clinical Director Dr. Gregory Curt expressed it well.

On Tuesday, September 11, 2001, America was diagnosed with a serious cancer. Worse, the disease is not local, or even loco-regional. Rather, it was already advanced at the time of detection.

This was not the first time that cancer and military language had crossed their respective borders. "'Cells,'" Dr. Curt went on, "which have often lived in apparent harmony with their neighbors for years, are 'activated' by an unknown and unheard 'signal.' The signal is only clear to the cells destined to develop malignant behavior, and this signal sets off a series of apparently irreversible events."

He was, of course, speaking of cancer cells, although it was identical verbiage to what was being used to explain the 9/11 chain of events. Dr. Curt ended his cleverly crafted piece with this hope: "During these difficulties, oncologists should not lose their sense of the importance of the War on Cancer. Cancer is to the patient and their family what terrorism is to a free society, a deeply personal threat that must be overcome."

Those not in white coats were also concerned about reduced attention to cancer research. In a December 2, 2001, letter to the editor in the St. George, Utah, *Daily Spectrum*, a cancer survivor wrote, "While we continue to grapple with the unconscionable issues of terrorism, we must ensure that we keep our eye on the imperatives of another battle—our nation's war against cancer."

In addition to the problem of sharing the sense of urgency directed toward fighting terrorism and other diseases, the war on cancer's bigger problem was measuring successful advances. On the thirtieth anniversary of Nixon's "Christmas Gift to the Nation," December 23, 2001, an article titled "After 30 Years, War on Cancer Is a Draw" listed conflicting statistics.

"The cost, in terms of deaths and dollars, is staggering," it read. Half of the men and a third of the women in the country would be diagnosed in their lifetimes. "One-fourth of all Americans will die from cancer," the article reported. "The overall rate of death from cancer is as high today as it was 30 years ago."

The few bright spots in this article came from NCI. Testicular cancer and Hodgkin's lymphoma (the name had changed some years earlier) death rates had dropped nearly 70 percent. Breast cancer deaths had dropped 14 percent, and death rates from seven other cancers were down as well. But for so many participants of the war—fighting on both sides of the hospital bed—the mission was still unaccomplished.

Other newspaper articles expressed similar disappointments.

"The 'war on cancer' is 30 years old today. Total victory is nowhere in sight. The cost, in terms of deaths and dollars, is staggering."

"Since President Nixon signed the National Cancer Act into law, more than 12 million Americans have died from cancer."

"The government has spent more than $45 billion on cancer research."

"While medical science has conquered other diseases, 'the big C' is still very much with us."

Perhaps saddest of all, and despite scientific evidence to the contrary, Americans still clung to the suggestion that Nixon had made thirty years earlier: cancer is curable. They hoped and expected, as Mary Lasker had proclaimed, that a simple pill would make it all go away. And they were frustrated that that lofty goal hadn't been reached.

In 1996, when President Clinton created the Office of Cancer Survivorship (OCS)—due in large part to the success of the NCCS congress a few months earlier and the white paper that came out of it—its assignment was clear and welcomed in the survivorship community: "To enhance the quality and length of survival of all persons diagnosed with cancer and to minimize or stabilize adverse effects experienced during cancer survivorship."

The OCS's first Request for Proposal (a call for research projects they might fund) was issued in September 1997. The inaugural grant applicants based their proposal and its ensuing work on "Long-Term Cancer Survivors: Research Initiatives." Susie's dream of survivorship research was finally coming to fruition. And because

OCS was a part of NIH, who included women and minorities in all its supported research projects, those groups also had to be included in other OCS grant recipients' work as well. That meant that the issue of quality of life for all survivor groups—regardless of who they were or where they were—would be brought to the forefront.

Another first for OCS occurred a few years later. Dr. Anna Meadows had been highly successful as the inaugural acting director. The time had now come to select a full-time director. They were big shoes to fill, but Dr. Julia Rowland stepped into the office in September 1999. As a former NCCS board member, and a highly respected psycho-oncology professor, she was the perfect pick.

"This office and this science is where the heart of the institute is," Julia remembered fifteen years later, "because it's all about the people who were touched by cancer and its treatment... What happens to them after cancer? We're trying to figure out what that impact is, and prevent adverse outcomes or mitigate them when they happen."

She spoke about the "lovely Rose Garden ceremony" establishing the office. "There's a great picture of [President Bill] Clinton signing the Ribbon of Hope. Ellen Stovall is there, Rick Klausner is there. It's a picture I have and I often want to trot it out for new NCI directors and say, 'See, we have this signed document. Make sure we're putting monies into the office!'"

Julia guided OCS with an eye to their five survivorship research goals: collecting information from current survivors to help guide future survivors' treatment decisions down the road; tailoring therapies to maximize benefit, while minimizing long-term adverse effects; sharing information about evidence-based interventions to reduce future diagnoses; improving the quality of care while controlling the costs; and equipping the next generation of physicians, nurses, and other health care professionals to, as Julia so eloquently put it, "...provide not just the science, but also the art of comprehensive cancer medicine."

She added that she felt her job was, "a deeply humbling and privileged position."

As the new year and the new century approached, the NCCS leadership realized it was time for them to reinvigorate the membership program, supplying each member with a library of the most popular NCCS publications and resources. The office itself would be relocating to an entire floor in their building, as opposed to rooms scattered across several floors. The most bittersweet of the millennium makeovers was the announcement that the much-cherished paper version of the Networker would be retired. Its replacement would come in the form of a weekly email, promising to cover survivorship issues like clinical trials and end-of-life decision-making.

Some things, however, would not spring into the new millennium with a fresh image. Despite all the medical advancements that had been made in oncology since the birth of NCCS thirteen years earlier, and despite the organization making great strides in the lives of the nation's millions of survivors, shadows remained. True, cancer survivors were no longer routinely shunned or discriminated against, although examples of both occasionally raised their ugly heads. Nonetheless, patients with cancer now dwelled in perhaps the worst kind of existence: indifference. It was a new demon of survivorship to add to the list. As Ellen had said several years earlier, survivorship "is one of those issues that make people yawn." Once finding them threatening and frightening, the healthy public had now come to take cancer survivors for granted, rarely understanding the threatening sword of Damocles hanging over them. After all, they had survived, hadn't they? And so had returned to their normal lives.

But cancer survivors' lives were anything but normal. Susie made that point clear in an interview for an international newsletter. "Obviously, it is good news that earlier diagnosis and better treatments are improving survival. The not-so-good news is that increased longevity increases our chances to develop other cancers and aftereffects from treatments."

Susie had firsthand knowledge of that last statement, a trend that also extended to her close survivor friends as well. For example, in addition to her lymphoma, Susie had had breast and bladder diagnoses since her original treatment, Ellen Stovall had experienced a 1983 recurrence of Hodgkin's lymphoma. Since Natalie Davis Spingarn's first diagnosis of metastatic breast cancer in 1974, she'd had multiple recurrences in her spine, hip, and other breast. Cancer had really "piled on" in Natalie's family. Her grandmother died of the disease, her two sisters had breast cancer (one had died of pancreatic cancer), and one of her two sons was a lymphoma survivor.

Natalie's cancer experiences, and her love of NCCS, led her to write her third book, *The New Cancer Survivors: Living with Grace, Fighting with Spirit*, published in 1999. In it, the dedication speaks to the NCCS vision of veterans and rookies: "For my fellow survivors, past, present future: 'Be strong. Be strong and let us strengthen one another'—adapted from II Samuel 10:12 and I Chronicles 19:13."

On a rainy, late-October night, more than 100 people showed up for Natalie's book-signing party at the Monocle, a well-known Capitol Hill watering hole on D Street. Of course, it didn't hurt that the party host was Connecticut Senator Joe Lieberman. He entertained the standing-room-only crowd with stories of coming to the city as a young intern, and being tutored on the ways of Washington by Natalie.

Seven months later, after being diagnosed with pancreatic cancer, Natalie succumbed to the disease she had fought for a quarter of a century. Soon afterward, Senator Lieberman gave this tribute on the floor of the US Senate. His words reflected the heaviness in the hearts of all who had known Natalie.

"Mr. President, on June 6, 2000, we lost a very courageous, brilliant, and dedicated American, Natalie Davis Spingarn. A noted writer, public servant, and leading advocate for cancer patients, Natalie was also a good friend who I miss greatly...she lived her life with purpose, grace, and humor."

It was 2004's must-wear fashion accessory: a yellow silicone gel wristband, inscribed "LIVESTRONG." It wasn't the first time adornments were used to create attention. Among the yellow bracelet's predecessors were ribbons in various colors given to European knights during the Middle Ages, ribbons tied around trees in support of the American embassy personnel held during the 1979 Iran hostage crisis, and the pink ribbons that first debuted on behalf of breast cancer in 1992. But this little yellow bracelet was an entirely different animal, and represented a stroke of marketing genius.

Here's what happened: On October 2, 1996, twenty-five-year-old American cyclist Lance Armstrong was diagnosed with Stage III testicular cancer. It had spread to his abdomen, lungs, and brain. Surgery removed the testicle, and it was followed by a rigorous twelve-week chemotherapy regimen. Armstrong vowed to return to racing. He did that and more. In 1997, he created the Lance Armstrong Foundation to raise awareness of symptoms and treatment for testicular cancer. The foundation's mission evolved two years later with a new focus on cancer survivorship, specifically the practical psychosocial needs of those affected by the disease.

To raise awareness and reach a $5 million fundraising goal for Armstrong's foundation, in May 2004, sports apparel giant Nike produced five million of the bright yellow bracelets and sold them for $1 apiece. The color of the bracelet was significant. The winner of the world's most famous—and grueling—bike race, the Tour de France, is given a yellow jersey, known as the *maillot jaune*. It is the world's biggest annual sporting event and nearly 200 cyclists race over 2,000 miles in just 23 days up hill and down dale. Armstrong had won it five times and would go on to win it another two, for a record seven *maillots jaunes*.

With the bracelets gracing the wrists of former President Bill Clinton, actors Ben Affleck and Gwyneth Paltrow (who lost her father to cancer), tennis champion Serena Williams, and even Armstrong's Italian biking rival Ivan Basso (whose mother was battling pancreatic cancer at the time), they were gone in ninety days. So Nike produced six million more, half of which were gone by early August.

While it is true that Armstrong's athletic career ended unhappily, what is less well known is the powerful message he, and his yellow bracelets, broadcast. "Young people with cancer should be empowered to fight hard, dream big and live strong," he had said when the bracelets debuted. In much the same way as Brad Zebrack had done with his 1988 bike trip to raise funds for NCCS, Armstrong was sending a message that cancer isn't just a disease of the elderly. It can be survived, and survivors can realize full and meaningful lives. Lance Armstrong became an important icon of what cancer survivorship could look like. Despite his later failings, he nevertheless forged a wide path, not only for cancer awareness, but for survivorship awareness.

Like all long-term survivors, Susie was sympathetic to the newly diagnosed. She also realized those cancer patients would join her and the legions of survivors for whom the future was filled with hundreds of question marks once treatment had ended. "How will we know if our cancer comes back? How do we learn to monitor our health? How do we live with the fear and uncertainty? Who will oversee our follow-up care? When will guidelines be developed so that non-oncology practitioners will know what to look for when our care is returned to them? Who will pay for this type of continued follow-up?"

In the article she wrote listing these questions, she astutely observed, "While the questions are many, the answers are, unfortunately, few."

Enter the Institute of Medicine (IOM). Established in 1970, it is a nonprofit component of the National Academy of Sciences, working outside the framework of government to provide evidence-based research and recommendations for public health and science policy. It was the IOM that established the National Cancer Policy Board in 1997, of which NCCS was a member.

An idea to embark on a major study of cancer survivorship had been shepherded by Ellen, who served as chairwoman of the Policy Board's Committee on Cancer Survivorship. The board's first published work, *Ensuring Quality Cancer Care*, was released in 1999. It focused primarily on treatment, but noted that survivorship issues needed attention. Given the intimidating scope of the topic of survivorship, the board created three reports.

While some approach monumental tasks by tackling the most challenging first, the IOM went in the opposite direction. Its first report, in 2003, addressed survivorship in childhood cancers, a subject on which significant research had already been done and the one that was supported by the greatest amount of advocacy. The second report, a year later, addressed, exclusively, the psychosocial needs of female breast cancer survivors. That group, too, had been well studied, providing a great deal of already published material.

When the third report, *From Cancer Patient to Cancer Survivor: Lost in Transition*, was finally published on November 7, 2005, it became clear why it took the IOM nearly three years to construct it. The title was the clue. Survivors were, indeed, often lost and forgotten as they transitioned from "patient" to "non-patient." The latter group comprised both those who were declared "free of disease," and those who had been told they had to live with their cancer.

The report's introduction stated some somber statistics. "The ranks of cancer survivors in the United States are 10 million strong and growing... Half of all men and one-third of women in the United States will develop cancer in their lifetime... Today, one in 30 Americans has a history of cancer, and among those 65 and older, the figure is one in 7."

Clearly, a program had to be created for a group whose numbers were now larger than the populations of many of the world's nations.

Within the 534 pages, the most dazzling voices from the survivorship movement could be heard. NCCS founding member Patti

Ganz was one of the editors, and Ellen served as vice chair of the committee. Susie was a member of the review committee, and she, Julia Rowland, and Barbara Hoffman were also thanked in the acknowledgments and for their commitment "to improving the lives of cancer survivors."

The Executive Summary outlined ten recommendations, all of which NCCS had worked toward for nearly twenty years, including the development of private and public partnerships, coordination of government organizations, ending discrimination against survivors, and assuring access to health insurance. But of the ten, the most important recommendations were the first two.

"Recommendation 1: Health care providers, patient advocates, and other stakeholders should work to raise awareness of the needs of cancer survivors, establish cancer survivorship as a distinct phase of cancer care, and act to ensure the delivery of appropriate survivorship care."

Then, as now, there was plenty of awareness of cancer's existence. Pink ribbons (the other colors hadn't fully caught on yet), celebrity testimonials, and national and grassroots organizations had seen to that. It was now survivorship's turn. While Lance Armstrong's yellow wristbands floated the first national balloon to bring awareness to survivorship, the purpose of Lost in Transition was to raise that awareness, encompassing the medical, functional, and psychosocial consequences of cancer and its treatment.

The recognition of cancer survivorship as a distinct phase of the cancer trajectory was not enough, however. The report was a battle cry for a new strategy for the ongoing clinical care of survivors. And that led to the second recommendation.

"Recommendation 2: Patients completing primary treatment should be provided with a comprehensive care summary and follow-up plan that is clearly and effectively explained. This 'Survivorship Care Plan' should be written by the principal provider(s) who coordinated oncology treatment. This service should be reimbursed by third-party payors of health care."

While they were exciting in concept, implementing the Survivorship Care Plans (SCP) was challenging. A consistent template to be used nationwide would be best, but it needed to be agreed upon by many. The plans would require multiple languages (consider just the number of Native American languages still in use today) and had to include information that could be understood by different cultures and regions across the country. Implementation would be far easier in larger cities than in the vast rural areas. Who would head up that challenge?

Obviously, the report introduced big topics that required big discussions. The first of those discussions began the day after Lost in Transition was released, when the IOM and ASCO (with additional support from NCCS) presented a one-day symposium. Held at the National Academy of Sciences building on Constitution Avenue in Washington, DC, the symposium would further disseminate the conclusions and recommendations of the report. Fitz (now Professor of Medicine and Health Policy at George Washington University), Ellen, Patti Ganz, and Susie were present, each playing a part in the conversation.

"It is a monumental piece of work," Fitz began the morning's plenary session. "... it takes issues that many of us have been grappling with for many years in happily lessening obscurity, but obscurity to begin with, and puts them between two hard covers and out into the public policy stream in a far more potent way than has ever happened before. So, it is terrific. The survivorship care plan concept," he continued, "an individualized roadmap for each survivor, ought to be part of what we do clinically, and what people in survivorship encounter. It is terribly important."

Soon afterward, Ellen spoke of the goals of those involved in creating the report. "The charge to the committee was to raise awareness of the consequences of cancer, to define quality care and outline strategies to achieve it, and to recommend policies to improve care and quality of life ... Simply and most importantly, we recommended that awareness of the needs of cancer survivors be raised; that cancer survivorship be established as a distinct phase of cancer care; and that responsible parties act to ensure the delivery of appropriate survivorship care."

Patti began her contribution to the symposium with enthusiasm. "I was one of the founding members of the National Coalition for Cancer Survivorship. When Fitz Mullan invited me to go to that small meeting in Albuquerque, I did not know it would lead to this. So, it is really exciting to be here today." Her presentation was an explanation of the concept of SCPs and what they should include: diagnosis and treatment details; expected short- and long-term effects; surveillance for recurrence or secondary cancers; psychosocial and vocational needs; and recommended preventative behaviors and interventions.

Patti moderated an afternoon breakout session titled "Developing and Testing Models of Survivorship Care." Even though Susie would later refer to Lost in Transition as the "big bang" for survivorship, the "bang" has faded and this all-important component is nonexistent for most who are still "lost in transition."

Two years later, in 2007, Patti edited another book: *Cancer Survivorship: Today and Tomorrow*. She dedicated it to the founding members of NCCS, saying, "We have learned a lot about cancer survivorship, but there is much more to discover." As would be expected, Susie authored a chapter from a nursing perspective. In speaking about attention to cancer survivorship, she said, "The tide is finally turning. My question remains, 'Why has it taken so long?'"

She went on:

> But hope is on the horizon. The book *The Tipping Point* [published in 2002 by Malcom Gladwell] is about a theory of social epidemics. It discusses the moment of critical mass, the boiling point when an idea or trend finally explodes and spreads to the masses ... So, maybe it is a critical mass of multiple exposures that have been building over the past three decades. Advocates, activists, physicians, researchers, social workers, mental health specialists, public policy makers, mayors—and of course, nurses—are all working together to help us survive survivorship. But our work has just begun.

Chapter 16: Helping Is Healing

In 2011, there are more than 11 million survivors in America, with another 1.6 million to be diagnosed that year.

The human heart beats 100,000 times per day, moving 2,000 gallons of blood. In a lifetime, those numbers leap to 2.5 billion beats, and one million barrels of blood. The heart is a vital, powerful, and miraculous machine. But it is *not* indestructible.

A 1967 "Medicine and You" newspaper column included a four-sentence description of something new for cancer survivors to consider. "The frequency of radiation-induced heart disease is probably more common than hitherto suspected, say medical investigators at Stanford School of Medicine."

This was eleven years after Dr. Henry Kaplan (also at Stanford) had begun successful radiation treatment with his linear accelerator of various cancers, including Hodgkin's lymphoma. "The significance of recognizing the complication," the article continued, "…is that doctors then are in a position to begin treatment of the complication."

There are three errors in that little piece. First, the "complication" typically doesn't show up immediately, as one would assume from the article. Second, doctors being aware of potential side effects of cancer treatment and communicating them to patients are two very different ends of the spectrum. This was at a time, you may recall, when doctors weren't keen to tell patients they had cancer in the first place, let alone that there was a "complication." Last, the 1960s-era medical community was anxious to land on treatments that extended cancer patients' lives. Radiation was turning a *sometimes* survivable disease into a *more likely* survivable disease. Spreading concern about side effects could persuade patients to decline treatment altogether.

A year later, another small blurb mentioned a potential problem with radiation treatment. "Although most cases of radiation-induced heart disease are mild and easily treated, severe cases occasionally appear among patients receiving very high radiation doses in the vicinity of the heart."

We now know this message, too, was erroneous. The radiation dosage level of the 1960s and '70s, whether considered "high" or not, required a significant number of sessions to move the needle in eradicating the patient's cancer. More sessions meant more total radiation exposure, and thus more potential damage to the heart. Many of those radiated in the chest area for Hodgkin's lymphoma and breast cancer during that era would find themselves, decades later, in the crosshairs of another terrifying demon of survivorship: long-term effects of previous treatments. Ellen Stovall was one of them.

Long-term issues which may seem "mild and easily treated," as the writer suggested, can become severe as time goes on. And it's been more than "occasional." Those treated with the early lifesaving radiation are thrilled to be alive. But the cost has been great.

In 2010, Ellen wrote in the forward to the book *Cancer Symptom Science*, "I was diagnosed with significant coronary vessel and valve damage, concluded to be consequential to radiation exposure." The Cobalt-60 machine that had saved her life in 1972 had now complicated it. But Ellen was encouraged that the tide was turning when it came to paying attention to those complications.

She continued:

Cancer... Symptom... Science. Simply reading the three words grouped together in the title of this book signals that we have indeed entered a new age in the way we will consider how to treat a person diagnosed with cancer…As this book [*Cancer Symptom Science*] so importantly points out, we now know how to measure the severity of symptoms that wreak havoc with a cancer patient's recovery.

Ellen also spoke of the painful neuropathy in her hands and feet, caused by the chemotherapy she received for her 1983 Hodgkin's recurrence. An accomplished pianist, she was never able to play at the same level after that treatment, although she kept her grand piano at the ready should her neuropathy abate. Then, not long after her heart disease was diagnosed, the other shoe dropped. Ellen was diagnosed with bilateral breast cancer, also most likely radiation-induced. A double mastectomy followed.

Of course, Susie was no stranger to fallout from early treatment, either. It was most probably the cause of her 1991 breast cancer. "For years, no one paid much attention to the continuing struggles that plagued cancer survivors," she told an interviewer. "Simply keeping patients alive for longer periods of time was major progress, especially since cancer had such a grim history."

Long-term survivors are truly the canaries in the coal mine, able to alert the medical community about what to watch for. But two years after *Lost in Transition* had called for SCPs, there was still no standardized survivor follow-up protocol in place. The lack of movement on that front took those involved with NCCS to a new level in frustration. Ellen's words spoke for them all: "Just because people are surviving isn't sufficient."

The last chapter in the 2007 book, *Cancer Survivorship: Today and Tomorrow* is titled "The Survivorship Care Plan: What, Why, How and for Whom." Building on the information in *Lost in Transition*, Patti, along with three other authors, clearly answered each of the subtitle's questions. "Most oncologists," they wrote, "focus on surveillance for recurrent cancer after primary treatment, but it is important to recognize that surveillance may also need to be considered for new primary cancers in the same organ, or for secondary cancers or treatment-induced late effects."

The authors continued by outlining three main reasons for the plans, the first being to communicate more easily with other oncology and non-oncology providers about a patient's care. Second, they suggested that these plans would also facilitate communication with the survivors. Patients would be calmed by the notion that their primary care physician had at his or her fingertips a document of what their treatment had been, what toxicities and other issues they might have developed during treatment, *and* a list of any red flags to be watched for in their particular case. Last, "having an explicit document that initially describes the treatment plan and follows with the treatment summary and survivorship care plan facilitates ongoing monitoring of quality of care."

Those points certainly zeroed in on the "what" and "why." The "how" was a different story. The authors acknowledged that "practically speaking, a formal survivorship care plan will take some time to implement and make a routine part of oncology care." But this is probably the most crucial "how" statement: "Changing the culture of medical records documentation will not be easy and, ultimately, will only be successful if it is linked to reimbursement and requirements from health care payors." And therein lies the rub.

In early 2007, the pooled knowledge, relationships, and resources of WellPoint, UCLA, NCCS, and pharmaceutical company Genentech formed the Journey Forward program, with a goal "to provide efficient ways to facilitate and simplify communication between doctors, clinicians, and survivors." Using ASCO's surveillance guidelines, and treatment plan and summary templates, the collaborative developed the Survivorship Care Plan Builder. ASCO later convened a special task force to refine its standards, and LIVEStrong created an SCP template as well.

But implementation of the SCPs stumbled on many barriers. On the provider and system side there were the financial questions described above, along with limited time and human resources to fill out the SCPs. Plus, there had been no large, randomized controlled trials on the effectiveness of the plans. Decisions in health care are nearly always based on evidence. No evidence means no decision.

On the patient side of things, there were a number of barriers as well. As previously mentioned, translation into multiple languages would have to be considered. Who would be in possession of the SCPs, the patient or their doctor? But the most substantial barrier was this: While an SCP would certainly assuage a survivor's feeling of "free fall" when released from acute or active treatment, most survivors had little to no awareness of the possibility of such a document. There was scarcely any press about them, and if physicians (primary care or oncologists) were familiar with SCPs, that information was often not paramount on the list of things to cover during an office visit. Consequently, survivors didn't even know to ask for one.

In 2010, NCCS became one of three patient-centered organizations invited to membership in the Commission on Cancer (CoC), part of the American College of Surgeons. The result of that membership was the creation of the first-ever patient-centered CoC Accreditation Standards, in 2013. Those included a CoC mandate that SCPs be prepared by the principal oncology provider and delivered to patients at the completion of treatment. Aggressive deadlines were set for this to happen at all CoC-accredited cancer programs across the county. The deadlines were revised, then revised again, and finally shelved, as the difficulties of SCP implementation have yet to be resolved.

When the new millennium dawned, Ellen's NCCS title changed from executive director to president and CEO. The organization was still on "full speed ahead" when it came to inventive programs that would help further their mission. In 2004, they launched a new program, "Cancer Advocacy Now!" Advocates from across the country who were interested in putting their self-advocacy skills to work to change cancer policy were asked to participate, giving them a voice in advocating for quality cancer care. The same year, NCCS expanded its definition of who a survivor is. In a *Journal of the National Cancer Institute* article, Ellen explained that because so many people are "touched by cancer," the NCCS definition of the term also included families and caregivers of cancer patients.

As a survivor and advocate, Ellen's dedication to her work often caused her sleepless nights. "Some days, she'd come in with a beautiful manicure," Donna Doneski explained. "I'd ask her if she had been able to sleep the night before. She'd say, 'Nope!' and we'd laugh. When her mind wouldn't rest, she'd do her nails, rearrange her cupboards, anything to make herself tired."

But after the cardiac issues and breast cancer, compounded by concern for her father (her mother had died in 2003), Ellen decided it was time to step away from her executive role at NCCS. However, she could not step away from the organization. She served as acting president in between others who had been hired for her position and then didn't fit. Finally, in 2011, Ellen slipped into a new NCCS role—senior health policy advisor.

It was perfect for her. She still participated in NCCS events, was still quoted in newspapers and asked to speak around the country. But the new position was without the everyday pressures, and it gave her more free time. She told the *Washington Post* that cancer had given her more of a spirit of adventure. "I am not as cautious," she said. "I could walk out on the street and get hit by the Number 52 bus. I am probably going to die of cancer, but maybe not. So why not try some things?"

In her new role, Ellen helped guide the passage of the Comprehensive Cancer Care Improvement Act. The act became law in February 2012, but Ellen explained its contents in a May 2008 ASCO publication:

> To further encourage care planning, NCCS and ASCO also support the Comprehensive Cancer Care Improvement Act, which includes a number of proposals that would advance a system of integrated cancer care and improved

communication between patients and their health care teams regarding treatment options and follow-up care.

By reforming Medicare reimbursement, enhancing training of professionals who treat cancer survivors, and testing and expanding model systems of integrated care, the Act would advance a system of quality, comprehensive cancer care.

This act was yet another monumental NCCS achievement in improving the lives of cancer survivors.

December 23, 2011: "Bombs rock Baghdad," claimed the *Arizona Daily Star.* "House Ready to OK Tax Bill," shouted the *Baltimore Sun.* "Win No. 2 Puts No. 1 Pick at Risk," pronounced the *Indianapolis Star.* The latter was a reference to the Indianapolis Colts' unexpected 19–16 win against the Houston Texans, which might have affected their first-place draft pick.

On that day, however, only a sprinkling of mentions appeared in any American newspaper about the fortieth anniversary of the war on cancer. It wasn't that the country hadn't been behind President Nixon's desire to cure cancer when he signed the National Cancer Act, proclaiming, "It is my hope that history would look back on this as being the most significant action taken during this administration." But in 2011, *Time* magazine health writer Alice Park wisely observed, "The disease that doctors thought they knew then is very different from the cancer they're studying today." Such a true statement, and perhaps an explanation of why the heady idea of curing this frightening disease had been replaced with slower, more methodical research.

Park quotes Dr. William Dalton, then-president and CEO of Tampa's Moffitt Cancer Center and Research Institute. "In the haste to continue research and fund it, you sometimes need to stop and turn around and look back at what we've accomplished. The reduction in death rates of many common cancers that has occurred over the last 40 years is incredible. That's important because that's huge progress against something that is probably the biggest health scare for any society."

And what did people see when they turned around and looked back? In 1991 (the twentieth anniversary year of the war on cancer), University of California, Berkeley professor and researcher Dr. Mary-Claire King and her team discovered the BRCA gene mutation. (The mutation's name is derived from the first two letters of "breast" and "cancer.") BRCA was the first cancer-related mutation to be found; there are now more than fifty. Testing for these mutations allows individuals and their doctors to be more vigilant about what their medical future holds. And vigilance, as we've seen, is crucial for survivors' quality of life.

The year prior to Dr. King's discovery, the Human Genome Project was launched with the objective of determining the DNA sequence of the entire human genome. Despite much wrangling between private corporations and governmental agencies, the project was declared complete on April 14, 2003. That, in turn, paved the way for The Cancer Genome Atlas (TCGA) project, begun in 2005. It was a joint effort of NCI and the National Human Genome Research Institute, with a goal of mapping the genetic makeup and variation of various types of cancer. It achieved that goal and more, transforming our understanding of the disease. And that, in turn, has aided researchers and doctors to better target a patient's treatment, based not just on the type of cancer they have, but on their cancer's specific genetic makeup. By the end of 2011, TCGA had made access to their data available to anyone, anywhere, via an online portal.

Another leap forward involved the human immune system. We have known for some time that it exists to conduct biological warfare on bacteria, viruses, and parasites. Doctors have used it as a trusted ally in health for centuries by vaccinating the population against deadly diseases. Then, in 2010, the FDA approved the first immunotherapy vaccine to combat cancer. The vaccine stimulates the natural defenses of the immune system so it works harder and smarter to find and attack cancer cells. Although immunotherapy seems to be more effective for some types of cancer than for others, it has proven to be an exciting weapon in the war.

American writer and biochemistry professor Isaac Asimov once observed, "The most exciting phrase to hear in science, the one that heralds new discoveries, is not 'Eureka!' but 'That's funny….'" While early troops in the war on cancer had hoped for more "eurekas" than they actually heard, the numbers of survivors continued to climb. More lives being saved was a good thing, and would keep NCCS busy for a long time.

As Susie pointed out in an interview in 2010, "Survivorship is the success story of oncology. We now have long-term survivors whom we have to care for."

In 2011, ONS published *Cancer Rehabilitation and Survivorship*. Susie was asked to write a chapter, which she did, titling it "From Anecdote to Evidence: The Survivor's Perspective." She admitted to always struggling "with the decision to include my cancer history within my writing as anecdotal accounts are usually considered 'unprofessional' in an academic sense." And yet, she wrote, "it is from these experiences that I have been able to make contributions to my chosen profession of oncology nursing."

Among those observations are seven important suggestions for her fellow oncology nurses. First, "Celebrate but With a Dose of Reality." The excitement of finishing treatment is sometimes only experienced by the medical staff. "…many survivors leave the clinic, sit in their cars, have panic attacks, and wonder 'What do I do now?'" Second, "Complete a Treatment Summary." These are a part of an SCP, but focus solely on the treatment aspect of care. She observed, "Hopefully, most survivors will soon have one of these important documents." Next, "Prepare Us to Leave Our Safety Net." She voiced what nearly all survivors feel. "It can be frightening to think about returning to primary care providers who may not know how to care for us, or know how to identify possible treatment-related problems."

That was dealt with in her next point: "Encourage Survivorship Care Plans." While the treatment summary is a static report, the survivorship care plan is an ever-changing, living document. Fifth, "Honor Our 'Labels.'" Some love the label of survivor, but as she pointed out, "If we prefer to call ourselves thrivers, victors, warriors, activists, cancer killers, or simply cancer patients, honor how individuals view themselves."

Sixth, "Look Outside the (Evidence-Based) Box." As discussed earlier, it was lack of evidence that was slowing the SCPs. Simply, Susie said, "Since there are few evidence-based guidelines that direct survivorship care, we can no longer use this lack of evidence to ignore appropriate follow-up." And finally, "Value Our Stories." Susie explained, "Storytelling is how we find meaning through our suffering ... Survivors continue to be guides to the unknowns."

Her speaking calendar remained full, including dates for Arizona Oncology, ONS, and Genentech, providing case managers of the latter survivorship education. But she was beginning to notice a difficulty in projecting when she spoke. And it was getting worse. She was scheduled to deliver the Mara Mogensen Flaherty Lecture at the ONS congress in May 2014. An annual and prestigious congress lecture since 1981, speakers addressed topics related to the psychosocial aspects of cancer diagnosis, treatment, and care. Susie certainly qualified. Being selected to address the entire congress assemblage was a huge honor and she wanted to be in top shape. So, she consulted a laryngologist and speech therapist.

Susie's presentation was titled "My Glass Half Full Keeps Spilling." That title was extremely prophetic given the laryngologist's assessment of Susie's problem: one of her vocal cords was in the early stages of paralysis. Like her breast cancer, it was probably a radiation-induced issue. Furthermore, the atrophy of her neck and upper chest muscles was also treatment-related. The serious condition could increase the risk of carotid artery disease. Susie had been given a cardiology workup in 2010, and was told all was well. But, she said later, "The cardiologist completely missed the boat."

About the time her vocal cord problem arose in 2013, Susie noticed she could barely roll her carry-on suitcase up a jetway and on to a plane without resting to catch her breath. Back home, she described her symptoms to a triage nurse at the VA, and was told to immediately see a nurse practitioner in the women's clinic. She arranged for an echo that same afternoon. The test found that her heart was only pumping at half capacity. Follow-up testing eventually showed the Susie had congestive heart failure, valve damage, and cardiomyopathy. Angiography showed that she had three blocked arteries, and because of prior radiation, surgery was not recommended. Instead, five stents were placed in the arteries.

Susie's original radiation caused more collateral damage. In 2014, she had a small heart attack. She experienced no pain, just pressure in her chest when walking. Another angiogram was done and two more stents were inserted. Then, in 2016, Susie was diagnosed with lung cancer. Her treatment would ordinarily have been surgery, especially since it was a single small tumor. But surgery was not a good option as the tumor was abutting her aorta. While she had originally been told in 1972 that she had maxed out on radiation, she was able to receive a very high, extremely targeted dose to treat the tumor. What a difference from her original radiation!

Given all of that, her ONS lecture's most poignant line resonated not only with her audience, but had significance for survivors, too. "Our glass isn't going to be half full all the time. That's okay. Just be thankful that you have a glass and that there's something in it."

———————————

Where Fitz got the illustrative phrase "the veterans guiding the rookies," which first appeared in print in a 1987 *Los Angeles Times* article, no one really knows. But most likely he had no idea what a profound effect that analogy would have on the survivorship movement in the years that followed.

His phrase is actually an illustration of prosocial behavior; that is, behavior that contributes to society as a whole. It takes many forms: helping, sharing, donating, cooperating. But its most common form is volunteering, the benefits of which have been studied for decades. Initially, volunteering was thought to improve someone only on a psychosocial level. Volunteers find a sense of purpose in their work. Their self-esteem increases and symptoms of depression decrease. Volunteering connects people to one another, giving them an opportunity to socialize. It enhances happiness, life satisfaction, and a person's sense of control over their life. All of which are traits of great importance to cancer survivors.

But impressive findings from a growing body of research now indicate that volunteering provides health benefits as well. The feelings of usefulness and altruism appear to cause the brain to release oxytocin, endorphins, and dopamine—the feel-good hormones that curb stress, reduce harmful inflammation, and create a euphoria that has been cleverly described as the "helper's high." Oxytocin also enhances empathy and "mind-reading" behavior. The British writer and lay theologian C.S. Lewis observed, "Friendship is born at that moment when one man says to another: 'What! You too? I thought that no one but myself…'" In that same vein, volunteers who work with people who share similar experiences—such as cancer veterans guiding rookies—can honestly say, "I know how you feel."

In 2010, United Healthcare and Volunteer Match embarked on a volunteer survey of over 4,500 American adults. Their findings were impressive. Seventy-three percent of those surveyed said volunteering lowered their stress; 68 percent said it made them feel physically healthier; and 29 percent suffering from a chronic disease (like cancer can be) said volunteering helps them better manage their condition.

Our lives unfold like acts in a play. There is a very definite division between life before cancer, the "1st Act," and life after cancer, the "2nd Act."

With all the evidence pointing toward the benefits of prosocial behavior, giving back is a most valuable addition to a survivor's 2nd

Act. From the beginning, those involved in NCCS were all about helping others, and thus ultimately themselves. It was the many hands on deck that made sure the ship sailed true. Fitz's monumental contributions to understanding survivorship, including *Vital Signs*, his article "Seasons of Survival," and helping to found NCCS, had a simple motivation. As he explained decades later, "My driving principal was that this [cancer] was a really shitty experience. If I could change that for someone, it would be some kind of recompense."

Catherine Logan-Carrillo's "2nd Act" (she had married her longtime sweetheart, Tino Carrillo, in the late '90s) was centered in peer support, often referred to prior to the 1990s as mutual aid, and was the basis for her organization LTC. "In a real sense," she wrote in 1987, "the concept of survivorship had to be developed among survivors themselves. It could have come from nowhere else, for it was built on the foundation of mutual aid—from a pooling of our own experiences, wisdom and support. For NCCS, mutual aid and survivorship go hand-in-hand; they are inseparable, and through networking and clearinghouse activities, they are the very foundation of NCCS."

Barbara Hoffman's work against cancer discrimination was an enormous gift to the survivorship population. From that moment as a student at Princeton when she learned firsthand from fellow student Peter Bastone about discrimination against cancer survivors, she made it her life's work to change that situation. Those who have been helped by her personal mission are so many, they cannot be counted.

Natalie Davis Spingarn's recognition of her "2nd Act" came later in her life. She had written tens of thousands of words about her own cancer experience and about cancer in general well before her association with NCCS. But the organization brought her clarity, as described in a 1996 *Networker* article. "As we have organized our forces and become more sure of our ability to speak up to national audiences as well as intimate groups, others begin not just to tolerate our participation, but to encourage (even court) it... To say we have come a long way is an understatement. We need to increase our participation wherever survivorship decisions are made."

The 1996 article that Ellen and Betsy wrote describing the "advocacy continuum" spoke of cancer as a "life transformation." They said, "With the underlying idea that they 'want to give something back,' in gratitude for their survival, many survivors seek out avenues to share their experience with others." That is the very essence of a 2nd Act. Ellen and Betsy also wrote about advocating for changes at a community level that would help future survivors, as would their third type, public interest advocacy, but on a larger scale. Each of those forms benefit the greater good, which in turn benefits the survivors doing the advocating.

Betsy spoke of the power of advocacy again in her chapter contribution to the 2019 book, *Cancer Survivorship: Interprofessional, Patient-Centered Approaches to the Seasons of Survival.*

"Existing information suggests that a critical task of the recovery process is for cancer survivors to regain a sense of control over their lives. Other challenges of the cancer experience include continuing personal growth,... maintaining a positive and hopeful outlook, and advocating for self and others."

When Susie wrote the article "Myths, Monsters, and Magic" in 1992, she referred to a piece she, Lois Loescher, and others had written for the *Oncology Nurse Forum* the year before. "After interviewing a number of long-term survivors," Susie wrote, "Loescher, et al., found that 'helping others represents a kind of end point at which survivors felt lucky and eager to use those painful and helpful parts of their experience to improve the lives of others and get on with living.'" Wendy Harpham had referred to Susie doing exactly that, remembering when she first saw her speak at an NCCS assembly. "She was using her experience to make survivorship better for others."

From the organization's inception and all along the way, those involved with NCCS have embraced the theory that helping is healing. In addition to their many other achievements, furthering that concept—in the form of "veterans guiding rookies"—has laid the groundwork for generations of survivors, ensuring they will always lend a hand to fellow survivors.

Cancer may never be "cured," in the sense that we have a pill or shot to prevent it. But the diligent and unceasing work of NCCS certainly cured cancer's myths. Betsy reflected on the early days, saying, "We worked really hard on survivorship. I'm not sure we saw the whole picture because there was always the next project. We accomplished so much with so little money and so few staff."

An outsider, however, has the luxury of seeing the whole picture, which captures how incredibly vast their grapevine has grown. The NCCS origins were based on two main goals: to improve survivors' lives, and to act as a clearinghouse for grassroots organizations across the country. It's thought that the origin of the term "grassroots" came from Indiana Progressive Party Senator Albert Jeremiah Beveridge, who, in 1912, said, "This party...has grown from the soil of people's hard necessities." While the NCCS began that way, it is now the nation's oldest survivor-led cancer advocacy organization.

When it made the move to Washington, DC, instead of the one-to-one survivor events that had been so important at its birth, NCCS evolved to bring the fourth realm of cancer into the light, and enabled a proliferation of new grassroots organizations in its wake. No longer chained to the earlier misconceptions about their disease that had kept them in hiding, advocates freely began creating their own survivorship groups, pursuing myriad missions. The survivorship movement has come full circle.

Cancer survivors have a complicated relationship with death. Simply put, cancer, like other life-threatening diseases, forces us to confront our own mortality. With the news of a diagnosis, survivors' first inclination is often an overwhelming desire to live at all costs. As time passes, so does the initial shock, and survivors try to keep the fear of death at bay. But with the possibilities of metastasis, recurrence, secondary cancers, and long-term effects, death lurks in the minds of even the most optimistic survivor.

Tani Bahti was drawn to oncology nursing as the result of the traumatic and unexpected suicide of her father. There was no preparation for his death, no closure, and no experience of healthy grieving. But being able to walk with her patients, to talk openly about dying and the legacy they were leaving behind, helped them get the closure she did not. And that in turn contributed to her own healing. She went on to educate about end of life for thirty-five of her forty-four years as a nurse. She went from hospice community educator to speaking at state and national levels, and eventually started a nonprofit with the goals of demystifying the dying process, navigating end-of-life decision-making, communicating with family, partnering with health care professionals, and more. Prior to his death, Tani's father, Tom, authored this thought-provoking haiku: "We admire the death of leaves, why not our own?"

Arthur Frank had a similar view of dying. In his 1991 book, *At the Will of the Body,* he wrote, "The ultimate value of illness is that it teaches us the value of being alive … Death is no enemy of life, it restores our sense of the value of living."

Frank's observation parallels beautifully with Betsy's lifelong work on the subject of hope. "Many people have never thought much about the role hope plays in their lives," she says in the revised edition of the *Almanac,* published in 1996. "Most people forget that while a person may be dying, they are also living. They should live as fully as possible in whatever time they have left."

That chapter was titled "Confronting the End of Life," a theme Betsy felt was important. So did the organizers of the 1996 NCCS assembly. They scheduled a Saturday-afternoon focus group on end-of-life issues. Seeing the offering, some of the attendees felt the topic was inappropriate and depressing, particularly as the assembly was the ten-year celebration of NCCS. In the next issue of the *Networker*, Betsy's message as president was titled "The Final Stage of Survivorship." She spoke about those who attended the focus group, who saw it as an essential issue for survivors to explore.

"The key to managing the entire cancer experience is understanding grief," Betsy said, alluding to the physical and psychological losses as a recurrent theme in cancer. Losses of hair, body parts, and autonomy are accompanied by financial losses and the loss of security. Grief accompanies every loss, and denying the significance of the loss makes grief harder.

Betsy had written the "Rights of the Bereaved" in her *Almanac* chapter. She added this right to her *Networker* article: "Perhaps the most important thing others can do to help friends or loved ones who are experiencing grief is to recognize their right to express their grief and to encourage them to verbalize their feelings and sadness."

The NCCS family was no stranger to grief. Wonderful volunteers and staff members who had given generously of their time and treasure were remembered in the paper version of the *Networker* and its digital replacement. The deaths of those who fueled early fire for the survivorship movement were difficult to process. On Tuesday, January 5, 2016, Ellen died suddenly of a heart attack. The shockwaves of grief reverberated within the survivorship world and beyond. Their words are profound and accurate.

Shelley Fuld Nasso (who became the CEO of NCCS in 2013, and under whose dedicated leadership NCCS continues to grow today): "I write to you with the devastating news that the cancer community lost a hero this week...Ellen was truly a legend in cancer advocacy...She touched thousands of lives, personally and through her advocacy. She believed in helping cancer survivors live as well as they can, for as long as they can. And she did exactly that in her own life, even if it was shorter than we would all have hoped."

Fran Visco (president of the National Breast Cancer Coalition): "I don't want to write about Ellen's numerous awards, where she went to school, what committees she sat on. I want to write about

Ellen. Because no matter what table she sat at or degree she held or plaque she was given, she wanted to cut through all the BS and do two things: help people and get the right things done…There are many, many egos in cancer advocacy. Ellen's wasn't one of them. I saw her time and time again step aside and let someone else take the mike."

Dr. Richard Klausner: "Ellen was, above all else, a friend. She was a truth teller, and there was no editing when Ellen and I talked. I met her soon after I became NCI director, and she was a guide, an advisor and a teacher…Her death is a shock, because she was always so alive bringing life and even humor to the most serious issues without ever diminishing their import."

A tribute was held on Wednesday, February 24, 2016, at the Carnegie Institution for Science in Washington, DC. Between the announcement of her death and the tribute, there were thousands more words about Ellen, written and spoken expressions of love and admiration. But ironically, the most appropriate were written by Ellen herself, in the Summer 1995 *Networker* honoring the life of NCCS volunteer Ellen Hermanson.

"…[Ellen was] stoic in the way she bore the physical and emotional pain of her illness, but, more importantly, a beloved friend to many of us with whom she shared her huge talent for writing about a subject we all know too well. We shall miss you, Ellen, and we will treasure the time you had with us."

When Catherine Logan-Carrillo died on Friday, February 25, 2018, having been diagnosed with dementia several years earlier, her NCCS cofounders gave her the kind of salute she deserved.

Fitz: "It was Cathy's hear-no-objections determination that really breathed life into NCCS. She was determined that a national cancer survivors' organization could be built and determined that we should do it. She was right and today the NCCS has a proud 32-year history of accomplishment thanks to her grit."

Susie: "Without Cathy, there would be no NCCS. She had a vision for cancer-related support that eventually expanded far beyond anything she or any of us could imagine. And her work in this area continued as long as her health permitted. I miss her not only as a cherished colleague, but also as a beloved friend."

Barbara: "Catherine Logan planted the seed for NCCS. She was one of the first to recognize that the most effective advocates for cancer survivors would be educated survivors themselves…Every cancer survivor now benefits from Catherine's foresight and dedication."

Cancer returned to Fitz's life in 2018. Its presence in his lungs was certainly a direct result of the aggressive radiation that saved his life forty-four years earlier. When he died on Friday, November 29, 2019, Susie, Julia Rowland, and Barbara Hoffman collaborated on this beautiful remembrance:

"It is with profound sadness that we acknowledge the passing of Fitzhugh Mullan, MD, the cofounder and first president of the National Coalition for Cancer Survivorship…With dignity, kindness, brilliance, and selfless energy, Fitz built the foundation upon which NCCS rests today. His work has enhanced the lives of countless cancer survivors through advocacy for their medical, emotional, financial, and social needs, from the moment of diagnosis and for the balance of their lives. We mourn the passing of our dear friend, mentor, and beloved colleague."

Well before the deaths of these giants in the survivorship movement, Betsy had observed in the 1996 version of the *Almanac*, "Even if hope for survival dims, individuals and families can find something else to maintain hope." She lists examples of what one might hope for at that point in a life: having a family reunion, seeing a child graduate from college, welcoming the birth of a new grandchild, experiencing a peaceful death.

Betsy herself died peacefully—albeit suddenly—on Saturday, May 23, 2020. She gave kindness and comfort to so many during her professional life, both as an oncology social work pioneer and as a steadfast pillar of NCCS. While Betsy had written hundreds of thousands of words on the subject of hope, these will be the most enduring, from her 2017 book *Choose Hope (Always Choose Hope)*.

"Hope is powerful—more powerful than fear or despair or even grief. Your hope always stands waiting, ready to help you cope and move forward. No matter how difficult or dire the situation, hope is possible and necessary. Never give in to hopelessness. Instead, choose hope. Always choose hope."

The unforgettable voices of these survivorship pioneers will continue to be passed down to the new legion of survivors. In honor of all those who brought survivorship out of the shadows and into the light, we must, indeed, choose hope. Hope to carry on their important work. Hope that science and government will continue striving to take care of those for whom hope is a rare commodity. Hope to live our best lives.

Epilogue

Courageous, compassionate, intelligent, resourceful, prescient. These words hardly seem significant enough to describe the people you've just read about. I could fill pages with so many more descriptions, but I'm assuming you don't need my suggestions. Because of their stories and their work, you began your own mental list of descriptions long ago.

In the summer of 2017, I was introduced to Susie Leigh through a contact in the Tucson cancer community. When I first emailed her, after having done considerable reading about her on the internet, I was unsure whether calling her "Susie" was appropriate. Her body of work and her tireless advocacy were the most impressive things I'd come across since my own cancer diagnosis six years earlier. I asked her name preference, as we set up a lunch. Her response still makes me smile.

"I have attempted to be called Susan over the years, but I just must be a 'Susie.' New people start out calling me Susan. Then we get around friends or colleagues, and 'Susie' is all they know. So Susie is just fine." In the same email, she added, "Survivorship has been my passion these past three decades, so I might talk your ear off."

Survivorship had become my passion, too, and in researching and writing this book, I have been astounded by how much I didn't know. Susie's story is amazing, as is that of each individual with whom she connected me. Some I came to know personally; some I became close to. And some I never met. As I worked through this history—our history as survivors—the sting of my own oncologist's words lessened. At the end of my treatment in 2011, when my issues of survivorship began raining down, I asked her politely why I hadn't been prepared for them. Her terse response was that she had been busy saving my life; giving me details about what was to come hadn't been necessary.

Yet, at the very same time, there was a group of people for whom sharing the details of survivorship was the most necessary thing in the world. Learning about them, hearing their voices—whether written or spoken—has driven me forward. Just as we've come to appreciate what other movements have done to improve our lives and those of our fellow humans, I want *every* cancer survivor to appreciate how the survivorship movement has changed our collective lives.

And the movement is ongoing. To be sure, those who have come before us have made tremendous strides. But there is still work to be done. Millions of survivors muddle through their challenges, unaware of how much support is available or where to find it. Millions do not receive the care they need because of where they live, who they are, what they can afford. All of us should have a survivorship care plan, "the blueprint," as Fitz called it, for the rest of what we hope will be long lives.

We mustn't waste a minute of those lives. What we do doesn't have to be grand. But we should experience a grand moment in helping another every day. As Ellen and Betsy described, there is a veritable buffet of advocacy work we can do, whether for ourselves, for others, or in the public policy realm. In the same way that medical researchers continue to improve detection and treatments of cancer, we survivors are best equipped to help improve one another's lives after cancer. As he always did, Fitz provided a creative and vivid image of this. Addressing the attendees at the 1989 NCCS assembly, he painted the scene of survivors crossing a river after their cancer experiences. They can never go back, he said, but they can start a new life on the other bank, populated by fellow survivors.

Susie spent hours schooling me in the history of survivorship. We talked on the phone, we met for lunch and dinner, and sometimes I became her house guest. Each time I stood on the terrace of her lovely adobe home overlooking the windswept Catalina Mountains, I considered how that vista represented the woman she is. The elements are harsh in that part of Arizona. Heat and drought in the summer, cold and gray in the winter. Susie's four cancer diagnoses and the ongoing long-term effects of treatment have been equally harsh on her body and mind. But like the spring wildflowers that appear every year in the desert, she has never failed to rise back up.

The sudden deaths of Ellen and Betsy shook Susie. I had come to know Betsy well during this project, and in mourning her death, Susie and I exchanged emails. I don't think she recalled the quote opening the prologue of this book when she wrote these words: "I am again wondering why I am so lucky to still be here. I guess I still have work to do."

Let the work continue.

Judy Pearson, May 31, 2020

Acknowledgments

According to ancient legend, the phoenix is a bird that burns to death and is reborn from its own ashes. As the symbol of renewal and rebirth, the phoenix is a perfect metaphor for cancer survivorship.

And while my name is on the cover, this book would not have been possible without the help of many. My persistent questions about tiny nuances may have seemed trivial, but it is my sincere hope that all of those who patiently answered me now see how they helped create this beautiful story. I had the good fortune to tap the memories of several founding National Coalition for Cancer Survivorship (NCCS) members: Dr. Patti Ganz, Al and Alice Hiat, attorney Barbara Hoffman, and Dr. Fitzhugh Mullan. Others who became involved with NCCS were equally generous with their time. They include Deborah Ash, Betsy Clark, Donna Doneski, Wendy Harpham, Lovell Jones, Julia Rowland, and Brad Zebrack. The current CEO of NCCS, Shelley Fuld Nasso, welcomed me to the office. She, along with her staff, combed through boxes of photos and hunted up documents, bolstering my drive to write their history.

Oncology Nursing Society members gave me insight into not only the growth of their specialty, but also the survivorship movement they helped foster. Tani Bahti, P.J. Haylock, Lois Loescher, and Debi Boyle are to be commended for all they have done throughout their careers. Audrey Wilson, a founding member of the early Albuquerque support group Living Through Cancer, gave me a glimpse into how far we've come in both treatment and survivorship, as did journalist Betty Rollin. Mary Dickson shared her experiences as a "downwinder," while Marion Kelly, Lee Magnuson and others opened my eyes to survivorship in minority communities.

The woman who truly launched this project deserves my greatest thanks, love, and respect. Founding NCCS member Susie Leigh promised to "talk my ear off" at our first lunch. She did, and went on to introduce me not only to many of those I've mentioned, but also to the heart of what being a cancer survivor really is. Her hesitancy to be in the spotlight, despite the fact that it's a position she has earned, makes her very special to all who know her. I am lucky to call her my friend.

Longtime friend and sister author Cindy Goyette served once again as a wonderful editor. This is the fifth book of mine that she has read in its formative state, and for that I'm forever grateful. After Cindy, Diedre Kaye Alexander became the perfect sounding board. She listened as I read each chapter aloud while she was going through chemotherapy. It allowed me to make certain every word was perfect and those hours will remain a very special memory for me. Once again, Peter Rubie, my agent of nearly two decades, and in the case of this book also my publisher, proved why he is the best in the business.

My grown sons, other family members, and many friends were enthusiastic cheerleaders. But at the heart of it all, I could never have written a word if it were not for my wonderful husband, David Martens. He encouraged me when the going got tough, and celebrated with me when I typed "The End." He is the best life partner anyone could ever ask for.

To all of you, a hearty thanks.

Notes

If three people tell the exact same story, it will still be quite different each time. The many voices in this book have come from myriad sources: extensive archival research; newspaper, magazine, and newsletter articles; book chapters; online videos; and personal interviews. While they often lived through shared experiences, their memories of those experiences vary. I have blended their words to the best of my ability to create this history of the survivorship movement.

That movement has required many individuals and much good work. Any omission of either has nothing to do with their value, and everything to do with space, time, and my own ignorance. My hope is that this book will encourage readers to learn more, research further, and create their own part in the survivorship movement.

I have chosen to use an informal style for this bibliography, and to eschew footnotes in the text itself. The intention behind these choices was to keep the story accessible. However, it is important to acknowledge the sources I've used in preparing this work. Here you will find them listed by chapter, with a brief nod to the location in which I have used them in the text.

One note: The cancer statistics that open each chapter of this book are drawn from various publications of the American Cancer Society. Unless otherwise indicated, other data related to the prevalence of various cancers, number of deaths from those cancers, and growth in numbers of survivors are also sourced from various publications of the American Cancer Society.

Prologue

Catherine Logan's life details taken from a presentation prepared by various individuals to honor her life.

Dr. Fitzhugh Mullan's life details taken from his book *Vital Signs: A Young Doctor's Struggle with Cancer* (New York: Farrar, Straus & Giroux, 1982).

Chapter 1

"In 1830s London ..."—Stone, Marvin J. "Thomas Hodgkin: Medical Immortal and Uncompromising Idealist" (Baylor University Medical Center, 2005).

"By the time of World War II ..."—Jacobs, Charlotte DeCroes. *Henry Kaplan and the Story of Hodgkin's Disease* (Stanford, CA: Stanford University Press, 2010), 82.

"At a 1951 cocktail party ..."—Ibid., 110.

"Scoring a grant of $18,381 ..."—"Cancer Research Funds Allocated," Associated Press, August 23, 1951.

"Kaplan next aimed ..."—"Experts Optimistic on Hodgkin's Disease Outlook," *Dayton Daily News*, Dayton, OH, April 8, 1971.

"A year later, in 1956..."—Mukherjee, Siddhartha, M.D., *The Emperor of All Maladies: A Biography of Cancer* (New York, NY: Simon and Schuster, 2010), 136.

"Research done in 1947 at New York's Memorial Hospital"— *California Bulletin of Cancer Control*, 1948.

"Among patients over 60 years of age ..."—Ibid.

"A University of Michigan study ..."—Ibid.

"In 1964..."—DeVita, Vincent T., Jr., M.D., *The Death of Cancer* (New York, NY: Sarah Crichton Books/Farrar, Straus & Giroux, 2015), 77.

"Along with another NCI researcher ..."—Ibid., 86.

"The treatments were tough ..."—"A History of Cancer Chemotherapy," *Cancer Research* 68, no. 21 (2008).

"But unlike his predecessor ..."—Califano, Joseph, Jr., *The Triumph & Tragedy of Lyndon Johnson: The White House Years* (New York, NY: Atria Books, 2015).

"The report was summarized..."—Letter from Dr. Michael E. DeBakey to President Lyndon Johnson, December 1, 1964.

"In an earlier briefing..."—"Johnson Vows $3 Billion Drive to Combat Disease," *Detroit Free Press,* December 10, 1964.

"Making good on their promise ..."—*Atlanta Constitution,* September 3, 1965.

"DeVita's MOPP..."—"Experts Say Improved Treatment Improves Hodgkin's Disease," *Arizona Republic,* April 8, 1971.

Chapter 2

"Fearing a 'falling domino theory'"—Dwight D. Eisenhower press conference, April 7, 1954. Retrieved from nps.gov/features/eise/jrranger/quotes2.htm

"A year after the French left"—Digital History. Retrieved from digitalhistory.uh.edu/disp_textbook.cfm?smtid=2&psid=3459

"President Kennedy quickly authorized..."—John F. Kennedy Presidential Library. Retrieved from jfklibrary.org/learn/about-jfk/jfk-in-history/vietnam

"I feel like a jackass..."—Burns, Ken, and Novak, Lynn (producers and directors). *The Vietnam War.* (Florentine Films, United States, 2017).

"Then, on August 2, 1964"—Real Clear Defense. Retrieved from realcleardefense.com/articles/2019/07/19

"Johnson handily won..."—Burns and Novak, op. cit.

"Sen. Robert Kennedy..."—"Well, That's Settled," *The Record,* Hackensack, NJ, January 4, 1966.

"But flowers and love..."—McLaughlin, Malcolm, *The Long, Hot Summer of 1967: Urban Rebellion in America* (London, U.K.: Palgrave Macmillan, 2014).

"At 7:55 p.m."—"Johnson Flies to Fund-Raiser in Los Angeles," *Oshkosh Northwestern,* Oshkosh, WI, June 24, 1967.

"The dawn of 1968"—Donna Doneski interview with the author.

"Over 2,000 miles away"—Susie Leigh interview with the author.

"On January 30..."—Wikipedia. Retrieved from en.wikipedia.org/wiki/Tet_Offensive#Phase_III

"After thirty-nine minutes…"—*Reel America*, C-SPAN3. Retrieved from youtube.com/watch?v=kxWGg3AARnI

"On his last day…"—"22 Presidential Medals Are Awarded by Johnson," *The Sentinel*, Carlisle, PA, January 23, 1969.

"Cancer came to Mary's…"—Cruikshank, Jeffrey L., and Schultz, Arthur W., *The Man Who Sold America* (Boston, MA: Harvard Business Review Press, 2010).

"In 1940…"—"A.D. Lasker Weds 3d Time; Bride from Wisconsin," *Chicago Tribune*, Chicago, IL, June 21, 1940.

"It was Albert's…"—Gourley, Catherine, *Flappers and the New American Woman: Perceptions of Women from 1918 Through the 1920s* (Minneapolis, Minnesota: Twenty-First Century Books, 2008).

"One of Mary's first…"—Columbia University Oral Histories, Notable New Yorkers. Retrieved from columbia.edu/cu/lweb/digital/collections/nny/laskerm/profile.html

"Then, in 1945…"—Ibid.

"As had other journalists…"—"The Enemy Within," *Pittsburgh Post-Gazette*, Pittsburgh, PA, April 23, 1945.

"In the first year…"—Mukherjee, op. cit., 113.

"As an ACS Washington lobbyist…"—Brazala, Jerry and Siwolop, Sana, "The Fairy Godmother of Medical Research," *Science & Technology* (Summer 1985).

"On the other side of the country…"—Susie Leigh interview with the author.

"Wounded servicemen…"—Wikipedia. Retrieved from en.wikipedia.org/wiki/Letterman_Army_Hospital

"The patients' monotonous…"—Nevidjon, Brenda (ed.), *Building a Legacy: Voices of Oncology Nurses* (Boston, MA: Jones and Bartlett Publishers, 1995), 283.

"I was so socially naive…"—Ibid.

"In its original form…"—US National Library of Medicine, Digital Collections. Retrieved from various documents.

"Despite the cutbacks…"—Ibid.

"In 1968…"—Ibid.

"And then it was all over"—Ibid.

Chapter 3

"Susie Leigh arrived…"—Susie Leigh interview with the author.

"Her approach was simple…"—Brazala and Siwolop, op. cit.

"…she told…Edward R. Murrow"—Murrow, Edward R., *Person to Person,* May 22, 1959.

"She personally gave…"—"Critiques Question Cancer Society," Tallahassee Democrat, Tallahassee, FL, April 21, 1978.

"Nobody lobbies…"—Ibid.

"I am just an agent…"—"When Mary Lasker Speaks, They Listen," *Indianapolis Star,* Indianapolis, IN, April 22, 1979.

"That position…"—Scharer, Gil, "It's Time to Think About Priorities," *Detroit Free Press*, Detroit, MI, July 20, 1969.

"This prompted Professor…"—Coleman, Michael P., "War on Cancer and the Influence of the Medical Industrial Complex," *Journal of Cancer Policy* 1, no. 3–4, September–December 2013.

"Dr. Jonathan E. Rhodes…"—"Current Decade Is Called Crucial in War on Cancer," *Fort Lauderdale News,* Fort Lauderdale, FL, April 6, 1970.

"So she created"—Coleman, op. cit.

"She persuaded him…"—Department of Health, Education, and Welfare, National Institutes of Health memo, March 5, 1971.

"Culling from her Christmas Card list…"—Department of Health, Education, and Welfare, National Institutes of Health, undated memo.

"Released in October…"—"Conquest of Cancer Is Group's Goal," *The Corpus Christi Caller Times,* October 25, 1970.

"But for Mary Lasker…"—"Disease Lobbies Are at the Heart of Funding," *The News Journal,* Willmington, DE, March 9, 1980.

"Before he left his Senate seat…"—"Conquest of Cancer," *Clarion-Ledger,* Jackson, MS, December 28, 1970.

"Nixon declared…"—Richard Nixon Foundation. Retrieved from youtube.com/watch?v=peb47Z-jPqc

"As a part…"—Hearings Before the Subcommittee of Health of the Committee on Labor and Public Welfare, Ninety-second Congress, March 9, 1971.

"NCI convened..."—Department of Health, Education, and Welfare, National Institutes of Health memo, March 5, 1971.

"It was time..."—"Bill S-34 Gets a Boost from Ann," *Tampa Tribune,* Tampa, FL, April 20, 1971.

"Under pressure from..."—"Reach Compromise on Cancer Fund Bill," *Ithaca Journal,* Ithaca, NY, December 8, 1971.

"On December 23, 1971..."—"Nixon Signs $1.6 Billion Cancer Bill," *Battle Creek Enquirer,* Battle Creek, MI, December 23, 1971.

"Two months earlier..."—Donna Doneski interview with the author.

Chapter 4

"One gave her..."—"Ellen Stoval...dies at 69," *Washington Post,* January 8, 2016.

"So there she was..."—"Artist Brushes Patients' Lives with Tranquility," *Tallahassee Democrat,* Tallahassee, FL, October 28, 1982.

"But she wasn't eligible..."—Cleeland, Charles S., Dunn, Adrian J., Fisch, Michael J. (eds.), *Cancer Symptom Science* (Cambridge, U.K.: Cambridge University Press, 2010).

"Ellen's sixty"—Ibid.

"The 1970s..."—Ibid.

"It was February..."—Susie Leigh interview with the author.

"As Susie explained..."—Leigh, Susie, "Cancer Survivorship," *American Journal of Nursing* 106, March 2006.

"Susie had..."—Susie Leigh interview with the author.

"Susie returned..."—Ibid.

"As noted by..."—American Cancer Society. Retrieved from cancer.org/cancer/cancer-basics/history-of-cancer/what-is-cancer.html

"Starting in the fifteenth century..."—Retrieved from cancer.org/cancer/cancer-basics/history-of-cancer/sixteenth-to-eighteenth-centuries.html

"The newspapers of the day..."—"Cancer Contagious," *Pittsburgh Weekly Gazette,* Pittsburgh, PA, November 14, 1901.

"Nineteen years…"—"Questions and Answers," *The Dayton Herald,* Dayton, OH, March 5, 1920.

"By 1940…"—"Cancer Misconceptions Still Persist in the US," *The Dayton Herald,* Dayton, OH, April 7, 1940.

"When a 1960…"—"Virus Type of Cancer Contagious?" *Miami News,* Miami, FL, July 31, 1960.

"Five years after that…"—"How to Keep Well," *Chicago Tribune,* Chicago, IL, February 12, 1965.

"When an…"—"Coffee Break," *Washington C.H. Recorder-Herald,* Washington Court House, OH, April 2, 1970.

"In 1972…"—"Evidence That Some Cancers Contagious," *Evening Independent,* Massillion, OH, March 22, 1972.

"Although the doctor stressed…"—Ibid.

"As chemotherapy…"—Susie Leigh interview with the author.

"Once a treatment…"—Ibid.

"On his way…"—Ibid.

"It was a…"—Ibid.

"The next time…"—Ibid.

"We are going…"—Ibid.

"Even as recently…"—"Can Better Bedside Manner Be Taught," *New York Times,* January 29, 2009. Retrieved from well.blogs.nytimes. com/2009/01/29/can-better-bedside-manner-be-taught/

"In the fifth century…"—"How the Doctor's Nose Has Shortened," *Journal of the Royal Society of Medicine,* December 2006.

"In the eighteenth century…"—Ibid.

"One of the…"—"Dr. Wainwright Read Report on Cancer Effects," *The Times-Tribune,* Scranton, PA, September 23, 1915.

"It wasn't until…"—Abrams, Ruth D. and Finesinger, Jacob M.D. "Guilt Reactions in Cancer Patients." Department of Neurology and Psychiatry, Harvard Medical School, 1953.

"Part of the problem…"—Ibid.

"Part of the non-communication…"—Dr. Patricia Ganz interview with the author.

"In a sad…"—"Psychiatrist Dies," *The Times-Tribune,* June 22, 1959.

"The nondisclosure drum..."—"Virginia Physicians to Meet," *Daily News*, Newport News, VA, June 15, 1971.

"The communication gap..."—Anonymous interview with the author.

"Even as this..."—Dr. Teresa K. Woodruff interview with the author.

"A final tale..."—Wikipedia. Retrieved from en.wikipedia.org/wiki/Lurleen_Wallace.

"Now it was Lurleen's..."—Ibid.

"George still lied..."—"Lurlene Wallace Contracts Cancer for 3rd Time," *Wisconsin State Journal*, Madison, WI, January 5, 1968.

"Dr. Arthur I. Holleb..."—Obituary, *Boston Globe*, Boston, MA, October 31, 2006.

"By early 1972..."—Holleb, Arthur I., M.D. "The Cancer Patient—Too Often Alone." *CA: A Cancer Journal for Clinicians*, 22, no. 2 (March/April 1972).

"Following up..."—*The Atlanta Voice*, Atlanta, GA, May 27, 1972.

"It was..."—"Julie to Speak at Forum Here," *The Atlanta Constitution*, Atlanta, GA, June 22, 1972.

"In the end..."—"Cancer Impact Also Emotional," *The Atlanta Constitution*, Atlanta, GA, June 25, 1972.

"You can write..."—Spingarn, Natalie Davis, *Hanging In There: Living Well on Borrowed Time* (New York, NY: Stein and Day, 1982).

"Natalie had seen..."—Ibid.

"Trusting the man..."—Ibid.

"Natalie continued..."—Ibid.

"After her second..."—"A Cancer Patient's Never-Never Land," *Washington Post*, Washington DC, April 27, 1980.

Chapter 5

"On the last page..."—*American Public Health Association News*, March 1973.

"The announcement..."—Ibid.

"...expected 100..."—Bullough, Vern L., RN, *American Nursing: A Biographical Dictionary*, Volume 3 (New York, NY: Springer Publishing Company), 15.

"Both of the ..."—Nevidjon, op. cit., 35.

"... she would later say ..."—Barckley, Virginia, "The Visiting Nurse and the Patient with Cancer," *CA: A Cancer Journal for Clinicians*, 15, no. 4 (July/August 1965).

"This tiny woman ..."—Nevidjon, op. cit., 35.

"After the conference ..."—Yarbro, Connie Henke, "The Early Days: Four Smiles and a Post Office Box," *Oncology Nursing Forum*, 12, no. 1.

"In the 1915..."—Peterson, Reuben, "How Nurses Can Aid in the Fight Against Cancer," *The American Journal of Nursing*, 15: no. 10 (July 1915).

"Earlier in his address ..."—Ibid.

"... one nurse remembered ..."—Nevidjon, op. cit., 88.

"We had no idea ..."—Pamela J. Haylock interview with the author.

"In 1975..."—Mullan, Fitzhugh M.D., *Vital Signs: A Young Doctor's Struggle with Cancer* (New York, NY: Farrar, Straus & Giroux, 1982).

"As a member..."—Fitzhugh Mullan, M.D., interview with the author.

"... this unfamiliar persona ..."—Mullan, op. cit., 15.

"... the tumor ..."—Mullan, op. cit., 20.

"an unusual ..."—Ibid.

"... as he explained ..."—Mullan, op. cit., 43.

"... the correct answer ..."—Mullan, op. cit., 108.

"Fitz had long ..."—Mullan, Fitzhugh, M.D., *White Coat, Clenched Fist* (New York, NY: McMillian and Sons, 1976).

"They had two ..."–Yarbro, op. cit.

"During a November ..."—Ibid.

"... the space allotted them ..."—*Oncology Nursing Newsletter*, 2, no. 2 (1975).

"They voted ..."—Yarbro, op. cit.

"Between Mother's Day ..."—Yarbro, op. cit.

"She couldn't imagine ..."—"Ellen Stoval ... dies at 69," *Washington Post*, January 8, 2016.

"She vowed ..."—Ibid.

"...Ellen asked ..."—"The Ellen Stovall Story," *NCCS InterActions*, 17, no. 1.

"Volunteering ran ..."—Ibid.

"The Leukemia Society ..."—Ibid.

"...headline had proclaimed ..."—"Cancer: Prevention Is the New Watchword," *Dayton Daily News*, Dayton, OH, July 12, 1971.

"The last television ..."—"History of Tobacco Regulation." Retrieved from druglibrary.org/Schaffer/LIBRARY/studies/nc/nc2b. htm

"concise when he wrote ..."—"Critics Question Cancer Society," *Tallahassee Democrat*, Tallahassee, FL, April 21, 1978.

Chapter 6

"Joseph Hixon to ask ..."—"Money Pours in but Cancer War Drags," *Pittsburgh Press*, Pittsburgh, PA, March 9, 1976.

"Dr. Donald Kennedy ..."—"Official: Cancer Fight Is a Medical Vietnam," *Fort Lauderdale News*, Fort Lauderdale, FL, April 2, 1978.

"Over a fourteen-year ..."—"US Spent $114 Billion in Vietnam," *Gettysburg Times*, Gettysburg, PA, April 12, 1975.

"Cell research scientist ..."—"Who's Winning the War on Cancer," *Tallahassee Democrat*, Tallahassee, FL, April 20, 1978.

"Susie remembered ..."—Susie Leigh interview with the author.

"We're expanding ..."—Ibid.

"The fee ..."—Oncology Nursing Society registration pamphlet.

"Susie returned ..."—Susie Leigh interview with the author.

"Leticia was ..."—Nevidjon, op. cit., 287.

"To that end ..."—"Disabled Soldiers to Get Vocational Education," *Tallahassee Democrat*, Tallahassee, FL, March 10, 1919.

"General George Patton ..."—"Congressmen Favor Probe of Patton Hitting Soldier," *Courier Post*, Camden, NJ, November 24, 1943.

"Vietnam Syndrome ..."—Friedman, Matthew J. "Post-Vietnam Syndrome: Recognition and Management," *Psychosomatics*, 22, no. 11 (1981).

"PTSD was exactly ..."—Susie Leigh interview with the author.

"There are people…"—"Combatting the Specter of Cancer," *Albuquerque Journal,* Albuquerque, NM, October 2, 1988.

"Some years earlier…"—Ibid.

"The experiences…"—"Local Cancer Conference Planned," *Albuquerque Journal,* Albuquerque, NM, July 24, 1983.

"By November…"—Audrey Wilson interview with the author.

"There's a misconception…"—"Combatting the Specter of Cancer," op cit.

"Ellen Stovall"—"The Ellen Stovall Story," *NCCS InterActions,* 17, no. 1.

"The someone…"—Ibid.

"Two days later…"—"Someone Who Knew My Terror," *Washington Post,* May 9, 1983.

"People got this…"—Fitz Mullan, M.D., interview with the author.

"Why was…"—Ibid.

"On the day…"—Ibid.

"In that moment…"—Ibid.

"It started with…"—Mullan, Fitz, M.D., "Seasons of Survival," *New England Journal of Medicine,* July 1985.

"She told him…"—Fitz Mullan, M.D., interview with the author.

"In early 1986…"—Ibid.

"Debi McCaffrey…"—Debi Boyle interview with the author.

"I didn't realize…"—Ibid.

"I remember…"—Nevidjon, op. cit., p. 289.

Chapter 7

"The first research…"—Abrams and Finesinger, op.cit.

"Unlike tuberculosis…"—Ibid.

"Two years after…"—Bard, Morton, Ph.D., and Sutherland, Arthur, M.D. "Psychological Impact of Cancer and Its Treatment: Adaptation to Radical Mastectomy," *Cancer,* 8, no. 4 (1955).

"…she was one…"—Cavallo, Jo and Piana, Ronald, "Celebrating the Life of Jimmie Holland, MD," *ASCO Post,* January 25, 2018.

"She called…"—Grisham, Julie, "Remembering Jimmie Holland, a Founder of Psycho-Oncology," Memorial Sloan Kettering

Cancer Center, January 9, 2018. Retrieved from mskcc.org/news/remembering-jimmie-holland-founder-psycho-oncology.

"Jimmie began research..."—Dr. Julia Rowland interview with the author.

"...psychooncology"—Ibid.

"As a first year..."—Patti Ganz interview with the author.

"It was..."—Ibid.

"Her work profoundly..."—Ibid.

"And when she attended..."—Ibid.

"Further north..."—Pat Fobair interview with the author.

"By this time..."—Ibid.

"After she graduated..."—Betsy Clark interview with the author.

"Betsy joined..."—Ibid.

"...empower the survivorship..."—Logan, Catherine. "National Planning Meeting on Cancer Survivorship, October 3–5, 1986." Sent to Barbara Hoffman, August 4, 1986.

"But Jewish invitee"—Susie Leigh interview with the author.

"Previously an apartment complex..."—"Hotels Struggle to Survive in City's Overbuilt Market," *Albuquerque Journal,* Albuquerque, NM, April 25, 1988.

"Catherine explained..."—Logan, Catherine, op.cit.

"The restaurant's owner..."—Jim Schumacher interview with the author.

"...later described as leaders..."—*NCCS Newsletter,* 1, no. 1, March 1987.

"Susie spent..."—Nevidjon, op. cit., p. 289.

"Each time..."—Susie Leigh interview with the author.

"They convened..."—Alice Hiat interview with the author.

"...this moment..."—*NCCS Newsletter,* II, no. 1 (Winter 1988).

"...as Fitz would say..."—Fitz Mullan, M.D., interview with the author.

"She described her..."—Nevidjon, op. cit., 289.

"Even more absurd..."—Fitz Mullan, M.D., interview with the author.

"They collected..."—These sums come from notes taken during the inaugural meeting.

"For example..."—Gillings School of Public Health, University of North Carolina. Retrieved from peersforprogress.org/pfp_blog/a-brief-history-of-peer-support-origins/

"As the weeks..."—American Childhood Cancer Organization. Retrieved from acco.org/history/

"She was so enthusiastic..."—Susie Leigh interview with the author.

Chapter 8

"The Rehabilitation Act of 1973..."—Information retrieved from ada.gov/cguide.htm

"A forty-two-year-old bookkeeper..."—"Cancer Patients Find Job Discrimination," *Pittsburgh Post- Gazette,* Pittsburgh, PA, October 3, 1985.

"Francis Wright..."—Ibid.

"Barbara had learned..."—Barbara Hoffman interview with the author.

"Peter's recent history..."—Peter Bastone interview with the author.

"After hearing her..."—Debi Boyle interview with the author.

"Debi created..."—Nevidjon, op. cit., 290.

"Susie and Lois..."—Lois Loescher interview with the author.

"For nearly twelve months..."—"The Impact of the Cancer Experience on Long-Term Survivors," *Oncology Nursing Forum,* 17, no. 2 (1990).

"Insomuch as U of A..."—Lois Loescher interview with the author.

"By the summer..."—*NCCS Newsletter,* I, no. 2 (Summer 1987).

"Bike America..."—Ibid.

"Best of all..."—*NCCS Newsletter,* I, no. 3 (Fall 1987).

"Washington-area psychiatrist..."—"Dating Service Helps Handicapped Overcome 'Disability of Loneliness,'" *The Palm Beach Post,* West Palm Beach, FL, September 14, 1987.

"...in July 1987..."—NCCS Board of Directors Meeting Notes.

"The following spring..."—Fitzhugh Mullan, M.D., interview with the author.

"The meeting..."—*NCCS Newsletter,* I, no. 3 (Fall 1987).

"Brad Zebrack..."—Brad Zebrack interview with the author.

"Brad and Joanne left..."—Ibid.

"Some years later..."—Ibid.

"There were..."—"Adoption and Cancer Survivors: Findings From a Learning Activity for Oncology Nurses," *Cancer,* American Cancer Survivorship, September 1, 2015.

"Survivors, like other..."—*NCCS Networker,* 2, no. 2 (Spring 1988).

"Fitz pointed out..."—*NCCS Newsletter,* II, no. 1 (Winter 1988).

"Amid the celebration..."—"Picnic Held for Cancer Survivors," *Asbury Park Press,* Asbury Park, NJ, June 6, 1988.

"In another article..."—*NCCS Networker,* 3, no. 1 (Winter 1989).

Chapter 9

"The Civil Rights Act..."—Retrieved from archives.gov/education/lessons/civil-rights-act

"It was introduced..."—"Cancer Patients, Handicapped Claim Job Bias," *The Dispatch,* Moline, IL, June 21, 1987.

"As Biaggi put it..."—Ibid.

"There is life..."—"Cancer Victims Want Employment Rights," *The Spokesman-Review,* Spokane, WA, June 18, 1987.

"Again Barbara..."—*NCCS Networker* 3: no. 3, Summer 1989.

"On July 26..."—Retrieved from ada.gov/ada_intro.htm

"The other new member..."—Betsy Clark interview with the author.

"Post-assembly comments..."—*NCCS Networker,* 4, no. 4 (Fall 1990).

"Most consumers..."—Hoffman, Barbara, J.D. and Mullan, Fitzhugh M.D., *Charting the Journey: An Almanac of Practical Resources for Cancer Survivors* (Mount Vernon, NY: Consumers Union, 1990), 3.

"What was needed..."—Hoffman and Mullan, op. cit., 2.

"Patti Ganz..."—Hoffman and Mullan, op. cit., 7.

"But, as she..."—Nevidjon, op. cit., 292.

"Women treated..."—Nevidjon, op. cit., 292.

"I may have..."—"Cancer Survivor Says She's Been There Done That," *The Morning Call,* Allentown, PA, February 12, 1999.

"Nurses taught..."—Ibid.

"Successful and..."—Rollin, Betty, *First, You Cry* (New York, NY: J.B. Lippincott Company, 1976), 185.

"In the late..."—Imbur, Gerald, M.D., *Genius on the Edge* (New York, NY: Kaplan Publishing, 2010), 282.

"Some of..."—Ibid.

"On June 25..."—"Rose Kushner Beat the Medical System," *Fort Lauderdale News,* Fort Lauderdale, FL, October 24, 1979.

"Her courage..."—Ibid.

"But the American..."—Ibid.

"Dr. Allen Lichter..."—Dr. Allen Lichter interview with the author.

"The process..."—Ibid.

"It was the surgeon's..."—Ibid.

"...if a person..."—"Breast Rebuilding More than Mere Vanity," *The Journal Times,* Racine, WI, July 12, 1980.

"...a woman in Indianapolis..."—Cynthia Martens interview with the author.

"...suggesting that..."—"Breast Reconstruction: Surgery Saddled with Myths," *Hartford Courant,* Hartford, CT, February 27, 1979.

"...which hovered..."—"Shirley Vanderberg Fought to Help Other Women Cancer Victims," *The Atlanta Constitution,* Atlanta, GA, August 30, 1980.

"...After Susie's..."—Susie Leigh interview with the author.

"Scientific data..."—"How Now, Dow," *The Philadelphia Inquirer,* Philadelphia, PA, January 1, 1992.

"In reality..."—"Dow Chemical Deceived Women on Breast Implants, Jury Decides," *New York Times,* August 19, 1997.

Chapter 10

"We will..."—Hearings before a Subcommittee of the Committee on Appropriations, United States Senate, Fiscal Year 1992, 682.

"This December..."—Ibid.

"They were missing..."—Lovell Jones interview with the author.

"Listening to music..."—Ibid.

"NCCS was growing..."—Fitzhugh Mullan, M.D., interview with the author.

"While Catherine..."—Ibid.

"But she wanted..."—Deborah Ash interview with the author.

"As it was for Catherine ..."—Ibid.

"Deb was inspired ..."—Ibid.

"Peer support ..."—"Book Can Help Survivors," *Albuquerque Journal*, Albuquerque, NM, May 26, 1991.

"It saddened ..."—Deborah Ash interview with the author.

"In her session ..."—"National Cancer Survivors Coalition Studying Universal Health-CarePlan," *The Pantagraph*, Bloomington, IL, November 9, 1991.

"...who shared a story ..."—*NCCS Networker*, 5, no. 4 (Fall 1991).

"Just as it had ..."—Susie Leigh interview with the author.

"Finding the ..."—"Cancer: The New Battlefront," *Los Angeles Times*, November 12, 1991.

"This sad but ..."—Ibid.

"The first prepaid ..."—"Statutes and Stories: Collections and Reflections on American Legal History." Retrieved from statutesandstories.com/blog_html/act-for-the-relief-of-sick-and-disabled-seamen/

"Another early ..."—*The United States Army and Navy Journal and Gazette of the Regular and Volunteer Forces*, 3 (May 19, 1865), 616. Retrieved from books.google.com/books?id=7KNMAAAAYAAJ&pg=PA616#v=onepage&q&f=false

"After the war ..."—Hendricks, Rickey, *A Model for National Health Care: The History of Kaiser Permanente* (New Brunswick, NJ: Rutgers University Press, 1993), 13.

"...which the NCCS ..."—*NCCS Networker*, 5, no. 3 (Summer 1991).

"The public ..."—"Nation Is Losing the War Against Cancer, Study Says," *The Miami Herald*, May 6, 1986.

"In her article ..."—"Search Persists for Magic Weapon in Cancer War," *Albuquerque Journal*, Albuquerque, NM, December 23, 1991.

"This was why ..."—Fitzhugh Mullan, M.D., interview with the author.

"The first hurdle ..."—Ibid.

"Meanwhile, Catherine ..."—Ibid.

"Realizing ..."—Ibid.

"The survivor..."—*NCCS Networker,* 7, no. 4 (Assembly Edition, 1993).

"Gathering information..."—"Breasts Get Shabby Treatment," *The Daily Herald,* Provo, UT, March 7, 1992.

"Breast cancer diagnoses..."—"Breast Cancer Activist Tired of Being Polite," *Austin American-Statesman,* Austin, TX, November 11, 1996.

"They also saw..."—"Breast Cancer: Activists Demand Their Fair Share," *The Record,* Hackensack, NJ, November 20, 1992.

"Speaking to..."—"Letters to Congress Show Plight of Women with Breast Cancer," *The Charlotte Observer,* Charlotte, NC, October 9, 1991.

"To gather attention..."—Ibid.

"If they want..."—"Votes Sought for Cancer Funds," *The Burlington Free Press,* Burlington, VT, June 14, 1992.

"On Tuesday..."—"1 in 8 Will Get Breast Cancer," *Press and Sun Bulletin,* Binghamton, NY, September 26, 1992.

Chapter 11

"In a soft..."—*Surviving Cancer* [Video file], November 3, 1994. Retrieved from c-span.org/video/?61342-1/surviving-cancer#

"Once the..."—Ibid.

"I thought if..."—Ibid.

"The night of..."—*NCCS Networker,* 8, no. 4 (Winter 1994).

"We have to figure..."—*NCCS Networker,* 7, no. 4 (Assembly Edition, 1993).

"The council..."—Ibid.

"Board member Dr. Lovell Jones..."—Ibid.

"Susie opened..."—*NCCS Networker,* 8, no. 4 (Winter 1994).

"It was..."— Betsy Clark interview with the author.

"Summing it up..."—*NCCS Networker,* 8, no. 3 (Summer 1994).

"Julia continued..."—Ibid.

"In the midst..."—*NCCS Networker,* 8, no. 4 (Winter 1994).

"In her gracious..."—Ibid.

"On the door..."—Mary Dixon interview with the author.

"Knowing it wasn't…"—Ibid.

"Mary had been…"—Ibid.

"A brilliant…"— "Range Explosion Wakens Sleepers," *Reno Gazette-Journal,* Reno, NV, January 27, 1951.

"The AEC…"—"Atomic Blast Rocks Nevada," *Tucson Daily Citizen,* Tucson, AZ, January 27, 1951.

"The third atomic…"—Ibid.

"So on…"—Buck, Alice, *The Atomic Energy Commission,* US Department of Energy, July 1983.

"Testing only…"—"Fox, Sarah Elizabeth, *Downwind: A People's History of the Nuclear West* (Lincoln, NE: University of Nebraska Press, 2014), 6.

"…according to an AEC…"—"The Forgotten Guinea Pigs," a report prepared for the Committee on Interstate and Foreign Commerce of the US House of Representatives, August 1980.

"…the AEC assured…"—"Scientists Refute Risks to Atomic Test Fall-out," *Daily Press,* Newport News, VA, March 24, 1955.

"It wasn't long…"—Fox, op. cit., 82.

"They took…"—Fox, op. cit., 110.

"A horrible irony…"—Mauer, Raymond J., "Bert Ducks and Covers," Archer Productions. Produced for the US Federal Civil Defense Administration, January 1952.

"The sickening picture…"—"The Forgotten Guinea Pigs," op.cit.

"Who would be…"—The Radiation Exposure Compensation Act (RECA). Retrieved from justice.gov/civil/common/reca

"What would be…"—Laura Taylor interview with the author. Ms. Taylor is an Arizona attorney who filed over 1500 RECA claims on behalf of thousands of clients.

"How would they…"—Ibid.

"And although…"—Mary Dickson interview with the author.

"Their illnesses…"—Ibid.

"A National Institutes…"—Retrieved from ncbi.nlm.nih.gov/books/NBK100842/

"In his 1999 book…"—Miller, Richard, *Under the Cloud: The Decades of Nuclear Testing* (Woodlands, TX: Two Sixty Press, 1999), 8.

"No one can ..."—Mary Dickson interview with the author.

"As of 2020..."—Retrieved from justice.gov/civil/awards-date-09252020.

"Ellen, too,..."—"Cancer Patients Won't Let Disease Get in the Way of Life," *Rocky Mount Telegram,* Rocky Mount, North Carolina, July 15, 1993.

"You get..."—Retrieved from washingtonpost.com/national/health-science/ellen-stovall-cancer-survivor-and-advocate-who-lived-beyond-her-disease-dies-at-69/2016/01/08/cd011e10-b624-11e5-9388-466021d971de_story.html.

Chapter 12

"Women of..."—Retrieved from ncbi.nlm.nih.gov/pmc/articles/PMC4800017/

"During her treatments..."—Skloot, Rebecca, *The Immortal Life of Henrietta Lacks,* (New York, NY: Random House, 2011), 4.

"According to a story..."—Retrieved from history.com/news/the-infamous-40-year-tuskegee-study

"In 1997..."—Ibid.

"In a 2016..."—"White–Black Differences in Cancer Incidence, Stage at Diagnosis, and Survival among Adults Aged 85 Years and Older in the United States," *Cancer Epidemiology, Biomarkers & Prevention,* November 2016.

"Marion Kelly..."—Marion Kelly interview with the author.

"When Darryl Mittledorf..."—Darryl Mittledorf interview with the author.

"For Lee Magnuson..."—Lee Magnuson interview with the author.

"It broke..."—Ibid.

"The seismic tremors..."—Tweedy, Damon, M.D., *Black Man in a White Coat: A Doctor's Reflections on Race and Medicine,* (New York, NY: Picador, 2016), 123.

"A different kind..."—"Cancer Survivor Chips Away at Fear," *The Santa Fe New Mexican,* Santa Fe, New Mexico, November 27, 1993.

"According to Mary..."—Ibid.

"Low numbers..."—*A Seat at the Table: Culturally based cancer research among American Indians and Alaska Natives,* video produced by the National Cancer Institute. Retrieved from cancer.gov/about-cancer/understanding/disparities/american-indian-alaska-native-video

"HPV is a..."—Dr. Erin Kobetz interview with the author.

"Hair is important..."—Ibid.

"Other cultures..."—Fernandez, Gerardo, 17th Annual Oncology Nursing Conference, "Survivorship: From Diagnosis and Beyond," November 21-22, 2014, Northwestern Memorial Hospital, Chicago, IL.

"Dr. Harold Freeman..."—"The History Makers," retrieved from thehistorymakers.org/biography/dr-harold-freeman-42.

"Poverty does not..." – *NCCS Networker,* Volume 8, Number 4, Winter, 1994.

"The poor also... – Dr. Lovell Jones interview with the author.

"I heard..." – *NCCS Networker,* Volume 9, Number 2, Summer, 1995.

"NCCS brought... – Betsy Clark interview with the author.

"Betsy had focused... – Clark, Elizabeth, "You Have the Right to Be Hopeful," (a publication of NCCS), 1995.

"In the early..."—"Artist Brushes Patients' Lives with Tranquility," *Tallahassee Democrat,* Tallahassee, FL, October 28, 1982.

"As Ellen described it..."—1995 Congress Program.

"Toughing it..."—*NCCS Networker,* 9, no. 4 (Winter 1995).

"Survival is..."—Ibid.

Chapter 13

"A few weeks later..."—*NCCS Networker,* 9, no. 3 (Fall 1995).

"Rick, I..."—Dr. Julia Rowland interview with the author.

"At the time..."—Ibid.

"In the ensuing..."—Ibid.

"Today I..."—Public Papers of the President of the United States, Administration of William J. Clinton, October 27, 1996, 1940.

"In 1992..."—Dr. Wendy Harpham interview with the author.

"The side effects..."—Ibid.

"The collective spirit…"—Leigh, Susie, "Cancer Survivorship: A First Person Perspective," *American Journal of Nursing*, 106 (March 2006).

"My passion…"—Ibid.

"As it was for Susie…"—"The Ellen Stovall Story," *NCCS InterActions*, 17, no. 1.

"Ellen and Betsy…"—Clark, Elizabeth J., and Stovall, Ellen, "Advocacy: The Cornerstone of Cancer Survivorship," *Cancer Practice*, September/October 1996, 4, no. 5.

"Survivorship…"—"Ellen Stoval…dies at 69," *Washington Post*, January 8, 2016.

"I'm not very…"—"Alive and Well," *Lansing State Journal*, Lansing, MI, August 20, 1995.

"Survivors and their…"—Hoffman, Barbara, *A Cancer Survivor's Almanac: Charting Your Journey* (New York, NY: John Wiley & Sons, 1996), 300.

"At dawn…"—Betsy Clark interview with the author.

"The war on…"—"Victims Desperate for Cancer War Victory," *Arizona Daily Star*, Tucson, AZ, July 4, 1996.

"Dr. Klausner…"—Ibid.

"The July 4…"—Ibid.

"As he had…"—Ibid.

"Instead…"—*NCCS Networker*, 10, no. 2 (Summer/Fall, 1996).

Chapter 14

"Susie was…"—"Tucsonan Leads Troops in Cancer War," *Arizona Daily Star*, Tucson, AZ, September 14, 1998.

"My God…"—Ibid.

"I've been taking…"—Betsy Clark interview with the author.

"After all…"—Ibid.

"Ellen was asked…"—*The Cancer Letter*, 23, no. 42 (October 31, 1997).

"During the commercial…"—Donna Doneski interview with the author.

"Ellen was…"—Ibid.

"The vision..."—*The Cancer Letter,* 23, no. 42, October 31, 1997.

"As soon as he..."—Betsy Clark interview with the author.

"In early spring..."—Donna Doneski interview with the author.

"'No,' the general..."—*The Cancer Letter,* 23, no. 42 (October 31, 1997).

"The March team..."—Betsy Clark interview with the author.

"As Ellen explained..."—"March on Mall Brings Cancer Survivors Together," *The Daily Herald,* Provo, UT, September 24, 1998.

"By his own..."—"March on Washington Seeks Cancer Funds, *The San Francisco Examiner,* San Francisco, CA, September 8, 1998.

"That's bad..."—Ibid.

"It wasn't all..."—Betsy Clark interview with the author.

"It's like..."—"March on Washington Seeks Cancer Funds," op cit.

"There were also..."—Betsy Clark interview with the author.

"At 3:00 a.m."—Ibid.

"From the beginning..."—Ibid.

"As Susie later..."—Retrieved from youtube.com/watch?v=Vncblke60UA

"My name is..."—"THE MARCH: Stand With Us and Say 'No More,'" *The Oncologist,* 3, no. 3 (June 1998).

"If you have..."—*NCCS Networker,* 12, no. 3 (Fall 1998).

"You must do..."—NCCS March brochure.

"Today we defy..."—*Cancer Education Rally* [Video file], September 26, 1998. Retrieved from c-span.org/video/?112344-1/cancer-education-rally

"Modest and humble..."—*March to Conquer Cancer—Sidney Kimmel* [Video file], September 26, 1998. Retrieved from c-span.org/video/?c4543057/user-clip-march-conquer-cancer-sidney-kimmel

"Teach your children..."—Retrieved from songfacts.com/lyrics/crosby-stills-nash-young/teach-your-children

Chapter 15

"I can..."—"The March...Coming Together to Conquer Cancer: Why?" *Oncology Times,* July 1998.

"Two years earlier…"—*NCCS Networker,* 10, no. 2 (Summer/Fall 1996).

"Those thoughts…"—*NCCS Networker,* 12, no. 4 (Special Edition: The March, 1998).

"I never…"—"Five Years After 'The March,' *Oncology Times,* 25, no. 18, September 25, 2003.

"Very few…"—Ibid.

"The Toolbox…"—"Cancer Program to Begin March 23," *The Times-Tribune,* Scranton, PA, March 12, 2000.

"Added to that…"—Susie Leigh interview with the author.

"On Tuesday…"—"Terrorism and Cancer," *Oncology Times,* 6, no. 5 (October 1, 2001).

"…a cancer survivor wrote…"—"We Can't Lose Sight of Fight With Cancer," *The Daily Spectrum,* Saint George, UT, December 2, 2001.

"On the thirtieth…"—"War On Cancer Is a Draw," *The Cincinnati Enquirer,* Cincinnati, OH, December 23, 2001.

"This office…"—"20 Years Later Series Wrap-Up: Julia Rowland Shares a History of the Imperatives and the Current Challenges in Survivorship," posted December 28, 2015. Retrieved from canceradvocacy.org/20-years-later-julia-rowland-shares-history-current-challenges-survivorship/

"Susie made…"—"My Journey Through Cancer As Nurse and Survivor," *Cured and Chronic,* II, no. 2 (May-August 2017).

"…her third book…"—Spingarn, Natalie Davis, *The New Cancer Survivors: Living with Grace, Fighting with Spirit* (Baltimore, MD: The Johns Hopkins University Press, 1999).

"On a rainy…"—*NCCS Networker,* 13, nos. 3 & 4 (Winter 2000).

"While the questions…"—Ganz, Patricia, M.D. (ed.), *Cancer Survivorship: Today and Tomorrow* (New York, NY: Springer Science + Business Media, LLC, 2007), 8.

"The ranks of…"—*From Cancer Patient to Cancer Survivor: Lost in Transition,* Institute of Medicine and National Research Council (Washington, DC: National Academies Press, 2005).

"Held at…"—Retrieved from nap.edu/read/11613/chapter/1

Chapter 16

"A 1967…"—"Medicine and You, *Independent Press-Telegram,* Long Beach, CA, July 16, 1967.

"A year later…"—"Radiation Treatments May Damage Heart," *The Gazette,* Cedar Rapids, IA, December 25, 1968.

"In 2010…"—Cleeland, Charles S., Dunn, Adrian J., Fisch, Michael J. (eds.), *Cancer Symptom Science: Measurement, Mechanisms, and Management* (Cambridge, U.K.: Cambridge University Press, 2011).

"For years…"—Retrieved from youtube.com/watch?v=Vncblke60UA

"The last chapter…"—Ganz, op. cit., 287.

"Some days…"—Donna Doneski interview with the author.

"I am not as…"—"Cancer Survivor Discusses Her Experiences," *Washington Post,* February 14, 1995.

"But in 2011…"—"In 40 Years of Cancer Research, How Far Have We Come?" *Time Magazine,* September 21, 2011.

"As Susie…"—Retrieved from youtube.com/watch?v=Vncblke60UA

"In 2011…"—Lester, Joanne L., Schmitt, Patricia (eds.), *Cancer Rehabilitation and Survivorship: Transdisciplinary Approaches to Personalized Care* (Pittsburgh, PA: Oncology Nursing Society, 2011), 7.

"As with her…"—Susie Leigh interview with the author.

"My driving…"—Fitzhugh Mullan, M.D., interview with the author.

"In a real…"—*NCCS Networker,* I, no. 3 (Fall 1987).

"As we have…"—*NCCS Networker,* 10, no. 2 (Summer/Fall 1996).

"The 1996 article"—Clark, Elizabeth J., and Stovall, Ellen, "Advocacy: The Cornerstone of Cancer Survivorship," *Cancer Practice,* 4, no. 5 (September/October 1996).

"Betsy spoke of…"—Curtiss, Carol and Haylock, Pamela (eds.), *Cancer Survivorship: Interprofessional, Patient-Centered Approaches to the Seasons of Survival* (Pittsburgh, PA: Oncology Nursing Society, 2019).

"We worked…"—Betsy Clark interview with the author.

"There was no…"—Tani Bahti interview with the author.

"In his 1991..."—Frank, Arthur, *At the Will of the Body: Reflections on Illness* (New York, NY: Houghton Mifflin Harcourt Publishing Company, 1991), 120.

"In the next..."—*NCCS Networker,* 11, no. 4 (Winter 1997).

"Shelley Fuld Nasso..."—Retrieved from canceradvocacy.org/honoring-ellen-stovall-a-hero-in-cancer-advocacy/

"Fran Visco..."—*The Cancer Letter,* retrieved from cancerletter.com/articles/20160108_1/

"Dr. Richard..."—Ibid.

"When Catherine..."—Retrieved from canceradvocacy.org/remembering-catherine-logan-carrillo-pioneer-survivorship-movement/

"Cancer returned..."—Retrieved from canceradvocacy.org/remembering-fitzhugh-mullan-md/

About the Author

Judy Pearson is a best-selling and award-winning author, an accomplished presenter, and a graduate of Michigan State University. But her favorite title is "storyteller," as exemplified by the biographies she writes. Her second book, *The Wolves at the Door: The True Story of America's Greatest Female Spy*, is not only a bestseller, but also has been purchased for a movie.

A diagnosis of triple-negative breast cancer caused Judy to found A 2nd Act. The nonprofit organization raises funds through live storytelling performances, publishes a book (an ever-growing collection of the stories told on their stages), conducts workshops helping women survivors discover their 2nd Acts, and makes micro-grants to survivors ready to launch or grow their 2nd Acts after cancer.

Honored in Washington, DC, by the American Association for Cancer Research and featured in their National Cancer Research Progress Report, Judy is also member of the Society of Integrative Oncology and the American Psychosocial Oncology Society. She is a founding board member of Arizona Women for the Arts, a member of the American Association for University Women, and a past board member of the Michigan State University Alumni Association.

Judy was named one of Chicago's Most Inspirational Women, was selected as a finalist for the Arizona Healthcare Leadership Awards and named a Phoenix Healthcare Hero the same year.

Judy and her husband, David, live at the base of the Phoenix Mountain Preserve.

Made in the USA
Las Vegas, NV
05 March 2021